Classroom Manual for

# Automotive Heating
# and
# Air Conditioning

### Third Edition

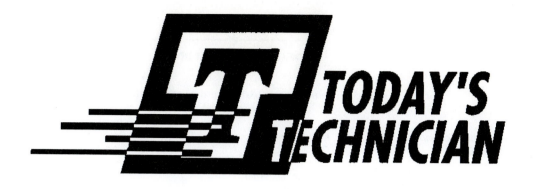

# Classroom Manual for
# Automotive Heating and Air Conditioning
## Third Edition

## Mark Schnubel
Naugatuck Valley Community College
Waterbury, Connecticut

## Jack Erjavec
Series Advisor
Professor Emeritus, Columbus State Community College
Columbus, Ohio

THOMSON ™
DELMAR LEARNING

Australia • Canada • Mexico • Singapore • Spain • United Kingdom • United States

## THOMSON

## DELMAR LEARNING

**Today's Technician: Automotive Heating and Air Conditioning, 3rd Edition**
Mark Schnubel

**Vice President, Technology
and Trades SBU:**
Alar Elken

**Editorial Director:**
Sandy Clark

**Acquisitions Editor:**
David Boelio

**Developmental Editor:**
Christopher M. Shortt

**Marketing Director:**
Cyndi Eichelman

**Channel Manager:**
Fair Huntoon

**Marketing Coordinator:**
Mark Pierro

**Production Director:**
Mary Ellen Black

**Production Manager:**
Larry Main

**Production Editor:**
Ruth Fisher

**Art/Design Specialist:**
Cheri Plasse

**Editorial Assistant:**
Kevin Rivenburg

Library of Congress Cataloging-in-Publication Data:

Schnubel, Mark.
   Classroom manual for Automotive heating and air conditioning / Mark Schnubel.—3rd ed.
      p. cm.—(Today's Technician)
   Rev. ed. of: Automotive heating and air conditioning / Boyce H. Dwiggins. 2nd ed. © 2001. Companion volume to Shop manual for automotive heating and air conditioning. 2005. The classroom and shop manuals are designed to be used together.
   Includes index.
   ISBN 1-4018-3552-X (core text) — ISBN 1-4018-3555-4 (IG) — ISBN 1-4018-3556-2 (e.resource)
   1. Automobiles—Heating and ventilation—Maintenance and repair. 2. Automobiles—Air conditioning—Maintenance and repair. I. Title: Automotive heating and air conditioning. II. Dwiggins, Boyce H. Automotive heating and air conditioning. III. Title. IV. Series.

TL271.D85 2005
629.2'772'0288—dc22        2003533100

## NOTICE TO THE READER

# CONTENTS

# PREFACE

Thanks to the support the *Today's Technician series* has received from those who teach automotive technology, Delmar Learning, a division of Thomson Learning, is able to live up to its promise to provide new editions every three years. We have listened to our critics and our fans and present this new revised edition. By revising our series every three years, we can and will respond to changes in the industry, changes in the certification process, and to the ever-changing needs of those who teach automotive technology.

The *Today's Technician series* by Delmar Learning features textbooks that cover all mechanical and electrical systems of automobiles and light trucks. Principal titles correspond with the eight major areas of ASE (National Institute for Automotive Service Excellence) certification. Additional titles include remedial skills and theories common to all of the certification areas and advanced or specialized subject areas that reflect the latest technological trends.

Each title is divided into two manuals: a Classroom Manual and a Shop Manual. Dividing the material into two manuals provides the reader with the information needed to begin a successful career as an automotive technician without interrupting the learning process by mixing cognitive and performance-based learning objectives.

Each Classroom Manual contains the principles of operation for each system and subsystem. It also discusses the design variations used by different manufacturers. The Classroom Manual is organized to build upon basic facts and theories. The primary objective of this manual is to allow the reader to gain an understanding of how each system and subsystem operates. This understanding is necessary to diagnose the complex automobile systems.

The understanding acquired by using the Classroom Manual is required for competence in the skill areas covered in the Shop Manual. All of the high-priority skills, as identified by ASE, are explained in the Shop Manual. The Shop Manual also includes step-by-step instructions for diagnostic and repair procedures. Photo Sequences are used to illustrate many of the common service procedures. Other common procedures are listed and are accompanied with fine-line drawings and photographs that allow the reader to visualize and conceptualize the finest details of the procedure. The Shop Manual also contains the reasons for performing the procedures, as well as when that particular service is appropriate.

The two manuals are designed to be used together and are arranged in corresponding chapters. Not only are the chapters in the manuals linked together, the contents of the chapters are also linked. Both manuals contain clear and thoughtfully selected illustrations. Many of the illustrations are original drawings or photos prepared for inclusion in this series. This means that the art is a vital part of each manual.

The page layout is designed to include information that would otherwise break up the flow of information presented to the reader. The main body of the text includes all of the "need-to-know" information and illustrations. In the side margins are many of the special features of the series. Items such as definition of new terms, common trade jargon, tools list, and cross-referencing are placed in the margin, out of the normal flow of information so as not to interrupt the thought process of the reader.

## Highlights of this Edition—Classroom Manual

The Classroom Manual content and organization has been based on ASE testing areas. All areas are expanded to include additional information relative to the latest service and troubleshooting techniques and technologies.

## Highlights of this Edition—Shop Manual

The Shop Manual has been updated to correlate with the new content of the Classroom Manual.

Job Sheets have been added to the end of each chapter. The Job Sheets provide a format for students to perform some of the tasks covered in the chapter. In addition to walking a student through a procedure, step by step, these Job Sheets challenge the student by asking why or how something should be done, thereby making the students think about what they are doing.

# Classroom Manual

To stress the importance of safe work habits, the Classroom Manual dedicates one full chapter to health and safety. Included in this chapter are common safety practices, safety equipment, and safe handling of hazardous materials and wastes. This includes information on MSDS sheets and OSHA regulations. Other features of this manual include:

## Cognitive Objectives

These objectives define the contents of the chapter and define what the student should have learned upon completion of the chapter.
*Each topic is divided into small units to promote easier understanding and learning.*

## Author's Notes

This feature includes simple explanations, stories, or examples of complex topics. These are included to help students understand difficult concepts.

## Terms to Know Definitions

New terms are pulled out into the margin and defined.

## Trade Jargon

These marginal notes give some of the common terms used for components and allow the reader to speak and understand the language of the trade, especially when conversing with an experienced technician.

## Cross-References to the Shop Manual

Reference to the appropriate page in the Shop Manual is given whenever necessary. Although the chapters of the two manuals are synchronized, material covered in other chapters of the Shop Manual may be funamental to the topic discussed in the Classroom Manual.

## Summaries

Each chapter concludes with a summary of key points from the chapter. These are designed to help the reader review the contents.

## A Bit of History

This feature gives the student a sense of the evolution of the automobile. This feature not only contains nice-to-know information, but should also spark some interest in the subject matter.

## Review Questions

Short answer essay, fill-in-the-blank, and multiple choice questions are found at the end of each chapter. These questions are designed to accurately assess the student's competence in the stated objectives at the beginning of the chapter.

## Terms to Know List

A list of new terms appears after the Summary.

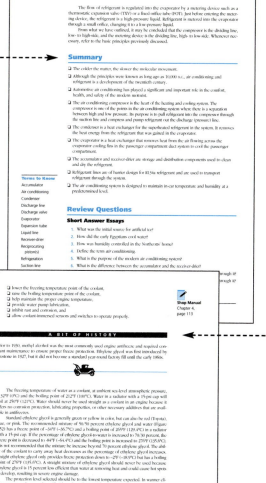

# Shop Manual

To stress the importance of safe work habits, the Shop Manual also dedicates one full chapter to safety. Other important features of this manual include:

## Performance Objectives

These objectives define the contents of the chapter and identify what the student should have learned upon completion of the chapter. These objectives also correspond to the list of required tasks for ASE certification. *Each ASE task is addressed.*

    Although this textbook is not designed to simply prepare someone for the certification exams, it is organized around the ASE task list. These tasks are defined generically when the procedure is commonly followed and specifically when the procedure is unique for specific vehicle models. Imported and domestic model automobiles and light trucks are included in the procedures.

## Photo Sequences

Many procedures are illustrated in detailed Photo Sequences. These detailed photographs show the students what to expect when they perform particular procedures. They can also provide a student a familiarity with a system or type of equipment, that the school may not have.

## Tools Lists

Each chapter begins with a list of the Basic Tools needed to perform the tasks included in the chapter. Whenever a Special Tool is required to complete a task, it is listed in the margin next to the procedure.

## Terms to Know Definitions

New terms are pulled out into the margin and defined.

## Customer Care

This feature highlights those little things a technician can do or say to enhance customer relations.

## Cautions and Warnings

Throughout the text, cautions are given to alert the reader to potentially hazardous materials or unsafe conditions. Warnings are also given to advise the student of what can go wrong if instructions are not followed or if a nonacceptable part or tool is used.

## Cross-References to the Classroom Manual

Reference to the appropriate page in the Classroom Manual is given whenever necessary. Although the chapters of the two manuals are synchronized, material covered in other chapters of the Classroom Manual may be fundamental to the topic discussed in the Shop Manual.

## Service Tips

Whenever a shortcut or special procedure is appropriate, it is described in the text. These tips are generally those things commonly done by experienced technicians

## Job Sheets

Located at the end of each chapter, the Job Sheets provide a format for students to perform procedures covered in the chapter. A reference to the ASE Task addressed by the procedure is referenced on the Job Sheet.

## Case Studies

Case Studies concentrate on the ability to properly diagnose the systems. Beginning with Chapter 3, each chapter ends with a case study in which a vehicle has a problem, and the logic used by a technician to solve the problem is explained.

## ASE-Style Review Questions

Each chapter contains ASE-style review questions that reflect the performance objectives listed at the beginning of the chapter. These questions can be used to review the chapter as well as to prepare for the ASE certification exam.

## ASE Practice Examination

A 50-question ASE practice exam, located in the Appendix, is included to test students on the content of the complete Shop Manual.

---

Figure 6-18 Connect a short hose to the inlet of the charging cylinder.

Figure 6-19 Attach the other end of the hose to a refrigerant source.

14. Observe the hoses and fittings for signs of the dye solution. If no signs of a leak are evident at this time, arrange to have the car available the following day for diagnosis and repair. If leak(s) are detected, make repairs as required. (The dye solution will remain in the system without causing harm or reduced performance.)
15. Close all valves: the refrigerant source valve, service hose shut-off valve, low-side manifold gauge valve, and compressor service valve(s), if equipped.
16. Remove the manifold and gauge set.
17. Remove the charging cylinder. Disconnect the hose from the refrigerant source. Remove the charging cylinder from the service hose. Remove the short hose from the charging cylinder.
18. Replace all protective caps.

Protective caps help guard against leaks and help to prevent the entrance of dirt and debris.

Freon is a generic term used to refer to R-12.

### CASE STUDY

A customer complained of an inoperative air conditioner and requested that Freon be added. The technician advised the customer that if refrigerant were needed, there must be a leak in the system. The customer responded "I have to add Freon every couple of months—just put it in."

The technician attempted to explain the problems with just adding refrigerant, such as loss of oil, harm to the environment, and possible damage to the air conditioner system components, such as the compressor. The customer still insisted that he only wanted Freon.

Politely and tactfully, the technician refused the service. "You have come to the wrong place," she told the customer. "This service facility employs only ASE-certified technicians who are dedicated to their profession. To perform a service in an improper manner violates the essence of ASE certification."

The somewhat surprised, but impressed, customer left the facility without further ado. He...

---

## Terms to Know

| | | |
|---|---|---|
| Can tap valve | Federal Clean Air Act | Recovery system |
| Charge | Gross weight | Standing vacuum test |
| Contaminated refrigerant | Pound cans | Stratify |
| Dry nitrogen | Purge | Triple evacuation |
| Evacuate | | |

## Terms to Know

A list of new terms appears after the case study.

## ASE-Style Review Questions

1. *Technician A* says that a system is contaminated if it contains more than 2 percent of a foreign substance. *Technician B* says that air is considered a contaminant if it exceeds 2 percent of the system capacity.
Who is correct?
A. A only    C. Both A and B
B. B only    D. Neither A nor B

2. *Technician A* says that tobacco smoke will not affect refrigerant leak detection. *Technician B* says halide is the best and an inexpensive method of leak detection.
Who is correct?
A. A only    C. Both A and B
B. B only    D. Neither A nor B

3. *Technician A* says that special electronic leak detectors are available that are used for HFCs. *Technician B* says that there are electronic leak detectors available that will detect CFCs as well as HFCs.
Who is correct?
A. A only    C. Both A and B
B. B only    D. Neither A nor B

4. *Technician A* says that the system is purged of refrigerant if the manifold gauges read a slight vacuum. *Technician B* says that the system may be purged of refrigerant even if the manifold gauges read a slight pressure.
Who is correct?
A. A only    C. Both A and B
B. B only    D. Neither A nor B

5. *Technician A* says that one need not evacuate the system if the "sweep and purge" method is used. *Technician B* says that one need not evacuate the system if it has been "opened" for less than five minutes.
Who is correct?
A. A only    C. Both A and B
B. B only    D. Neither A nor B

6. *Technician A* says that "purging" is the same as "evacuation." *Technician B* says that "pumping down" is the same as "evacuation."
Who is correct?
A. A only    C. Both A and B
B. B only    D. Neither A nor B

7. *Technician A* says when it is used improperly, refrigerant can cause blindness. *Technician B* says when it is used improperly, refrigerant can create a harmful vapor.
Who is correct?
A. A only    C. Both A and B
B. B only    D. Neither A nor B

8. *Technician A* says that the minimum pressure recommended for leak testing a CFC-12 system is 60 psig (414 kPa). *Technician B* says the minimum recommended pressure for leak testing an HFC-134a system is 60 psig (414 kPa).
Who is correct?
A. A only    C. Both A and B
B. B only    D. Neither A nor B

---

### APPENDIX A

### ASE Practice Examination

#### Final Exam Automotive Heating and Air Conditioning A7

1. What component part of the air conditioning system causes the refrigerant to change from a liquid to a vapor?
A. Evaporator
B. Compressor
C. Condenser
D. Metering device

2. Which of the following statements about the engine cooling fan are most correct?
A. The electric engine cooling fan may start and run when the air conditioning system is turned on.
B. The electric engine cooling fan may start and run when the ignition switch is turned on.
C. The electric engine cooling fan may start and run when the ambient temperature is high.
D. The electric engine cooling fan may start and run at any time.

3. A 17-psi radiator pressure cap is replaced with a 7-psi radiator pressure cap. Which of the following is least likely to occur as a result?
A. The engine will overheat.
B. The engine will not reach operating temperature.
C. The coolant will boil over.
D. Engine performance will be degraded.

4. Latent heat can be measured with:
A. A spirit thermometer
B. An electronic thermometer
C. Either A or B
D. Neither A nor B

5. Heat required for a change of state, say, from a liquid to a vapor is called:
A. Sensible heat
B. Latent heat
C. Superheat
D. Subsurface heat

6. All of the following may cause a compressor clutch to slip, except:
A. Overcharge of refrigerant
B. Loose drive belt
C. Improper air gap
D. Low voltage

7. The ohmmeter reading in the illustration below is 0. The most probable cause of this problem is that the:
A. Windings are shorted
B. Windings are open
C. Brushes are defective
D. Motor is seized

Volt meter

Blower motor relay

Blower motor

---

# Instructor's Guide

The Instructor's Guide is provided free of charge as part of the *Today's Technician Series* of automotive technology textbooks. It contains Lecture Outlines, Answers to Review Questions, a Pretest, and a Test Bank including ASE-style questions.

# E-Resource

The e.resource is a robust ancillary that contains all preparation tools to meet any instructor's classroom needs. It includes PowerPoint slides that coincide with each chapter's coverage, a computerized testbank containing hundreds of test questions, an image library with hundreds of images for instructors to import into the PowerPoint slides where they deem necessary, worksheets in Microsoft Word format for instructors to hand out to students, the job sheets from the Shop Manual in Microsoft Word format, a NATEF/ASE chart that correlates the classroom and shop manual pages to the matching NATEF and ASE tasks, and the entire Instructor's Guide in electronic format.

# Reviewers

I would like to extend special thanks to those instructors who reviewed this material:

Rick Mcallister
Automotive Technology Department
Lake Region State College

Jack Devine
Renton Tech
Renton, WA

Tammy Eaton
Gateway Community College
Transportation Technology Department
North Haven Campus, CT

RJ Ehlers
Albany, OR

George Panagiotou
Ford Service Training Instructor
Boston, MA

I would also like to extend thanks to those who reviewed the second edition of this text:

Richard J. Sweat
Statesboro High School

Charles Ginthen

Glen Hammonds
Rancho Santiago College

Ray Taylor
Copiah-Lincoln Community College

Brian Coppola
Eastern Arizona Community College

David Washington
Northwest Los Angeles Technical College

Daniel Hall

Michael Francis
Owens Community College

# Contributing Companies

I would also like to thank these companies who provided technical information and art for this edition:

American Honda Motor Co., Inc.
AMMCO
Bendix Brakes
Brake Parts
Branick Industries, Inc.
Brodhead-Garrett
Central Tools, Inc.
Century/Lincoln Service Equipment
DaimlerChrysler
CRC Industries
Dalloz Safety
DuPont Automotive Finishes
EIS Brake Parts
Federal-Mogul Corp.

Fluke Corporation
The Ford Motor Company
General Motors
Goodson Shop Supplies
Gutman Adversing Agency
Hunter Engineering Company
IDSC Holdings, Inc.
ITT Automotive
Lincoln Automotive
LucasVarity Automotive
Mettler-Toledo, Inc.
Mine Safety Appliances Co.
Mitchell Anti-Lock Brake Systems, Mitchell Repair Information Co., LLC

Mitsubishi Motor Sales of America, Inc.
NAPA
Nelson Australia Pty Ltd
Nissan North America, Inc.
Parker Hannifin Corp.
Pro-Tech Respirators, Inc.
Pullman/Holt
Raybestos/Brake Parts, Inc.
Rolero-Omega
Securall Safety Storage Equipment
Snap-on, Incorporated

# Health and Safety

Upon completion and review of this chapter, you should be able to:

❑ Explain the importance of the ozone layer.

❑ Discuss what industry is doing about the ozone depletion problem.

❑ Discuss what government is doing about the ozone depletion problem.

❑ Describe how ozone is created.

❑ Describe how ozone is destroyed.

❑ Identify potential hazards in the automotive shop.

❑ Recognize hazards before they become a problem.

## Introduction

Since the discovery of the hole in the ozone layer over Antarctica, there has been widespread concern about the consequences for human health and for the environment. Ozone depletion, together with global warming resulting from the greenhouse effect, have attracted widespread media attention and well-founded concern around the world.

This chapter will explain:

❑ The importance of the ozone layer
❑ How the ozone layer is formed
❑ How the ozone layer is being depleted
❑ What is causing ozone depletion
❑ What industry is doing to correct the damage
❑ What government is doing to correct the damage

### What is Ozone?

**Ozone** is a molecular form of **oxygen** having a different chemical property. Thus, it is an **allotrope** of oxygen. In large concentrations, ozone is considered to be a poisonous gas. The ozone layer, however, protects life on earth from damaging ultraviolet (UV) radiation.

Ozone has a very pungent odor described by many as irritating. In high concentrations it has a pale blue color. This is in contrast with oxygen (O) which is colorless, tasteless, and has no odor. Each molecule of ozone ($O_3$), an allotropic form of oxygen, contains three atoms of oxygen in contrast to the diatomic form, which contains two atoms of oxygen ($O_2$).

### The Earth's Atmosphere

The earth's **atmosphere** is composed of a thin covering of gases that surround the globe and comprise an enormous mass. This mass is equivalent to about 1 million tons for every person living on earth. The atmosphere extends skyward for hundreds of miles (Figure 1-1). The lowest part of the atmosphere, up to about seven miles (11 kilometers), is known as the troposphere. Above that to an altitude of about 30 miles (48 kilometers) is the stratosphere, which contains the ozone layer.

Ozone ($O_3$) is a form of oxygen.

**Ozone ($O_3$)** is an unstable, pale-blue gas with a penetrating odor; it is an allotropic form of oxygen (O) that is usually formed by electrical discharge in the air.

**Oxygen (O)** is an odorless, colorless, tasteless element that forms 21 percent of our atmosphere. It is an essential element for plant and animal life.

**Allotropes** are structurally different from elements. For example, though different in structure, the properties of charcoal and diamond are the same as the element carbon; they are both made up of the same element in differing combinations.

**Atmosphere** is a general term used to describe the gaseous envelope surrounding the earth to a height of 621 miles (1000 km); it is 21 percent oxygen, 78 percent nitrogen, and 1 percent other gases.

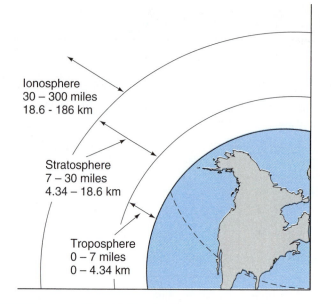

Ionosphere
30 – 300 miles
18.6 - 186 km

Stratosphere
7 – 30 miles
4.34 – 18.6 km

Troposphere
0 – 7 miles
0 – 4.34 km

**Figure 1-1**   The atmosphere extends skyward for hundreds of miles.

Nitrogen is an odorless, colorless, tasteless element that forms 78 percent of our atmosphere. It is an essential element for plant and animal life.

The air we breathe contains 1 percent rare gases, such as krypton (Kr).

The major gases in the atmosphere are **nitrogen** (N), an inert gas, which comprises 78 percent of the atmosphere by volume, and oxygen, which is vital for life and comprises 21 percent. Water ($H_2O$) vapor, a portion of which is seen as clouds, accounts for less than 1 percent. The composition of atmospheric gases are as shown in Table 1-1.

Several trace gases are also included in the other 0.00276 percent of the earth's atmosphere. Though very small in volume, they play critical roles in the atmosphere. Carbon dioxide ($CO_2$), for example, is a trace gas with a concentration of only 350 parts per million by volume (ppmv). This accounts for less than 0.3 percent but absorbs infrared radiation, thus warming the atmosphere through the phenomenon of the greenhouse effect.

Without its ability to retain this heat, the earth would be about 60°F (33°C) colder and could not support life as we know it. An increase of some 25 percent in the concentration of carbon dioxide over the past century is one of the primary causes of global warming.

Ozone ($O_3$), another trace gas, occurs at concentrations of only about 0.4 ppmv (0.000004 percent), but it is also essential for absorbing UV radiation from the sun. Excessive UV radiation is very damaging to life on earth.

## TABLE 1-1   COMPOSITION OF THE EARTH'S ATMOSPHERE

| GAS | PPM by VOLUME | PERCENTAGE |
|---|---|---|
| Nitrogen (N) | 780,840 | 78 |
| Oxygen (O) | 209,460 | 21 |
| Argon (Ar) | 9,340 | 0.0934 |
| Carbon dioxide ($CO_2$) | 350 | 0.0035 |
| Neon (Ne) | 18.18 | 0.0002 |
| Helium (He) | 5.24 | 0.00005 |
| Methane ($CH_4$) | 2.00 | 0.00002 |
| Krypton (Kr) | 1.14 | 0.00001 |
| Hydrogen (H) | 0.50 | 0.000005 |
| Nitrous oxide ($N_2O$) | 0.50 | 0.000005 |
| Ozone ($O_3$) | 0.40 | 0.000004 |
| Xenon (Xe) | 0.09 | 0.0000009 |

# Ozone in the Atmosphere

Unlike other gases, which are concentrated in the troposphere, about 90 percent of the ozone occurs in the stratosphere, from an altitude of about 9–22 miles (15–35 km). Even at its highest concentration, ozone does not exceed 10 ppmv—equivalent to 1 ozone molecule in every 100,000 molecules. For example, if all the ozone in the atmosphere were concentrated at sea level it would form a layer less than 0.125 in. (3 mm) thick. There are about 3,000 million tons of ozone in the atmosphere, equivalent to about 1,600 lb. (726 kg) per person on earth. Compared with the total mass of the atmosphere, however, the amount of ozone is negligible.

Ozone is formed by the action of electrical discharges. For this reason, it is sometimes detected by odor near electrical equipment or just after a thunderstorm. More frequently, however, ozone is formed by the action of **ultraviolet (UV) radiation** on oxygen in the stratosphere. The atoms in the oxygen molecules split apart, and the separated atoms recombine with other oxygen molecules to form the triatomic ozone ($O_3$).

Because sunlight is essential for the formation of stratospheric ozone, it is formed mainly over the equatorial region, where solar radiation is highest. From there it is distributed throughout the stratosphere by the slight global wind circulation. Stratospheric ozone levels vary throughout the world, being highest at the equator and lowest toward the poles.

## Absorption of Ultraviolet Radiation

Incoming radiation from the sun is of various wavelengths, ranging from UV to visible light to infrared. Ultraviolet radiation can cause sunburn, skin cancer, and damage to eyes, including cataracts. It can also cause premature aging and wrinkling of the skin. Ultraviolet radiation breaks down the food chain by destroying minute organisms such as plankton in the ocean, thereby depriving certain species of their natural food. Plant life and crops can also be devastated by excessive UV radiation.

Fortunately, the damaging forms of UV radiation are absorbed by ozone in the atmosphere and do not reach the earth. The minute amount of atmospheric ozone is sufficient to absorb this radiation. The ozone layer, then, acts as a giant sunscreen or umbrella enveloping the earth, protecting life from the dangerous UV radiation. **Ozone depletion** results in weakening of this protective shield, however, and allows more UV radiation to strike the earth and living organisms, as shown in Figure 1-2.

**Ultraviolet (UV) radiation** consists of invisible rays from the sun that have damaging effects on the earth. Ultraviolet radiation causes sunburns.

Ultraviolet (UV) radiation is to be avoided whenever possible.

**Shop Manual**
Chapter 1,
page 3

**Ozone depletion** is the reduction of the ozone layer due to contamination, such as the release of chlorofluorocarbon (CFC) refrigerants into the atmosphere.

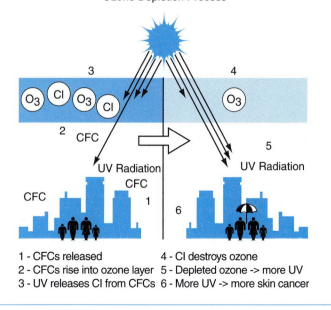

Ozone Depletion Process

1 - CFCs released
2 - CFCs rise into ozone layer
3 - UV releases Cl from CFCs
4 - Cl destroys ozone
5 - Depleted ozone -> more UV
6 - More UV -> more skin cancer

**Figure 1-2** Ozone Depletion Process

Another consequence of the absorption of solar energy by ozone is that the upper stratosphere is somewhat warmer than at lower altitudes, which helps to regulate the earth's temperature. Stratospheric ozone absorbs about 3 percent of incoming solar radiation, thus serving as a heat sink. Loss of this ozone will decrease the temperature of the stratosphere, which will, in turn, affect the troposphere and consequently the weather and climate on the earth's surface.

## Measurement of Ozone

Although the ozone depletion problem was not to be officially addressed for another 50 years or so, the measurement of ozone in the atmosphere began in the 1920s.

The standard term for measuring ozone levels is the **Dobson Unit (DU)** named after the British meteorologist, Gordon Dobson, who was the first to use a spectrophotometer. This device is used to determine the intensity of various wavelengths in a spectrum of light and can thereby measure the density of the ozone layer.

# The Ozone Hole

The term *ozone hole* refers to the loss of the blocking effect of ozone against UV radiation. With the depletion of the ozone barrier, a "hole" has been created that allows a much greater amount of UV radiation to penetrate to the earth. Like an umbrella with holes in it that allows the rain through, holes in the ozone layer allow dangerous UV radiation to pass through to the earth's surface.

When ozone measurements were first taken at the British base at Halley Bay in the Antarctic, levels were found to fall drastically in September and October to 150 DU—half the normal level. This is also half the levels measured in the northern hemisphere in the spring. Levels again rose in November to the expected pattern, confirming that the atmosphere over Antarctica differs from elsewhere in the world.

At the center of the depleted area almost all of the ozone had disappeared. At Halley Bay between mid-August and early October, levels fall by 97 percent at a height of 10.25 miles (16.5 km). The hole occurs between 10.6 and 13.7 miles (17 and 22 km) above the earth.

Recent studies by NASA indicate that by the year 2030 climate change may surpass chlorofluorocarbons as the main cause of ozone depletion. Greenhouse gases like methane and carbon dioxide are changing the earth's climate. These effects could delay the recovery of the ozone layer even though most of the industrialized nations have signed international agreements to ban the production and use of CFCs. CFCs once used in the production of refrigerant and other commercial applications will last for decades in the upper stratosphere.

Ozone thinning can also occur when water vapor makes its way to the stratosphere. At these high altitudes, water vapor can be broken down into molecules that attack the ozone molecules. This can occur when methane emissions that migrate to the stratosphere are transformed into water vapor. The greenhouse effect also heats up the lower stratosphere where most of the ozone is concentrated. As it heats up, the chemical reactions that destroy ozone are also accelerated. Computer modeling suggests that ozone levels will reach their lowest levels in recorded history around 2006. Another study indicates that, as the level of CFCs decline and their affect on the ozone layer is taken by itself, the ozone layer will make a full recovery by the year 2040. Unfortunately, the same study indicates that when the other variables such as the greenhouse effect and water vapor in the stratosphere are added back into the equation, the ozone layer will only make a slight improvement by 2040. There is still hope, but CFC reduction is only one piece of the puzzle.

Ozone is measured in Dobson Units (DU).

**Dobson Unit (DU)** is a measure of ozone density level named after Gordon Dobson, a British meteorologist who was the inventor of the measuring device (called a spectrophotometer).

# How Ozone Is Being Destroyed

Ozone is both created and destroyed by the action of UV radiation on oxygen molecules. **Chlorine** (Cl) is the major gas causing the destruction of ozone and starts chain reactions in which a single molecule of chlorine can destroy 100,000 ozone molecules. Such reactions can continue for many years, even a century or more, until the chlorine drifts down into the troposphere or is chemically bound into another compound.

The main sources of chlorine are chlorofluorocarbons (CFCs). **CFCs** (Figure 1-3) are artificially-made chemicals first developed in 1928 and are comprised of:

- ❏ Chlorine (Cl)
- ❏ Fluorine (F)
- ❏ Carbon (C)
- ❏ (Often) hydrogen (H)

CFCs are very stable chemicals and are nonflammable, nonirritating, nonexplosive, noncorrosive, odorless, and relatively low in **toxicity**. They vaporize at low temperatures, which makes them very desirable for use as refrigerants in air conditioners and refrigerators. CFCs were also used as solvents for cleaning electronic components, for blowing bubbles in certain types of foam-blown plastics such as sponges and food packaging, in dry cleaning solvent, and as an aerosol propellant. Figure 1-4 depicts the areas of the United States where CFCs were used to produce goods and services prior to the restriction in production under the Clean Air Act. As can be seen, refrigerant made up a large portion of the overall use of CFCs.

During the 1960s and 1970s, aerosol use was widespread due to the stable nature and nonflammability of CFCs. Peak worldwide use of CFCs in the 1970s was on the order of about 700,000 tons (635,460 metric tons) each year. The scheduled phaseout caused drastic reductions, however, and with the decline in the use of aerosols, nonaerosol use has risen.

**Chlorine (Cl)** is a poisonous, greenish-yellow gas used in some refrigerants and known to be harmful to the ozone layer.

**CFC** stands for chlorofluorocarbon, a man-made compound used in refrigerants such as CFC-12 (R-12).

**Toxicity** refers to the toxic or poisonous quality of a substance.

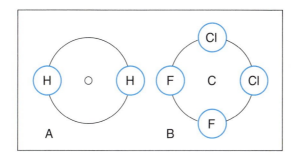

**Figure 1-3**   Chemical structure of (A) Water (B) CFC-12.

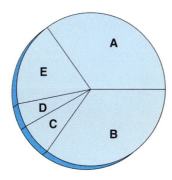

**Figure 1-4**   United States' consumption rates prior to CFC use being restricted by the Clean Air Act: (A) A/C-Ref 35%, (B) Foam Blowing 35%, (C) Other 7%, (D) Sterilants 5%, (E) Solvents 18%. (Consumption rates are prior to CFC being restricted)

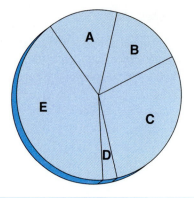

**Figure 1-5**  Consumption of CFCs at the time of the signing of the Montreal Protocol, by country/region: (A) The former Soviet Republics 14%, (B) Developing Nations 14%, (C) United States 29%, (D) China and India 2%, (E) Other Developed Nations 41%.

The chlorine atoms in CFCs are hazardous to the ozone layer.

The consumption of CFCs on a per-capita basis in the United States is among the highest in the world (Figure 1-5), a reflection of our affluence and the popularity and use of air conditioners. While industrialized nations are the major consumers of CFCs, developing nations such as China and India, because of their large populations, have enormous potential to require CFCs for refrigerators and other uses.

In 1974 two chemists at the University of California, Mario Molina and Sherwood Rowland, asked the simple question: "What has happened to the millions of tons of CFCs released over the previous four decades?" The only "sink" they could suggest was the stratosphere. They hypothesized that the chemical stability of CFCs would enable them to reach the stratosphere, be broken apart by the intense UV radiation, and release chlorine by a process known as photolysis. The chlorine would then react with the ozone, causing its depletion.

It is not the CFCs, as such, that cause the destruction but rather the chlorine released by the CFCs. The research of the British scientists at Halley Bay, together with international research programs in which samples of stratospheric air are obtained by high-altitude flights over Antarctica, have proven the link between CFCs and ozone destruction. A further factor identified as contributing to the loss of ozone is the polar stratospheric clouds that form during the Antarctic winter in the very cold stratospheric air. These comprise tiny particles of frozen water vapor, which condense and form clouds in spring. The clouds act as reservoirs of frozen chlorine during winter until thawed in spring. At that time the chlorine is released and begins to react with the ozone over the following five to six weeks, then the vortex breaks up and the stratosphere becomes less stable.

Chlorine atoms split ozone molecules to form chlorine monoxide.

A chlorine atom reacts with an ozone molecule, splitting it apart and attaching itself to one of the oxygen atoms to form chlorine monoxide. A free oxygen atom splits the chlorine monoxide molecule to reform a molecule of oxygen ($O_2$), and the chlorine atom is free to attack another ozone molecule (Figure 1-6).

The CFCs take six to eight years to rise up through the atmosphere. Chlorine as used in swimming pools and bleach is unstable and breaks down rapidly without rising into the atmosphere. The concern is that the current hole and depletion that have resulted from CFCs released in early years will only worsen as their full effects are manifested over time in the stratosphere.

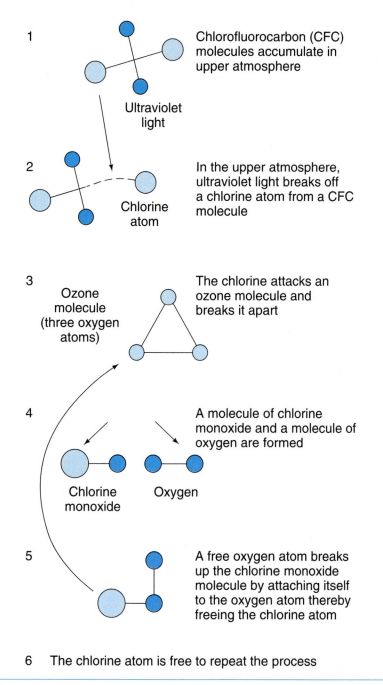

1    Chlorofluorocarbon (CFC) molecules accumulate in upper atmosphere

Ultraviolet light

2    In the upper atmosphere, ultraviolet light breaks off a chlorine atom from a CFC molecule

Chlorine atom

3    Ozone molecule (three oxygen atoms)

The chlorine attacks an ozone molecule and breaks it apart

4    A molecule of chlorine monoxide and a molecule of oxygen are formed

Chlorine monoxide    Oxygen

5    A free oxygen atom breaks up the chlorine monoxide molecule by attaching itself to the oxygen atom thereby freeing the chlorine atom

6    The chlorine atom is free to repeat the process

**Figure 1-6**    How CFCs destroy the ozone.

# Effects of Loss of Ozone on Human Health

As we have seen, ozone protects life on earth from damaging UV radiation. It acts as a giant sunscreen absorbing the UV rays, preventing a certain percentage of them from reaching the earth. As already noted, loss of ozone will only allow more UV radiation to penetrate to the earth and adversely affect human health and the environment. The three areas of our bodies that are adversely affected are the skin, eyes, and the immune system.

Exposure of skin to UV radiation can initially result in sunburn and suntan. If the exposure continues over a long period, as with those who work outdoors, the skin protects itself from UV radiation by gradually thickening and darkening as a pigment called melanin is released in the skin. Continuous exposure of the skin to UV radiation results in its aging and wrinkling and increases the risk of skin cancer.

Excessive UV exposure to the eyes will increase the risk of cataracts, which cause cloudiness in the lens of the eye, limiting vision. Other eye problems such as retina damage, tumors on the cornea, and "snow blindness" may also be caused by exposure to increased levels of UV radiation.

The body's immune system protects it from foreign chemicals and infections. If damaged, the immune system cannot protect the body and infections spread more rapidly. Ultraviolet radiation reduces the ability of the immune system to reject cancers, although not much is known about why this happens. Overall, increased UV radiation resulting from ozone depletion has the potential of significantly increasing human skin cancers and cataracts and damaging the human immune system. It also adversely affects marine and terrestrial plants and animals.

The extent of the damage will depend on the degree to which the earth's ozone layer is depleted. To date it has been reduced by about 2.5 percent, and it remains to be seen if the actions taken to control the release of ozone-depleting substances will be sufficient.

## Ozone and the Greenhouse Effect

**Greenhouse effect** is a term based on the fact that a greenhouse is warmed because glass allows the sun's radiant heat to enter but prevents radiant heat from leaving. Likewise, global warming is caused by some gases in the atmosphere that act like greenhouse glass.

**Global warming** is the gradual warming of the earth's atmosphere due to the greenhouse effect.

The loss of ozone and the greenhouse effect are separate phenomena, although CFCs are a common agent in both. The **greenhouse effect**, or **global warming**, is the result of the release of increasing amounts of so-called "greenhouse gases" into the atmosphere, gases such as carbon dioxide ($CO_2$), methane ($CH_4$), and CFCs. These gases trap some of the heat from the sun as it is reradiated out from the earth, thus acting as a blanket that retains the heat. As mentioned above, without the greenhouse effect, the earth would be about 60°F (33°C) colder, too cold to support life as we know it.

In 1992 the National Climatic Data Center (NCDC) declared that the winter of 1991–1992 was the warmest U.S. winter in the 97 years that the federal government had kept a record of climatic conditions. The average temperature was 36.87°F (2.7°C). The previous low average temperature of 36°F (2.22°C) was recorded in 1953–1954. In 1999 the NCDC declared that 1998 was the warmest year on record. During the twentieth century, the ten warmest years occurred during the last fifteen years of that century (Figure 1-7). This increase in global warming has also

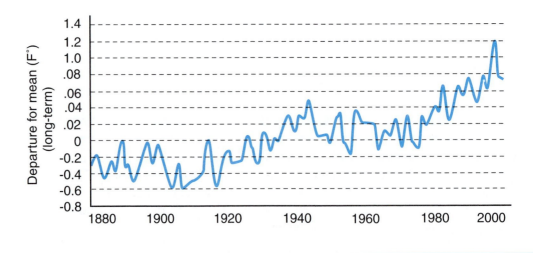

Figure 1-7 U.S. National Climate Data Center 2001 showing an increase in global temperature.

8

increased worldwide rainfall amounts by about 1 percent. Some scientists predict that global surface temperatures could rise 1–4.5 percent over the next fifteen years and by 2–10 percent during this century. This could result in sea levels rising by as much as 2 feet along most of the U.S. coastline. In 1997, the United States was responsible for emitting 20 percent of the total global greenhouse gases.

The greenhouse effect is a natural process of warming, just as the ozone layer is a natural function of the earth's atmosphere that protects life. Both have been affected by the release of pollutants from human activities, pollutants that have accelerated the greenhouse effect, resulting in increased warming and depletion of the ozone layer, exposing life to damaging UV radiation.

# The Clean Air Act

The most significant legislation to affect the automotive air conditioning industry in the United States is the **Clean Air Act (CAA)**. The CAA was signed into law by President George H. W. Bush on November 15, 1990. Most of the rules and regulations of the CAA were a result of the recommendations made at the Montreal Protocol.

The Montreal Protocol and later amendments deal with the environmental problems and issues created by certain refrigerants depleting the ozone on an international level. The CAA deals with this problem on a national level. The Montreal Protocol is structured so that periodic meetings must take place in order to reassess the ozone problem. As new facts about the impact of refrigerants are brought to light, the protocol will be modified accordingly. The majority of protocol modifications will also result in the CAA being modified accordingly.

Language exists in the CAA stating that the Environmental Protection Agency (EPA) can accelerate schedules for the phaseout of refrigerants if it is deemed necessary and practical. The CAA also mandates that phaseout may be accelerated if required by the Montreal Protocol.

The CAA is somewhat more specific than the Protocol in addressing the ozone depletion problem. The Clean Air Act gives the EPA the authority to establish environmentally safe procedures with respect to the use and reuse of refrigerants. In addition, the EPA will establish standards for certifying those who service refrigeration equipment and for that service itself. These standards will be derived from the information furnished mainly by private sector organizations.

**Clean Air Act (CAA)** is a Title 6 Amendment signed into law in 1990 that established national policy relative to the reduction and elimination of ozone-depleting substances.

# Stratospheric Ozone Protection—Title VI

Title VI of the CAA concerns stratospheric ozone protection. It establishes regulations for the production, use, and phaseout of CFCs, halons, and HCFCs. Other chemicals such as carbon tetrachloride ($CCl_4$), also covered by Title VI, are not covered in this text. Title VI divides the substances to be regulated into two classes: Class I and Class II.

The chemical that we are primarily concerned with in the automotive industry is CFC-12, a Class I refrigerant. Manufacture of this refrigerant ended in the United States on December 31, 1995.

# Technician Certification

Automotive technicians who wish to service mobile air conditioning systems and refrigeration equipment must be certified by an appropriate agency approved by the EPA. This includes all who work with CFC-12, the accepted replacement HFC-134a, or any of the blend refrigerants available and approved for automotive use.

## CFC-12 (R-12)

Those who wish to service or repair motor vehicle air conditioners (MVACs) using CFC-12 as a refrigerant, must be trained and certified by an EPA-approved organization. The training program must include pertinent information on the proper care and use of equipment, the regulatory requirements, the importance of refrigerant recovery, and the environmental effects of ozone depletion. To be certified, a technician must pass a test designed to demonstrate his or her knowledge in all of these areas.

## HFC-134a (R-134a)

Any automotive technician who wishes to repair or service HFC-134a MVACs must also be trained and certified by an EPA-approved agency. If, however, a technician is already trained and certified to repair and service CFC-12 systems, he or she does not have to be recertified to service HFC-134a systems.

## Characteristics of HFC134a (R-134a)

The automotive industry has chosen R-134a as the replacement refrigerant for CFC12 (R-12). R-134a is a Hydro-Fluorocarbon (HFC) and does not contribute to the depletion of the ozone layer. HFC134a is classified as a contributor to global warming though and, as such, is regulated. HFC refrigerants replace the chlorine atom with hydrogen atoms. It is a single-composition refrigerant that changes state at a specified temperature and pressure and has similar performance and vapor pressure characteristics to that of R-12. The power consumption is slightly higher for R-134a, and it has a slightly lower refrigeration capacity of between 3-5 percent compared to R-12. The properties of R-134a also require the use of different refrigerant oils to provide proper compressor lubrication which are not compatible with R-12. Components have been redesigned for the different characteristics of R-134a.

## Blend Refrigerants

Automotive technicians who service or repair MVACs that use a blend refrigerant must be trained and certified by an EPA-approved agency. However, a technician that is already trained and certified to handle CFC-12 or HFC-134a does not have to be recertified to handle a blend refrigerant.

## Certificating Agency

If there is any doubt about the integrity of the agency offering training and certification, check with the EPA. The EPA maintains an updated list of all of the approved agencies. The EPA has little mercy for anyone issuing bogus technician certificates to those who have not taken the required exam and can impose prison sentences and/or fines.

# Safety in the Shop

**Shop Manual**
Chapter 1,
page 6

Many studies have been made to determine which of the school shops are the more hazardous. The automobile mechanics shop, it has been found, ranks third in frequency of accidents. It is exceeded only by the wood shop and the machine shop.

Principal hazards and injuries in the automotive shop are:

❏ Flammable materials
❏ Bruised and cut fingers
❏ Acid burns
❏ Strains and hernia
❏ Falls
❏ Eye injuries

There is little manual lifting required in the modern automotive repair shop. Most lifting, when required, is accomplished with hoists, jacks, and other lifting devices. When using such equipment, understand and follow all applicable safety procedures. When manual lifting is required, lift with the legs—not with the back (Figure 1-8). Get help for heavy or bulky objects.

Many schools have designated their shops "total eye protection areas." This means that everyone who enters the shop must wear eye protective equipment. It is essential to wear safety goggles on any job where the eyes may be endangered, such as when grinding, using compressed air, working underneath cars, or servicing an air conditioning system.

Chemical or splash-proof goggles as well as a face shield (Figure 1-9) should be worn when servicing batteries or when boiling out or testing radiators for leaks.

Sparks near an automobile battery may create a hazard and can cause an explosion. The accumulation of hydrogen vapor at the top of the cell being charged is very explosive. Do not test a battery by "flashing" or "sparking" the terminals with a piece of wire to see if it has a charge.

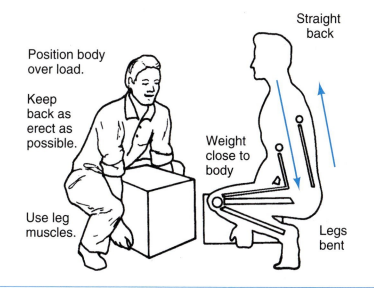

Position body over load.

Keep back as erect as possible.

Use leg muscles.

Straight back

Weight close to body

Legs bent

**Figure 1-8**  Lift with the legs, not the back.

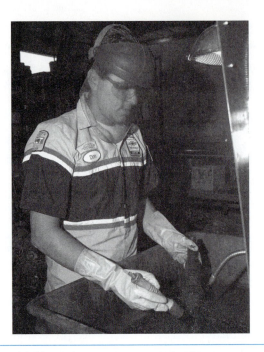

**Figure 1-9** A face shield may be worn over goggles for more protection.

Use only extension lights, cords, and sockets that are in good condition. Portable lights should be protected by a rubber- or neoprene-covered steel guard. All portable lights should have a third-wire ground. Do not place cords or wires across the floor where they may become a tripping hazard. Do not use portable electric tools unless they are electrically grounded with a third wire or are designated "double insulated." Be sure that the extension cables used with portable electric tools are in good condition and are of the proper size.

Do not attempt to use any power tools or equipment in the automotive shop until the proper and safe use has been fully explained by the instructor.

Hammers with broken handles, defective screwdrivers, and greasy tools can all be the cause of serious accidents. Keep all tools clean and free from grease.

Never engage in horseplay of any kind in the auto shop. This includes running, scuffling, and throwing tools or materials. Never use compressed air except for the purpose for which it is intended. Horseplay with compressed air equipment or dusting off clothing or work benches with compressed air is extremely dangerous. Flying particles of metal or glass may be blown into the eyes or the skin. Also, compressed air blown into the skin or body openings can cause serious injury and even death.

An approved hoist should be used for work underneath a car. The proper instruction, use, and operation of a hoist should be a work assignment for each learner in any automotive technician training program.

Vehicles raised by jack, chain hoist, or end lift should always be supported with safety stands (Figure 1-10) or with other approved safety devices. Before use, these devices should be carefully inspected for damage. Never crawl or work under a vehicle that is not supported by safety stands. This precaution should even be followed for inspection purposes.

When working under a vehicle:

❏ Use a creeper.
❏ Keep legs and arms clear of passageways.
❏ Keep vehicle doors closed.
❏ Do not place tools above the technician.

**Figure 1-10** Always use safety stands.

❏ Other technicians should not work on top of the vehicle.

❏ Wear safety glasses, goggles, or face shield.

❏ Do not leave creepers, tools, or other equipment where anyone can step on or trip over them.

Burns may result from working on a car that has not cooled off, most frequently by coming in contact with the manifold, exhaust pipe, or engine coolant.

Gasoline and diesel engines should only be operated in a shop or other area where there is adequate ventilation or there are provisions to connect the exhaust to an approved system that is designed to remove harmful exhaust fumes from the work area.

Before starting the engine, make sure the car is out of gear. On cars with automatic transmissions, make sure the gear select lever is in the neutral or park position when the motor is running. Set the parking brake. Ensure that there is no one working under the hood of the vehicle.

Be especially cautious around moving parts such as the flywheel, fan blades, belt, gears, and alternator pulley. Keep long sleeves rolled up when working on any moving machinery. Do not lubricate an engine while it is running, and do not attempt to wipe moving parts of the engine. Keep hands out of the area of moving parts.

Handle fluids carefully so that they do not splash in the eyes. Use a syringe when transferring fluids. It is important that brake fluid and some synthetic lubricants not be allowed to come into contact with a painted surface. Many such fluids contain ingredients that can soften, blister, and remove paint.

To avoid burns from accidental short circuits and to prevent accidental engagement of the starting motor, be sure to disconnect the battery ground cable and insulate the connection before working on the electrical system of the car.

Never consider a job complete until a check has been made to ensure that all parts that were removed have been replaced. Also, observe the following rules:

❏ Always refer to manufacturer's specifications.

❏ Keep tools clean and in good condition. Screwdriver blades should be kept sharp and square; handles should be of a nonconducting material.

❏ Use the proper type and size of tool. Use box wrenches in preference to open-end wrenches; use adjustable wrenches as little as possible. Do not use files as punches or chisels; they are brittle and may shatter.

Disconnect the battery ground cable before servicing the vehicle. See manufacturer's precautions.

Figure 1-11 Always wear safety glasses.

❏ Use handles on files.
❏ Do not put sharp-edge tools—such as chisels, punches, and open knives—in your pockets, even temporarily; keep guards on sharp edges or points of tools in tool kits.
❏ Push sharp tools away from you instead of drawing them toward you.
❏ Whenever possible, do not hold the screw or work piece with one hand and the screwdriver or tool with the other hand.
❏ Keep your face away from tools.
❏ Wear goggles when grinding or when working on any job that may involve flying debris (Figure 1-11).
❏ When working around moving machinery, do not wear gloves, ties, or loose clothing that may become caught in the machine and cause you severe injury.
❏ Rings should not be worn when working.
❏ Remove all loose jewelry, such as chains and watches.
❏ Use the proper fuel. Some vehicles use fuels other than gasoline and diesel fuel, such as liquified petroleum gas (LPG) and compressed natural gas (CNG) as well as alcohol and alcohol blends. Hydrogen gas may be used in the future.

Refrigerant pressure can exceed 300 psig (2,068 kPa).

## Injuries as a Result of High Pressure

A basic characteristic of a mechanical refrigeration system is the use of a fluid, both gas and liquid, that is at pressures above atmospheric pressure. The fluid must therefore be maintained and transmitted in tanks, pipes, and other vessels that do not allow the fluids to leak and that are strong enough to withstand maximum pressures without splitting or bursting under extreme conditions of use.

It is also a basic characteristic of mechanical refrigeration that these pressures change with fluctuations in temperature or are increased by compressors or pumps. We must, therefore, guard against extra pressures caused by compressors and pumps, as well as the pressures existing in the system because of variations of temperature.

**Figure 1-12** An accumulator is a pressure vessel designed to withstand normal pressures of an air conditioning system.

Pressure-containing vessels (Figure 1-12) and tubes are designed and constructed to withstand normal pressures caused by normal temperatures and by normal degrees of compression and normal filling of the vessels. If the vessel or tube is overheated, if an attempt is made to put too much fluid in it, or if the fluid is compressed above the pressure for which the vessel is designed or constructed, the vessel will "give" somewhat until it reaches its limit of elasticity; then the vessel will burst, often with explosive violence.

Overpressure may cause large parts to be blown out, such as the welded ends of dryers or of receivers. Overpressure may also drive plugs or other small parts out with projectile speed and force.

Explosions or bursting of vessels from overpressure sometimes start with overfilling the vessels with liquids at lower temperature. Then when the completely filled vessel warms up, the liquid expands and exerts tremendous pressure, known as **hydrostatic pressure**. As a result, something has to give, and it is the weakest part that gives. Oftentimes it is a hose or hose connection. Sometimes it is the compressor head gasket or a head, which may be most dangerous.

> Pressure relief valves are provided to release excess pressure.

> **Hydrostatic pressure** is the pressure exerted by a fluid.

## Special Safety Precautions

Because it is very important that the student be aware of the hazards involved in the use of any refrigerant, the following safety procedures must be observed at all times.

Recall that refrigerant is:

❏ Odorless
❏ Undetectable in small quantities
❏ Colorless
❏ Nonstaining

However, refrigerant is *dangerous* because of the damage it can cause if allowed to strike the human eye or come into contact with the skin. Suitable eye protection must be worn to protect the eyes from splashing refrigerant (Figure 1-13). If refrigerant does enter the eye, freezing of the eye can occur with resultant blindness. The following procedure is suggested if refrigerant enters the eye(s):

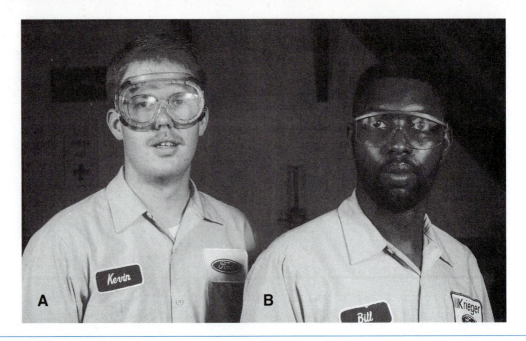

**Figure 1-13** Wear suitable eye protection: (A) monogoggle; (B) safety glasses.

Do not attempt self-treatment for injury.

1. Do not rub the eye.
2. Splash large quantities of cool (not hot) water into the eye to raise the temperature.
3. Tape a sterile eye patch over the eye to prevent dirt from entering. *Do not* use salves or ointments.
4. Go immediately to a doctor or hospital for professional care.

If liquid refrigerant strikes the skin, frostbite can occur. The same procedure outlined for emergency eye care can be used to combat the effects of refrigerant contact with the skin. Refrigerant in the air is harmless unless it is released in a confined space. Under this condition, refrigerant displaces oxygen in the air and may cause drowsiness or unconsciousness—even death. However, the automobile owner and the service technician need not be overly concerned about the safety of the automotive air conditioning system under normal conditions. The small capacity of the system compared to the large area of the car interior or work area minimizes the concentration of any contamination.

Refrigerant must not, however, be allowed to come into contact with an open flame or a very hot metal. Tests made by Underwriters' Laboratory, Inc. (UL) in 1933, shortly after the development of CFC-12, indicated that it produced a highly toxic gas known as phosgene during decomposition. Tests in recent years, however, prove that phosgene gas is not a product of decomposition in this manner. Decomposition does, however, result in the formation of carbonyl fluoride ($COF_2$) and carbonyl chlorofluoride ($COClF$) with small amounts of free chlorine ($Cl_2$).

Though 20–50 times less toxic than phosgene, as discussed earlier, the decomposed gases of CFC-12 must be avoided. At high concentrations, the lack of oxygen, which results in asphyxiation, is the real hazard. A primary rule, then, is to avoid breathing these or any other fumes. The human body requires oxygen in the quantity found in noncontaminated air. Diluting air with any foreign gas can reduce the available oxygen to a level that may be harmful or, in some cases, fatal.

The following rules must always be observed when handling refrigerants:

1. Never heat a refrigerant cylinder above 125°F (51.7°C) or allow it to reach this temperature. Above 130°F (54.44°C), expanding liquid refrigerant completely fills the container and hydrostatic pressure builds up rapidly with each degree of temperature rise.

**Figure 1-14** Use only DOT-approved recovery cylinders.

2. Never apply a direct flame to a refrigerant cylinder or container. Never place an electrical resistance heater near or in direct contact with a container of refrigerant.

3. Do not abuse a refrigerant cylinder or container. To avoid damage, use an approved valve wrench for opening and closing the valves. Secure all cylinders in an upright position for storing and withdrawing refrigerant. Carefully invert a refrigerant cylinder to dispense liquid refrigerant (first ensuring that the compressor is not running). Recovery cylinders are not to be inverted; use the liquid valve for dispensing liquid refrigerant (again ensuring that the compressor is not running).

4. Do not handle refrigerant without suitable eye protection.

5. Do not discharge (vent) refrigerant into the atmosphere. Remove refrigerant from a system using approved recovery equipment only.

6. Use only Department of Transportation (DOT) approved refrigerant recovery cylinders (Figure 1-14). Do not fill recovery cylinders beyond 80 percent of their rated capacity.

7. Do not mix refrigerants. Cross-contaminated refrigerants must be destroyed or separated by an approved reclamation center.

8. For an automotive air conditioning system, do not introduce anything but refrigerant acceptable under EPA's SNAP program into the system.

9. Use only lubricant recommended for the refrigerant type.

10. Properly identify, by label and fittings, refrigerant used.

11. Keep refrigerant containers out of direct sunlight.

12. Always work in a well-ventilated area. DO NOT work in a confined area.

Do not refill disposable cylinders.

# Ozone Protection Regulations

For decades, R-12, more properly known as CFC-12, was used as the refrigerant in motor vehicle air conditioning systems. However, since the discovery that CFCs damage the ozone layer, the production of ozone-depleting substances has ended. To help ensure that existing CFC-12 is used and reused rather than being wasted and released to the atmosphere, the EPA has issued regulations under Section 609 of the CAA to require that automotive shop technicians use special machines to recover and recycle CFC-12.

On December 31, 1995, the production of CFC-12 in the United States essentially ceased. It is legal, however, to use existing stockpiles of CFC-12, and several companies have also developed several new substitutes. These substitute refrigerants have been reviewed by the EPA's Significant New Alternatives Policy (SNAP) program. It is also illegal to release these substitutes to the atmosphere. As of June 1, 1998, the EPA has allowed refrigerant blends used in motor vehicle air conditioning systems to be recycled. The EPA stipulates that the equipment used must meet Underwriters Laboratories (UL) standards, and the refrigerant must be returned to the vehicle from which it was removed only.

The California Automotive Repair Bureau (CARB) passed a law that went into effect on January 19, 2001, requiring that every shop in the state that performs mobile air conditioning service have a minimum set of diagnostic equipment.

## Refrigerant Cylinders

Refrigerant cylinders (Figure 1-15) are designed and constructed for definite maximum pressures and for definite quantities of refrigerant that are based on specified maximum temperatures, usually 130°F (54°C). If the cylinders are subjected to temperatures above those specified, the liquid expands to entirely fill the cylinder; extremely high hydrostatic pressures develop, and the cylinder may burst.

If the cylinders are filled with a greater amount of refrigerant than specified, hydrostatic pressures may develop at ordinary room temperatures, and the cylinder may burst.

Flying pieces of the cylinder may travel at bullet velocity, or in case of small cylinders or light containers, the container itself may travel like a rocket at projectile speed. Sometimes of equal or greater danger, the refrigerant itself may burst from the cylinder; technicians have been blinded or suffered freezing injuries from being sprayed with refrigerant.

Many factory cylinders are equipped only with fusible plugs, which offer no protection against overfilling; nor do they offer adequate protection on most cylinders against excessive temperatures. Fusible plugs melt at about 160°F (71°C) and most cylinders are liquid-full at 130°F (54°C), so the fusible plug gives no protection between 130°F and 160°F.

All refrigerant cylinders should be protected by means of pressure-activated relief valves, especially service cylinders, because they are more often abused by overfilling than factory-filled cylinders. Small combination service valves, with built-in pressure-relief safety valves, were devel-

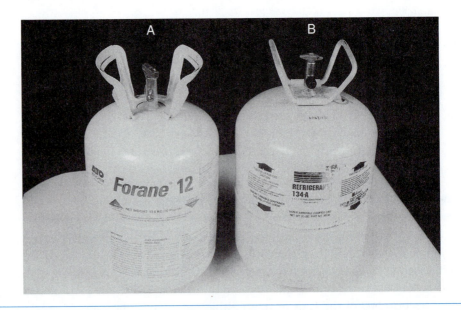

**Figure 1-15** Refrigerant cylinders are designated for a particular type refrigerant; 30 pounds (12.08 kg) cylinder R-12 (A) and 30 pounds (12.08 kg) cylinder R-134a (B).

**Figure 1-16** Cylinders must be reinspected every five years.

oped by valve manufacturers in cooperation with the Refrigeration Service Engineers Society (RSES) Safety and Educational Department and are available at moderate prices from refrigeration supply wholesalers. Every service cylinder should be equipped with one of the safety valves.

Even with the best of care, cylinders become rusted, damaged, or otherwise weakened after several years of use and should be retested by a hydraulic test approved by the Interstate Commerce Commission (ICC). The ICC requires a retest of all service cylinders and most factory cylinders once every five years (Figure 1-16). Do not use cylinders beyond the five-year period without having them retested. It may save your life or prevent serious injury. Your refrigerant supplier should be able to suggest a laboratory for retesting refrigerant cylinders. If not, consult the Yellow Pages of your local telephone directory under *Hydrostatic Testing* for the nearest facility.

Corrosion may occur inside a refrigerating system and may also affect external parts. It is commonly due to rusting in damp atmospheres or in areas in which there is a great deal of acidity in the air. As a rule, the parts most likely to be seriously affected are bolts, screws, nuts and rivets, or comparatively thin-walled vessels or tubes, especially those made of iron or steel. Particularly in damp or acid atmospheres, these parts should be inspected occasionally and repaired or replaced if necessary. Keeping parts subject to corrosion properly painted will greatly extend their useful life and lessen the possibility of suddenly giving way and causing an accident. Using protective paints and greases is an inexpensive preventative maintenance that guards against dangerous and costly breakage of corroded and weakened parts. Water supply lines, gate valves, fittings, and automatic pressure and control valves should be inspected periodically; badly corroded or weakened parts should be replaced.

It is a violation of federal law to reuse a disposable refrigerant cylinder.

# Antifreeze/Coolant

There are four key areas of engine protection. These are:

- ❏ Freeze protection
- ❏ Boil-over protection
- ❏ Corrosion prevention
- ❏ Adequate heat transfer

**Shop Manual**
Chapter 1,
page 5

### Ethylene Glycol-based Antifreeze

Ethylene glycol (EG) is the main ingredient of all major antifreeze brands and has long been known to be poisonous. When ingested, EG converts to oxalic acid that damages the kidneys and may cause kidney failure and death.

Just 2 oz. of undiluted EG antifreeze (Figure 1-17) can kill a dog; one teaspoon can be lethal to a cat; and two tablespoons can be hazardous to children.

Data compiled by the American Association of Poison Control Centers (AAPCC) show that about 3,400 poisonings related to EG occur annually. About 20 percent of these incidents are reported among children under six years of age.

### Propylene Glycol-based Antifreeze

A "new" antifreeze, formulated with propylene glycol (PG) is less toxic than EG antifreeze. Therefore, PG antifreeze (Figure 1-18) is much safer for children and animals. Actually, PG is used in specific amounts in the formulation of many consumer products. These products include, but are not limited to, cosmetics, pet food, and certain over-the-counter medications. Nonetheless, PG-based antifreeze should be considered toxic and handled as a hazardous substance.

In areas where recycling antifreeze is required, one may locate a facility through a local automotive parts house or in the telephone book's Yellow Pages under *Recycling Centers* or *Hazardous Materials and Waste Contractors.*

### Mixing EG and PG

It should be noted that EG-based antifreeze should not be mixed with PG-based antifreeze. Most antifreeze manufacturers caution against mixing the various types and suggest recovery and storage of the different types in separate containers. Also, most vehicle manufacturers require the

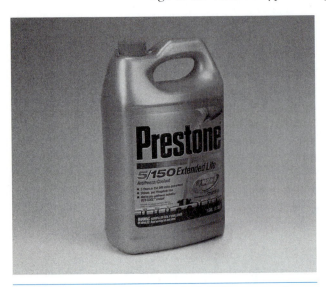

**Figure 1-17**  Ethylene Glycol Antifreeze.

**Figure 1-18**  Propylene Glycol Antifreeze.

same type antifreeze be used for top-off or refill that was originally installed in the factory fill to avoid warranty problems. It should be noted that there may be different formulations of antifreeze specified by some vehicle manufacturers. Always refer to manufacturer's specifications before changing or adding antifreeze to a cooling system.

## Vehicle Engine Protection

Either EG- or PG-based antifreeze offers excellent protection for vehicle engines against corrosion, freezing, and overheating. A 50/50 blend of ethylene glycol antifreeze and water has a freezing point of –34°F (–36.7°C). If a lower temperature protection is required, it can be attained by increasing the concentration of antifreeze. A 60/40 blend, for example, gives antifreeze protection to –54°F (–47.8°C). It also helps to prevent corrosion in all metals used in automotive cooling systems, including aluminum, brass, copper, cast iron, steel, and the elements contained in solder.

## Disposal

Used coolant must be properly disposed of in compliance with local rules and regulations. In areas where recycling is available, both used EG and PG coolants should be offered to recyclers for recycling and reuse.

# Hazardous Materials

Refrigerants, refrigeration lubricants, solvents, and other chemicals used in an automotive repair facility may be considered hazardous materials and will include warning and caution labels that should be read and understood by everyone who uses them.

All hazardous materials should be properly labeled, indicating what health, fire, or reactive hazard it poses and what protective equipment is necessary when handling each chemical. The manufacturer of the hazardous material must also provide all warnings and precautionary information that must be read and understood by all users before the material is used. One should pay particular attention to the label information. Using the product according to label directions helps to ensure the proper and safe methods, thereby preventing a hazardous condition.

A list of all hazardous materials used in the shop should be posted for all employees to see. Shops must also maintain documented records of the hazardous chemicals in the workplace, training programs, accidents, and spill incidents.

**Shop Manual**
Chapter 1,
pages 1–2, 4–5

## Material Safety Data Sheet

Every employee in a shop is protected by "right-to-know" laws concerning hazardous materials and wastes. The general intent of the law is to ensure that the employer provide a safe work environment. All employees must be trained about their rights under the legislation, the nature of the hazardous chemicals in their workplace, the labeling of chemicals, and the information about each chemical listed and described on Material Safety Data Sheets (MSDS). These sheets (Figure 1-19) are available from the manufacturers and suppliers of the chemicals. They detail the chemical composition and precautionary information for all products that can pose health or safety hazards.

Employees must be familiar with the contents of the MSDS that contains information relative to the intended purposes of the substance, the recommended protective equipment, accident and spill procedures, and any other information regarding safe handling. Training must be provided by the employer annually, and new employees must be trained as a part of their job orientation. When handling any hazardous material, always wear the appropriate safety protection. Always follow the correct procedures while using the material, and be familiar with the information given in the MSDS for that material.

**Shop Manual**
Chapter 1,
page 4

Figure 1-19 Typical Material Safety Data Sheet (MSDS) manual.

## Hazardous Waste

Waste is considered hazardous if it is on the EPA list of known harmful materials. Those materials generally have one or more of the following characteristics:

❑ Ignitable
❑ Corrosive
❑ Reactive
❑ Toxic

Many service procedures also generate products that may be considered hazardous wastes. Contaminated refrigerant or antifreeze are typical examples of hazardous waste.

## Safety Precautions

The following safety precautions in working with hazardous materials should always be observed:

❑ Do not overfill refrigerant cylinders.
❑ Do not allow pressure-containing vessels to become overheated.
❑ Do not put a flame on a refrigerant cylinder, accumulator, receiver, or any other vessel that may contain refrigerant.
❑ Do not steam clean any vessels that may contain refrigerant.
❑ Do not change or add refrigerant to any system without first determining system compatibility.
❑ Always connect both low- and high-pressure gauges before servicing a system. Observe these gauges frequently.
❑ Before loosening bolts or screws, see that the pressure in the part has been relieved. Gaskets may hold the pressure temporarily, then release suddenly, throwing a full charge of refrigerant in the technician's face.
❑ Use pressure relief valves on all refrigerant cylinders and other vessels that may be subject to excessive pressures.
❑ Do not allow a compressor to pump liquid or "slug oil."
❑ Wear suitable protective gear when handling any materials that may be considered toxic.

It is a violation of federal law to intentionally vent refrigerant to the atmosphere.

22

❏ Keep your mind on what you are doing.

❏ Be vigilant.

❏ If you are tired, take a break.

❏ Read and heed all caution labels. Those warning of high pressures, as in the antilock brake systems and the dangers of unexpected air bag deployment, are most important.

❏ Be aware of underhood hazards and avoid their danger.

**AUTHOR'S NOTE:** When you first begin a new job in an automotive shop, you will have many concerns on your first day. Pay particular attention to the location of all exits from the building, fire extinguishers, eye wash stations, the emergency shower, and where the MSDS data book is located in case of emergency. An emergency situation is not the time to try to locate safety equipment or exits.

# Breathing Toxic Gases

Literally the word *toxic* means "poisonous," so "toxicity" is the condition of being "poisonous." In refrigeration terms, "toxic" is more frequently used with gases that we may breathe and that poison us by being taken into our blood by means of the lungs.

Refrigerants vary a great deal in their degrees of toxicity. Some refrigerants, such as ammonia ($NH_3$), are so highly toxic that it is dangerous, as well as unpleasant, to breathe air that has only a few parts per million of these gases. Others, such as R-12, may be breathed in large percentages with air without noticeably harmful effects.

It must be remembered, however, that the gas we are suited to breathe is air, and that any other gas is harmful. Harmful effects depend upon:

❏ the nature of the gas itself,

❏ its concentration in air, and

❏ how long a time it is breathed.

## Decomposition of Gases

Some gases that may have a high safety rating or moderate safety ratings in their natural state become highly toxic if they are exposed to flames or hot surfaces. The heat "decomposes" these relatively safe gases and causes them to form other gases that are very toxic.

The refrigerants thus decomposed are those that contain one or more of the **halogens**, a group of elements that includes chlorine (Cl), fluorine (F), bromine (Br), and iodine (I). Any of the refrigerants that have the symbols "Cl" or "F" in their chemical structure may be subject to hazardous decomposition.

Refrigerants should not be allowed to come into contact with an open flame or a very hot metal. Until recently it was believed that fluorocarbon refrigerants, such as R-12, produce phosgene gas when exposed to hot metal or an open flame. The original tests, made by Underwriters' Laboratory (UL) shortly after the development of R-12, indicated that it produced this highly toxic gas during decomposition. Recent tests, however, have shown that phosgene gas is not produced in this manner.

According to a technical specialist for SUVA® Refrigerants at DuPont Chemicals, which was one of the major manufacturers of R-12, commonly known as Freon®, the only products of decomposition of R-12, when in contact with an open flame or glowing metal surface, are hydrofluoric and hydrochloric acids.

**Shop Manual**
Chapter 1,
pages, 2, 3, 6

**Halogen** refers to any of the five chemical elements that may be found in some refrigerants: astatine (At), bromine (Br), chlorine (Cl), fluorine (F), and iodine (I).

Though as much as 50 times less toxic than phosgene gas, the decomposed gases of R-12 must be avoided. At high concentrations, lack of oxygen, which results in asphyxiation, is the real hazard. Avoid breathing these or any other *fumes*. The human body requires oxygen in the quantity found in noncontaminated air. Diluting air with any foreign gas can reduce the available oxygen to a level that may be harmful or, in some cases, fatal.

These gases of decomposition may not noticeably affect the person breathing them for several hours, so you should vacate the area contaminated by them as soon as you detect them by smell. Also, beware of the gases from burning plastics; one of these is the extremely dangerous phosgene ($COCl_2$).

## Other Gases

Acetylene, a gas used in welding, brazing, and soldering operations, is not highly toxic. Nonetheless, it should not be breathed unnecessarily.

Nitrogen (N) is an inert gas, and is not absorbed by the lungs. It is, therefore, harmless in itself if sufficient oxygen is present. The air in our atmosphere is 78 percent nitrogen.

Carbon (C) is the element in coal, oil, natural gas, or wood, that "burns." In burning, it unites with oxygen, thus forming the gas carbon dioxide ($CO_2$), one part carbon, two parts oxygen. It is a comparatively harmless gas but can result in oxygen deficiency if it is in the air in too great a percentage.

Carbon monoxide (CO) is also formed during combustion (Figure 1-20). It is one part carbon and one part oxygen, highly toxic, and very dangerous. Carbon monoxide is doubly dangerous in that it has no odor and can therefore kill without warning. It is the gas that is chiefly responsible for deaths in closed garages or even in a closed automobile with the engine running.

### Precautions

If the nature of the various refrigerants and other gases and fumes are understood and if reasonable care is exercised, a refrigeration service technician need have no fear of possible toxic hazards from refrigerants.

One must use care, however, and in particular observe the following:

❑ Do not breathe any gas any more than is absolutely necessary. None of them is harmless under all conditions.
❑ Do not ignore the possible danger of a gas just because it has very little odor. The odor of a gas is no indication of its toxicity.

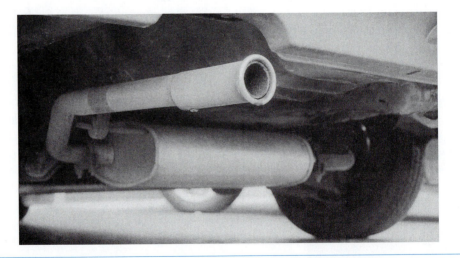

**Figure 1-20** Carbon monoxide, a deadly gas from the exhaust pipe, must be avoided. Work in a well-ventilated area.

❏ Do not discharge any gas into any unventilated area.

❏ Do not discharge any of the hydrocarbon gases into a room in which there is a fire, flame, or electric heating element.

❏ Do not hesitate to use a gas mask if it is necessary to enter a room that you know or suspect has any of the toxic gases in it.

❏ Do not leave leaks in refrigerating equipment that may fill the room with gas and pose a danger to someone.

❏ Do not run an automobile engine in a closed garage; do not sit in a closed car with the engine running.

❏ Do not allow liquids to boil over on a gas stove; they may put out the flame, but the gas continues to escape.

❏ Do not use questionable tubing, flexible hose, or connectors.

❏ Do not work in an unventilated room with a heater having an open flame.

❏ Do not vent refrigerant. The EPA requires that all refrigerant be recovered.

❏ Do not breathe fumes from acids, caustics, carbontetrachloride ($CCl_4$), benzol, ketone, xylene, or other toxic cleaning materials. Always keep rooms well ventilated when using cleaning solvents.

❏ Do not breathe fumes from broken fluorescent lamps; they are poisonous.

## Summary

❏ The ozone layer protects all life on earth from excess UV radiation.

❏ Ozone depletion seems to be the greatest during the early winter months.

❏ The mandatory phaseout in the manufacture and the eventual reduction of use of CFCs is expected to have a positive effect on the ozone.

❏ Increased UV radiation affects the eyes, skin, and the immune system.

❏ The greenhouse effect is also affected by the release of pollutants.

❏ All areas of safety should be practiced at all times.

**Shop Manual**
Chapter 1,
page 26

## Review Questions

### Short Answer Essays

1. What would you do if you had to enter a room that you suspected contained hazardous vapors?

2. How would you detect the presence of ozone or any other gas?

3. Describe the location and conditions of the troposphere.

4. What does it mean to say the ozone measurement is 125 DU?

5. Compare the ozone layer to an umbrella.

6. What is the intent of Title VI of the Clean Air Act?

7. Give and explain three reasons why horseplay cannot be tolerated in the shop.

8. Briefly describe the term *hydrostatic pressure*.

9. What are the precautions to observe before loosening bolts and screws of a pressurized system?

10. What are some of the factors that contribute to ozone depletion?

**Terms to Know**

Allotrope
Atmosphere
CFCs
Chlorine (Cl)
Clean Air Act (CAA)
Dobson unit (DU)
Greenhouse effect
Global warming
Halogens
Hydrostatic pressure
Nitrogen (N)
Oxygen (O)
Ozone ($O_3$)
Ozone depletion
Toxicity
Ultraviolet radiation (UV)

## Fill-in-the Blanks

1. Most of the earth's ozone is found in the _____ _____.
2. The air we breathe is made up of 21 percent _____.
3. Increased UV radiation is damaging to the eyes, skin, and _____.
4. Chlorofluorocarbons (CFCs) are also known as _____.
5. The element for the chemical symbol $O_3$ is _____.
6. The Clean Air Act was signed into law by _____.
7. The most hazardous shop in a school is the _____ shop.
8. The fluid in an air conditioning system is called ____.
9. Factory cylinders are equipped with _____ plugs.
10. ____ ____, a very dangerous gas, has no odor.

## Multiple Choice

1. The air we breathe is being discussed:
   *Technician A* says that this air is made up of 12 percent nitrogen.
   *Technician B* says that the most essential gas is oxygen.
   Who is correct?
   **A.** A only
   **B.** B only
   **C.** Both A and B
   **D.** Neither A nor B

2. *Technician A* says that chlorine (Cl), an ingredient of CFC refrigerants, is harming the ozone layer.
   *Technician B* says that the ozone layer is important for protection from ultraviolet (UV) radiation.
   Who is correct?
   **A.** A only
   **B.** B only
   **C.** Both A and B
   **D.** Neither A nor B

3. *Technician A* says that the main source for ozone-depleting chlorine is chlorofluorocarbons (CFCs).
   *Technician B* says that chlorine used in swimming pools contributes to ozone depletion.
   Who is correct?
   **A.** A only
   **B.** B only
   **C.** Both A and B
   **D.** Neither A nor B

4. *Technician A* says to lift heavy objects using the legs, not the back.
   *Technician B* says one should get help when lifting heavy objects.
   Who is correct?
   **A.** A only
   **B.** B only
   **C.** Both A and B
   **D.** Neither A nor B

5. *Technician A* says that an automotive air conditioning system contains a fluid under high pressure.
   *Technician B* says that the fluid in an air conditioning system is at a high temperature.
   Who is correct?
   **A.** A only
   **B.** B only
   **C.** Both A and B
   **D.** Neither A nor B

6. *Technician A* says that refrigerant gases, in contact with a heated surface, produce a toxic vapor.
   *Technician B* says that refrigerant gases, in contact with a heated surface, decompose.
   Who is correct?
   **A.** A only
   **B.** B only
   **C.** Both A and B
   **D.** Neither A nor B

7. *Technician A* says that cleaning fluids used in automotive service are toxic and their fumes must be avoided.
   *Technician B* says that brake fluid may be used to clean up a synthetic lubricant spill before it damages a painted surface.
   Who is correct?
   **A.** A only
   **B.** B only
   **C.** Both A and B
   **D.** Neither A nor B

8. *Technician A* says that a toxic product may not be classified as a hazardous substance.
   *Technician B* says that contaminated CFC-12 is not considered a hazardous substance.
   Who is correct?
   **A.** A only
   **B.** B only
   **C.** Both A and B
   **D.** Neither A nor B

9. *Technician A* says that carbon monoxide is very dangerous.
*Technician B* says that carbon dioxide is very dangerous.
Who is correct?

A. A only
B. B only
C. Both A and B
D. Neither A nor B

10. *Technician A* says that one should always use a three-wire grounded extension cord.
*Technician B* says that tools designated "double insulated" may be used safely with a two-wire extension cord.
Who is correct?

A. A only
B. B only
C. Both A and B
D. Neither A nor B

# Temperature and Pressure Fundamentals

Upon completion and review of this chapter, you should be able to:

❏ Discuss the fundamentals of temperature and pressure.

❏ Explain the nature of atoms and molecules.

❏ Describe the differences between sensible, latent, and specific heat values.

❏ Discuss the measurement of heat energy.

❏ Describe how heat flows.

❏ Explain effects of radiation, conduction, and convection on personal comfort.

❏ Describe the difference between humidity and relative humidity.

## Introduction

Before we can enter into a discussion about the automotive heating and air conditioning system, you must first have a basic understanding of the chemistry and physics involved in order to properly analyze both systems. The concepts and principles covered in this chapter will form the foundation for understanding heat transfer and the three changes in state of matter, which are the operating principles behind the climate control systems used on today's vehicles. Diagnosing and servicing comfort control systems will become more clear after learning how and why heat transfer takes place. Theories are critical in developing your skills as a technician and, in turn, will increase your productivity and overall worth to the trade.

## Elements and Matter

Everything in nature is known as **matter** and is made up of one or more of the 106 known basic elements. Some of the more common and better known of these elements are:

### Carbon

Carbon (C) is a nonmetallic element found in many inorganic compounds and in all organic compounds. Carbon is present in many chemical compounds and gases such as Refrigerant-12, a **chlorofluorocarbon (CFC)** refrigerant, and Refrigerant-134a, a hydrofluorocarbon (HFC) refrigerant. At atmospheric pressure and temperatures, carbon normally exists as a solid.

### Chlorine

Chlorine (Cl) is a heavy, greenish-yellow gas used for the purification of water ($H_2O$) and the manufacture of CFC and HCFC refrigerants. Chlorine, it has been determined, is causing problems with the ozone layer of the atmosphere.

### Aluminum

Aluminum (Al) is a lightweight, ductile metal that does not readily tarnish or corrode. Aluminum and aluminum alloys have widespread use in the manufacture of automotive components and parts.

**Matter** is anything that occupies space and possesses mass. All things in nature are composed of matter.

Nearly pure carbon (C), in crystalline form, is known as a diamond.

**Chlorofluorocarbon (CFC)** is a man-made compound used in refrigerants such as R-12, more accurately designated CFC-12.

## Lead

Lead (Pb) is a heavy, soft, blue-gray metal that was once used extensively as a filler material for soldering. It has now been determined that lead is a health hazard, and its use is limited and, in many cases, prohibited.

## Nitrogen

Ordinary air that we breathe is about 78 percent nitrogen (N). Nitrogen normally exists as a gas and is a very important element in plant life. Nitrogen is a compound of all living things.

## Oxygen

Oxygen (O) makes up 21 percent of the air we breathe. It is absolutely essential to all animal life. Oxygen is a very active element and combines readily with most of the other elements to form oxides or more complex chemicals. Oxygen normally exists as a gas.

## Other Gases

The remaining 1 percent of the air we breathe consists of argon (Ar), hydrogen (H), neon (Ne), krypton (Kr), helium (He), and xenon (Xe), and other trace nonelement gases, such as carbon dioxide ($CO_2$) and ozone ($O_3$).

**Hydrogen. Hydrogen** (H), an important element in oil, fuels, acids, and many other compounds, is odorless, tasteless, and colorless. It is normally a gas and is the lightest of the elements. Hydrogen rarely exists alone in nature; its most commonly known mixture is with oxygen to form water ($H_2O$).

# The Atom

Each of the elements consists of billions of tiny particles called atoms. An **atom** is so small that it can only be seen with the most powerful microscope. Scientists, however, can measure it and weigh it, and they have learned a great deal about its nature.

An atom is the smallest particle of which an element is composed that still retains the characteristics of that element. For example, an atom of copper (Cu) is copper (Cu), and it is different from, say, an atom of aluminum (Al). For our purpose, consider the atom as indivisible and unchangeable. That is, it cannot be divided by ordinary means. Whenever we divide an atom physically and chemically, it retains the characteristics of that element. Atoms of all of the elements are different. Iron (Fe) is composed of iron atoms; lead (Pb) of lead atoms; tin (Sn) of tin atoms, and so on.

An atom (Figure 2-1) is composed of still smaller particles called protons, neutrons, and electrons. The proton has a positive (+) charge; the electron has a negative (–) charge; and the neutron has neither a negative (–) nor a positive (+) charge.

Scientists have been able to split some kinds of elements, such as uranium (U). For our purpose, however, we will focus on the following facts regarding atoms:

❏ The atom is the very smallest possible particle of matter.
❏ All of the elements are composed of atoms.
❏ The atoms of the different elements are different.

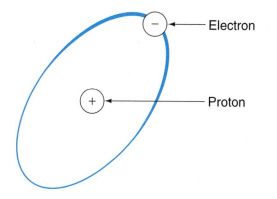

Electron

Proton

**Figure 2-1** A simple hydrogen (H) atom is composed of one proton and one electron.

# The Molecule

The next larger particle of a material is called a **molecule**. If the molecule contains only one kind of atom, the molecule will be a molecule of an element. The molecule of most of the elements has only one atom in it. However, a molecule may have several atoms in it, even though they are all the same kind. For example, a molecule of oxygen (Figure 2-2) contains two atoms of oxygen, a molecule of iron has but one atom of iron, and so on for all of the elements. Any element consists of billions of molecules, and each of those molecules consists of one, two, or several atoms of that element.

A **molecule** is two or more atoms chemically bonded together.

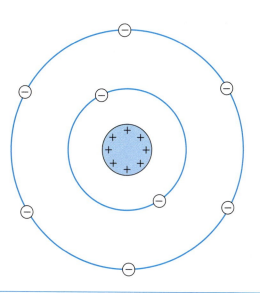

**Figure 2-2** An oxygen molecule ($O_2$) has two atoms of oxygen (O).

# Chemical Compounds

When hydrogen (H), a flammable gas, and oxygen (O), required for combustion, are combined water ($H_2O$) is produced, which is not flammable.

A molecule may consist of two or more atoms of different elements. In such an instance, the material becomes entirely different and usually does not resemble either of the elements that constitute it. For example, if the molecule consists of one atom of iron (Fe) and one atom of oxygen (O), it becomes iron oxide (FeO), which is quite different from either iron (Fe) or oxygen (O).

How different the compound material itself can be from the elements of which it is composed is illustrated by water ($H_2O$). The molecule of water, in any form, consists of two atoms of the element hydrogen (H), which is a very light, highly flammable gas, and one atom of the element oxygen (O), which is also a gas that aids combustion. The combination of these two elements, each a gas in its natural state, produces a liquid, water, which is unlike either hydrogen or oxygen.

The molecule is often quite complex and may have several kinds of elements in it. Refrigerant-12 (CFC-12), which is normally a colorless gas, is a good example of this. The CFC-12 molecule consists of one atom of carbon (C), normally a black solid; two atoms of chlorine (Cl), normally a yellow-green gas; and two atoms of fluorine (F), normally a pale-yellow gas. The chemical symbol for CFC-12 is $CCl_2F_2$ (Figure 2-3). HFC-134a, an ozone-friendly refrigerant developed to replace CFC-12, consists of two carbon (C) atoms, four fluorine (F) atoms, and two hydrogen (H) atoms. The chemical symbol for HFC-134a is $CF_3CH_2F$ (Figure 2-4).

## Motion of the Molecules

Since mechanical refrigeration is a physical rather than a chemical process, we deal with molecules and their movement. Rarely do we have a need to go into chemical processes that involve breaking down the molecules. It is nonetheless necessary to have an elementary understanding of the composition of matter to more easily understand how gases, liquids, and solids behave under various conditions.

If the matter is a solid, such as copper (Cu) or ice ($H_2O$), the molecules are held together by their mutual attraction to each other. The mutual attraction of like molecules is called cohesion. The molecules are not tightly bound together, and they are not motionless (Figure 2-5). There are spaces between them, and while their motion is limited, they move somewhat.

**Absolute zero** is the complete absence of heat, believed to be −459°F (−273.15°C).

The colder the solid, the less motion of the molecules. If the matter had absolutely no heat, if it were at a temperature of **absolute zero** (−459.67°F), there would be no motion of the molecules. If the absolute cold matter were heated, the molecules would begin to move. The motion of the molecules becomes greater the warmer the matter becomes.

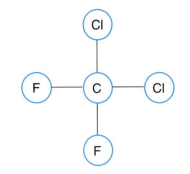

Figure 2-3 Composition of Refrigerant-12.

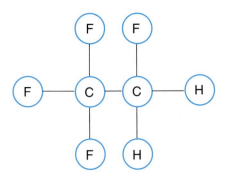

Figure 2-4 Composition of Refrigerant-134a.

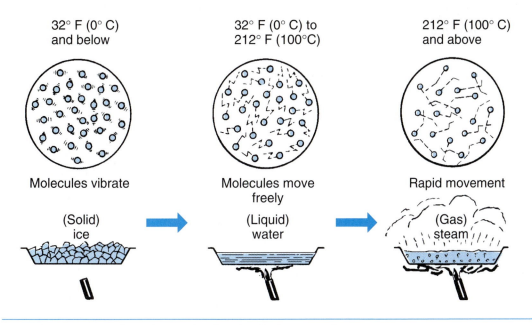

32° F (0° C)
and below

32° F (0° C) to
212° F (100°C)

212° F (100° C)
and above

Molecules vibrate

Molecules move
freely

Rapid movement

(Solid)
ice

(Liquid)
water

(Gas)
steam

**Figure 2-5** Freedom of water (H$_2$O) molecules in states of matter.

# Heat and Cold

An appropriate definition of **heat** is the sensation of warmth or hotness. The definition of cold, then, is feeling no warmth; uncomfortably chilled. If you sense a temperature above the normal body temperature of 98.6°F (37°C), you tend to feel warm; if the temperature is below normal body temperature, you feel cool. To understand what heat and cold are, you must first understand the law of heat.

## The Law of Heat

Heat is ever-present in all matter. There are three basic terms used to describe the three types of heat: sensible, latent, and specific.

**Sensible Heat. Sensible heat** is any heat that we can feel and that can be measured with a thermometer. For example, water boils at 212°F (100°C) at sea-level atmospheric pressure. The temperature of water from a spigot may be 58°F (14.4°C). From the spigot temperature to the boiling point, the increase in temperature is 154°F (85.6°C). That increase in temperature is known as sensible heat.

**Latent Heat. Latent heat** cannot be measured with a thermometer. To explain, we know that a pan of boiling water does not all turn to steam (gas) as soon as it reaches its boiling point. If the pan is left on the burner and allowed to boil long enough, however, all of the water will boil away. The heat that is added to the boiling water to cause all of it to vaporize is called latent heat. Though it cannot be measured with a thermometer, latent heat is required to cause a change of state in matter.

We cannot heat water at atmospheric pressure (sea level) hotter than 212°F (100°C). The steam form of this water as it boils is also at 212°F (100°C). We will discuss later the fact that water in a sealed container, such as an automobile radiator, may not boil until the temperature is

**Heat** is any temperature above absolute zero.

**Sensible heat** causes a change in the temperature of a substance but does not change the state of the substance.

**Latent heat** is the amount of heat required to cause a change of state of a substance without changing its temperature.

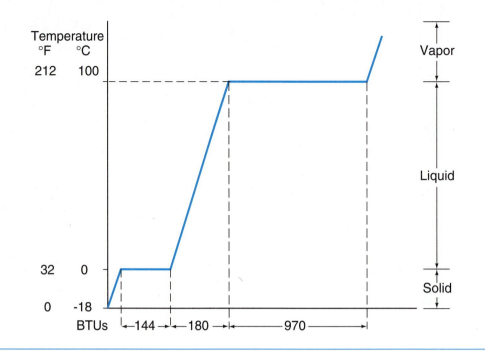

**Figure 2-6** Sensible and latent heat values required to effect a temperature and/or physical change in 1 lb. (0.4536 kg) of water ($H_2O$) from the freezing to boiling temperature at sea level atmospheric pressure.

**British thermal unit (Btu)** is a measure of heat energy; one Btu is the amount of heat necessary to raise one pound of water 1°F.

further increased if the system is pressurized. Also, if the pressure is reduced or at a vacuum, water may boil at temperatures much below 212°F (100°C). In fact, we will demonstrate how, under certain conditions, water will boil at 32°F (0°C)—its normal freezing point (Figure 2-6).

As indicated earlier, latent heat must be added to the water to cause it to change to a gas. Since we cannot measure latent heat on a thermometer, we use as a unit of measure the **British thermal unit (Btu)**. One Btu will cause a change of temperature of one degree Fahrenheit (1°F) in one pint (1 lb. or 16 oz.) of water ($H_2O$). Metrically, one calorie (1 cal) will cause a change of temperature of one degree Celsius (1°C) in one gram (1 g) of water ($H_2O$).

One pound (0.4536 kg) of ice taken from the refrigerator at 32°F (0°C) requires 144 Btu of latent heat to cause a change in state to liquid at 32°F (0°C). An additional 180 Btu of sensible heat will bring the liquid to its boiling point of 212°F (100°C), and another 970 Btu of latent heat are required for a change in state to a gas, again at 212°F (100°C).

**Specific Heat.** Everything in nature has a **specific heat**. We are not to be particularly concerned with this term. It is important, at this time, to know that refrigerant used in automobile air conditioning systems has an appropriate specific heat value for its application. It is interesting to note that water also has an appropriate specific heat value for its application as an engine coolant.

**Specific heat** is the quantity of heat required to change one pound of a substance by 1°F.

# Sensible Heat of a Solid

Energy is required to cause movement or to do work. The molecules must be given heat, a form of energy, in order to give motion. The more heat energy present, the greater the motion and the faster they move.

The heat added to raise the temperature of the solid matter and give the molecules more movement is called sensible heat, for we can tell that heat has been added by one of our senses, the sense of feeling, which tells us that the solid is warmer than before.

If we continue to add heat energy to the solid, it becomes warmer and the molecules move faster, but still within a very limited space, because they are still held to one another by their mutual attraction.

> **AUTHOR'S NOTE:** Air conditioning systems are based on the laws of physics, and it is essential that technicians understand the principles of latent and sensible heat if they are to properly diagnose system function later in this text.

# Melting or Fusion

Finally, when sufficient heat is added to the molecules, they receive enough energy to partially overcome their attraction for each other. At that time, the molecules can move about freely and change state to become a liquid. The process of the molecules breaking away from each other and changing state from a solid to a liquid is called melting or fusion.

The attraction of the molecules of a solid for one another is great; therefore, a considerable amount of heat energy is required for a solid to become a liquid. The heat energy required to melt a solid is relatively more than the amount required to warm it by raising its temperature a few degrees.

The heat required to effect a change of state of matter from a solid to a liquid is called the latent heat of melting or, more correctly, the latent heat of fusion. The word *latent* means hidden. It is a term that is used to identify something that is present, but not visible. The heat that causes a change of state cannot be measured on a thermometer; in this sense, it is hidden heat. Latent heat, then, is heat required to cause a change of state of matter without changing its temperature.

The temperatures of the solid immediately before it melts and immediately afterward when it has become a liquid are exactly the same. For example, if the matter (Figure 2-7) were water, its temperature as a solid (ice) and as a liquid would be 32°F.

The molecules, now moving more freely, are not held together. The matter can no longer stand rigidly by itself and must have a container to support it. The speed of the molecules is much greater as a liquid, yet not great enough to overcome the force of gravity. The molecules are therefore held downward in the container. The liquid, however, can be poured from a higher container to a lower one, or pumped from a lower container to a higher container.

Matter in the liquid state has more heat in it than when it is in the solid state; and, except at the exact melting temperature, it will always be warmer.

Since the liquid molecules are much freer in a liquid than in a solid, they are farther apart and require more room to move. Assuming the same matter and the same weight, the volume of a liquid, then, is greater than the volume of a solid.

Latent means hidden.

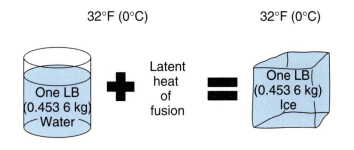

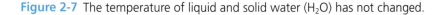

**Figure 2-7** The temperature of liquid and solid water (H$_2$O) has not changed.

# Sensible Heat of a Liquid

Sensible heat is heat that is added to matter to cause it to become warmer.

Since the molecules of a liquid have considerable heat energy, they move about in a lively manner and at a rapid speed. They constantly bump into each other and into the side of their container.

As heat energy is added to a liquid and it becomes warmer, the speed of its molecules increases. The heat energy that is added to it is called sensible heat.

# Evaporation

Evaporation is the process of forming a vapor.

Not all of the molecules in the liquid move at the same speed. In fact, some of the molecules at the top of the liquid may attain enough speed to fly out of the liquid and into the space of air above the liquid and escape. Some of them escape from the liquid temporarily but do not have enough speed nor energy to entirely escape and fall back into the liquid.

Some molecules, however, do escape to mix with the air or other gas above the liquid. Some of the molecules, then, are constantly escaping. They form a gas or vapor blanket above the liquids and tend to diffuse into and mix with the air. The process of the molecules escaping from the surface of the liquid is called **evaporation**.

A good example of evaporation of a liquid is water ($H_2O$) in an open container (Figure 2-8). When water is placed over heat and its temperature exceeds 212°F (100°C), it slowly evaporates into a gas (water vapor). Eventually all of the water evaporates. The warmer the water, the faster it evaporates. The more heat energy added, the more molecules gain sufficient velocity to escape from the liquid.

## Boiling or Vaporization

If more heat is added to the liquid above the boiling temperature, it becomes warmer and warmer and the molecules move faster and faster. When enough heat energy has been added, the molecules are moving so rapidly that they lose all restraint and fly out of the liquid, much the same as in evaporation, but in far greater numbers.

At this very high temperature, the liquid disintegrates and breaks loose even from the force of gravity. The molecules fly in all directions. This condition is referred to as a gas or a vapor. As a vapor, the matter requires a great deal more space than when it was a liquid or a solid. The molecules are flying about and are, therefore, widely separated. The volume of the vapor, then, is much greater than when the matter was a liquid.

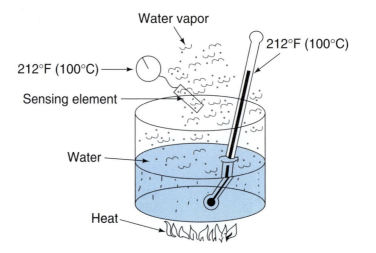

**Figure 2-8** Evaporation of liquid water ($H_2O$) by boiling.

The process of changing from a liquid to a vapor is called boiling or vaporization. The temperature at which this occurs is called the boiling temperature.

A great amount of heat energy is required to boil a liquid and give the molecules enough energy to escape and form a vapor. This is referred to as the latent heat of boiling or, more correctly, the latent heat of vaporization. Note that this heat, too, is referred to as latent heat. It is heat that is required for a change of state without a change of temperature.

If the liquid is water ($H_2O$) in an open container, the molecules that escape into the air form what is known as water vapor. Another term for water vapor is "moisture in the air." A liquid can and does have its own vapor that forms just above its surface. It also diffuses or spreads through the space above the surface of the liquid.

## Sensible Heat of a Vapor

Matter in any state can be warmed; a vapor or gas can be warmed just as a solid or liquid can be warmed. If heat energy is added, the speed—or velocity—of the molecules increases and the matter is said to be warmer. The heat that is added to a vapor and causes it to become warmer is called the sensible heat of the vapor. It is also called superheat.

Sensible heat can be measured with a thermometer.

## Measuring the Amount of Heat Energy

To understand and apply these principles, we must measure temperature changes and the amounts of heat. If we cannot, for example, measure a material, an action, a process, or an energy, we really cannot properly understand it.

Heat is one of the three forms of energy. Energy does work by causing things to happen. Energy is not a solid, liquid, or gas; and it cannot be measured in traditional terms, such as inches, feet, quarts, or cubic feet. Energy must be measured by what it does, by the effects it produces.

The term *thermal* defines heat.

Adding heat to water raises its temperature. We measure this heat by how much it raises the temperature of the water. For example, 1 lb. (0.45 kg) of water ($H_2O$), approximately 1 pt. (0.47 L), is at about 63°F (15.6°C). It takes a certain amount of heat (Figure 2-9) to raise its temperature 1°F, from 63°F to 64°F (15.6°C to 17.8°C).

Most countries are on the metric system. The calorie is the heat unit in the metric system. The calorie is now used in the United States only in some scientific laboratories. The calorie is the amount of heat required to raise 1 gr. (0.035 oz.) of water ($H_2O$) 1.0°C.

The Btu is the standard measure of the amount of heat, and the degree of temperature is the standard measure of the effect of that heat on 1 lb. (0.45 kg) of water ($H_2O$). The amount of

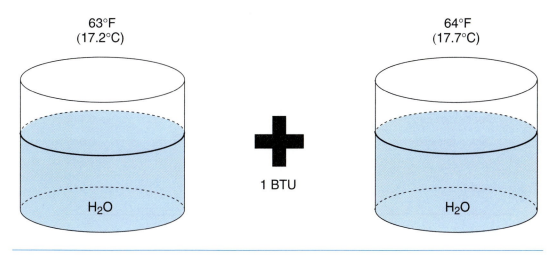

63°F
(17.2°C)

64°F
(17.7°C)

+

1 BTU

$H_2O$

$H_2O$

**Figure 2-9** One Btu raises 1 lb. (0.436 kg) of water ($H_2O$) 1°F (0.56°C).

water must be known. Obviously, it will take two times as much heat (2 Btu) to warm 2 lb. (0.91 kg) of water ($H_2O$) 1°F (0.56°C), as it would to warm 1 lb. (0.45 kg). It would also take twice as much heat (2 Btu) to warm 1 lb. (0.45 kg) of water ($H_2O$) 2°F (1.1°C) as it would to warm 1 lb. (0.45 kg) of water ($H_2O$) 1°F (0.56°C).

To warm 10 lb. (4.54 kg) of water ($H_2O$) 10°F (5.56°C) would require 100 Btu of added heat.

$$10 \times 10 = 100$$

The amount of heat required, in Btu, to warm any amount of water through any known temperature change is found by multiplying the number of pounds of water by the number of degrees Fahrenheit the temperature is to be raised. The answer is the number of Btu of heat that must be added.

Do not forget that the heat energy added to the water results in an increase in the active movement of the molecules to give them more rapidity of motion. This increased rapidity of motion produces the effect of a rise in temperature.

# Specific Heat

Materials vary in the amount of heat required to raise their temperature (Figure 2-10). Compared to most other materials—whether solid, liquid, or gas—water requires a great deal of heat energy to raise its temperature. Oil requires only about one-half as much heat energy as water, so it takes only 1/2 (0.5) Btu to warm 1 lb. (0.45 kg) of oil 1°F (0.56°C). Mercury (Hg) requires only about 1/30 (0.034) Btu; alcohol about 3/5 (0.6) Btu; and so on.

Gases vary greatly in the amount of heat required to warm them, depending upon their original temperature and their pressure. At atmospheric pressure and room temperature:

❑ air: oxygen, nitrogen, and carbon dioxide require 1/5 to 1/4 Btu per pound per degree;
❑ sulphur dioxide requires about 1/6 Btu per pound per degree;
❑ ammonia requires about 1/2 Btu per pound per degree; and
❑ Refrigerant-12 or Refrigerant 134a requires about 1/7 Btu per pound per degree.

The amount of heat required to raise 1 lb. (0.45 kg) of matter 1°F is called its specific heat. For water, the specific heat is 1.0. It takes 1 Btu to raise 1 lb. (0.45 kg) of water ($H_2O$) 1°F, as demonstrated earlier. The specific heat of oil is 1/2 (0.5) Btu. Tables of specific heats are usually given in decimals, as ice (at 20°F) 0.48, water vapor 0.46, iron 0.13 to 0.17, and so on.

| | | |
|---|---|---|
| Air..................................................0.240 | Nitrogen . . . . . . . . . . . . . . . . . .0.240 |
| Alcohol ...........................................0.600 | Oxygen . . . . . . . . . . . . . . . . . . .0.220 |
| Aluminum .......................................0.230 | Rubber . . . . . . . . . . . . . . . . . . .0.481 |
| Brass...............................................0.086 | Silver . . . . . . . . . . . . . . . . . . . . .0.055 |
| Carbon dioxide.............................0.200 | Steel . . . . . . . . . . . . . . . . . . . . .0.118 |
| Carbon tetrachloride ...................0.200 | Tin . . . . . . . . . . . . . . . . . . . . . .0.045 |
| Gasoline.........................................0.700 | Water, fresh . . . . . . . . . . . . . . .1.000 |
| Lead...............................................0.031 | Water, sea . . . . . . . . . . . . . . . .0.940 |

Figure 2-10 Specific heat values of selected solids, liquids, and gases.

To calculate the amount of heat required to raise matter from one temperature to a higher temperature, first figure the number of Btu just as if the material were water ($H_2O$), by multiplying the number of pounds (kg) of the matter by the number of degrees F (C) that it is to be warmed. Next, multiply this amount by the specific heat of that particular matter.

## Example

How many Btu are required to raise the temperature of 20 pounds of ice from 20°F to 32°F? If the ice were water, it would require

$$20 \times 12 \times 1 \text{ or } 240 \text{ Btu}$$

The specific heat of ice, however, is 0.48, so

$$20 \times 12 \times 0.48 = 115.2 \text{ Btu}$$

# Latent Heat of Fusion

To change 1 lb. (0.45 kg) of ice at 32°F to water at 32°F requires that the value of the latent heat of fusion of ice be added—144 Btu per pound (0.45 kg):

$$144 \times 20 = 2,880 \text{ Btu}$$

Accordingly, 2,880 Btu are required to melt 20 lb. (9.1 kg) of ice.

To warm the 20 lb. (9.1 kg) of water to 50°F (an additional 18°F), we would have to supply another 20 × 18 or 360 Btu.

If, however, we want to heat the water from 32°F to the boiling point of 212°F (through 180°F), instead of just to 50°F, we will have to add 3,600 Btu (20 × 180 = 3,600 Btu).

The latent heat of fusion also varies with the matter. For some other solids, the latent heats of fusion are:

| | |
|---|---|
| Aluminum (Al) | 167.5 Btu per pound |
| Copper (Cu) | 78.0 Btu per pound |
| Silver (Ag) | 43.9 Btu per pound |
| Gold (Au) | 28.7 Btu per pound |
| Tin (Sn) | 25.4 Btu per pound |
| Lead (Pb) | 9.8 Btu per pound |

# Latent Heat of Vaporization

To boil water at 212°F and turn it into steam, also at 212°F, requires latent heat of vaporization. For water in an open pan, the latent heat of vaporization is 970 Btu per lb. (0.45 kg), so 20 lb. (9.1 kg) at 212°F requires 20 × 970 or 19,400 Btu to turn it into steam or water vapor also at 212°F.

If we want to superheat this steam to 250°F, raise its temperature above the 212°F, we must add 20 × 38 × 0.46 (the specific heat of steam) or 349.6 Btu.

To warm 20 lb. of ice from 20°F to 32°F, change it to water, heat the water to 212°F, change it to vapor (steam), and then heat the steam to 250°F will require:

❑ To warm 20 lb. of ice from 20°F to 32°F: 20 × 12 × 0.48 = 115.2 Btu
❑ To change the 32°F ice to water at 32°F: 20 × 144 = 2,880.0 Btu
❑ To warm 20 lb. of water from 32°F to 212°F: 20 × 180 × 1 = 3,600.0 Btu
❑ To change the 212°F water to steam at 212°F: 20 × 970 = 9,400.0 Btu
❑ To warm 20 lb. of steam from 212°F to 250°F: 20 × 38 × 0.46 = 349.6 Btu
❑ The total required to change 20 lb. of ice at 20°F to steam at 250°F is 26,344.8 Btu

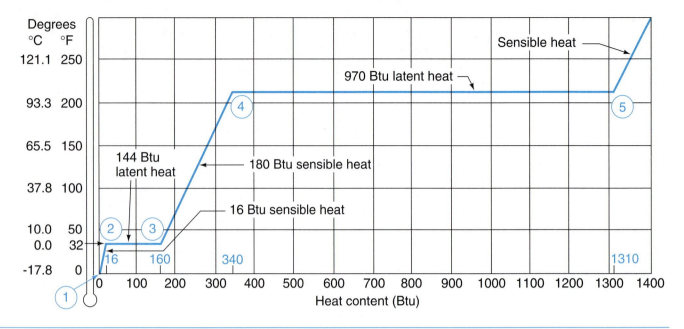

**Figure 2-11** Latent and sensible heat values for water ($H_2O$).

From this example, it may be seen that the latent heats of fusion and of vaporization are very large compared with the sensible heats. Moreover, the latent heats of fusion and vaporization of water, to change their states from a solid to a liquid and from a liquid to a vapor, are quite large compared to other matter. Most matter has far less heat capacity than ice, water ($H_2O$), and steam (Figure 2-11).

## Heat Flow

Heat has been defined as the energy of the molecules in motion. Motion is transmitted to other molecules that have less motion. Some of the molecules give up some of their energy to other molecules that have less energy. Another way of saying this is that heat flows from the matter at a higher temperature to a matter at a lower temperature.

Heat transfer, therefore, is always downward; from hot to warm, warm to cool, or cool to cold. Heat never flows from low-temperature matter to high-temperature matter. Natural heat flow from a warm to less warm area or surface is called gravity.

One method of studying heat flow is to place a hot object near, or touching, a colder object. Heat will flow from the hot object to the colder object. Actually, heat is neither added nor removed. It is simply transferred from one place where it is not wanted to another place where it is accepted.

Heat moves in either or all of three ways. Heat moves by:

❏ Radiation
❏ Conduction
❏ Convection

## Radiation

If a hot object is placed near or against a cooler object, heat is transferred by **radiation** (Figure 2-12) across the space between the two objects to warm the cooler object. There does not have to be any gas or other material in the space. An excellent example of radiation is how we receive heat from the sun. This heat radiates through some 92 million miles of vacuum to heat the earth without heating the space between.

*Natural heat flow from a warm to less warm area or surface is called gravity.*

*Radiation is the transfer of heat without heating the medium through which it is transmitted.*

Radiation

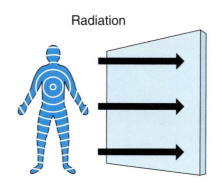

**Figure 2-12** Heat is transferred by radiation.

# Conduction

If one side of a material is heated, the heat will travel through it from the hot side to the cooler side. In turn, heat may be conducted to another cooler object touching it or radiated to a cooler object some distance away.

The transfer of heat through a material is known as **conduction** (Figure 2-13). The warmer side gives motion to the molecules which, in turn, give motion to nearby molecules and so through the material. In doing so, some of the heat energy is given up to the molecules and remains as heat energy. All of the heat, therefore, does not pass through the material.

A material that transmits heat easily, with little loss, is called a conductor of heat. Some of the best conductors are also good conductors of electricity. They are copper (Cu), silver (Ag), and aluminum (Al).

A material that does not conduct heat through itself easily is called an insulator. Some of the better insulators are cork, cotton, air, and other materials that are composed of thousands of tiny air cells. A good insulator is a poor conductor.

> **Conduction** is the transmission of heat through a solid.

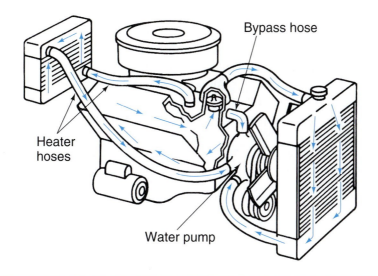

**Figure 2-13** Heat is transferred by conduction.

Convection

**Figure 2-14** Heat is transferred by convection.

# Convection

**Convection** occurs only in fluids—liquids and gases or vapors. When a material is warmed, it expands in volume and, therefore, becomes lighter per cubic foot of volume. In the case of fluids, the cooled fluid is heavier and, as a result, crowds out the lighter, warmer fluid. This pushes the warmer fluid upward, setting up a cycle of circulation. This circulation of the fluid carries heat upward on one side and downward on the other side. This means of conducting heat is called convection (Figure 2-14). It is very important in refrigeration and heating where a large part of the process is cooling or heating fluids. In many applications, the fluids are cooled as a means of carrying heat away from or to foods, human beings, or other objects.

# Personal Comfort and Convenience

The normal body temperature of a human adult is 98.6°F (37°C). This temperature is sometimes called **subsurface** or **deep-tissue temperature**, as opposed to surface or skin temperature. An understanding of the process by which the body maintains its temperature is helpful to the student because it explains how air conditioning helps keep the body comfortable.

## How the Body Produces Heat

All food and beverage taken into the body contains heat in the form of calories. The calorie is a term used to express the heat value of food. The calorie is the amount of heat required to raise one kilogram of water ($H_2O$) one degree Celsius (C). There are 252 calories in one Btu.

As calories are taken into the body, they are converted into energy and stored for future use. The conversion process generates heat. All body movements use up the stored energy and, in doing so, add to the heat generated by the conversion process. The body consistently produces more heat than it requires. Therefore, for body comfort, all of the excess heat produced must be given off by the body.

The constant removal of body heat takes place through three natural processes (Figure 2-15) discussed earlier, which all occur at the same time. These are:

❏ Convection
❏ Radiation
❏ Evaporation

**Convection** is the transfer of heat by the circulation of a vapor or liquid.

Twenty-five pounds of ice is equal to 150 British thermal units in today's terms.

**Deep-tissue** or **subsurface temperature** is the core temperature of the body.

Water ($H_2O$) weighs 8.3453 pounds (3.11 kilograms) per gallon (3.785 liters). For practical purposes, it is considered that 1 pound (0.4536 kilogram) of water ($H_2O$) is equal to 1 pint (0.473 liter).

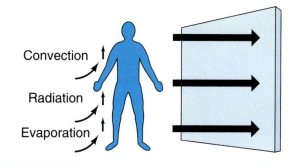

**Figure 2-15** The body gives up heat by convection, radiation, and evaporation.

## Convection

The convection process of removing heat is based on two natural phenomena:

- ❑ Heat flows from a hot surface to a surface containing less heat. For example, heat flows from the body to the air surrounding the body when the air temperature is lower than the skin temperature (Figure 2-16).
- ❑ Heat rises. This is evident by watching the smoke from a burning cigarette or the steam from boiling water.

When these two natural phenomena are applied to the bodily process of removing heat, the following changes occur:

- ❑ The body gives off heat to the surrounding air (which has a lower temperature).
- ❑ The surrounding air becomes warmer and moves upward.
- ❑ As the warmer air moves upward, air containing less heat takes its place. The convection cycle is then completed.

> Gravity causes warm air to rise. Cool air is heavier than warm air, and as warm air rises, cool air falls to take its place.

## Radiation

Radiation is the process that moves heat from a heat source to an object by means of heat rays. This principle is based on the phenomenon that heat moves from a hot surface to a surface containing less heat. Radiation takes place independently of convection. The process of radiation does not require air movement to complete the heat transfer. This process is not affected by air temperature, although it is affected by the temperature of the surrounding surfaces.

> Radiation is the transfer of heat without heating the medium through which it is transmitted.

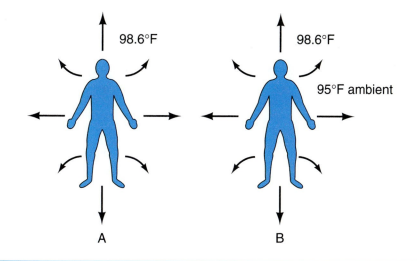

**Figure 2-16** The body rapidly gives up heat when the surrounding air temperature is below body temperature (A), and slows as the surrounding air temperature increases (B).

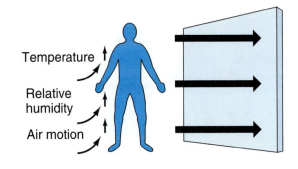

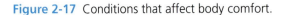

Figure 2-17 Conditions that affect body comfort.

The body quickly experiences the effects of sun radiation when one moves from a shady area to a sunny area.

## Evaporation

Evaporation is the changing of a liquid to a vapor while picking up heat.

Perspiration is the salty fluid secreted by sweat glands through the pores of the skin.

Evaporation is the process by which moisture becomes a vapor. As moisture vaporizes from a warm surface, it removes heat and thus lowers the temperature of the surface. This process takes place constantly on the surface of the body. Moisture is given off through the pores of the skin. As the moisture evaporates, it removes heat from the body.

**Perspiration** appearing as drops of moisture on the body indicates that the body is producing more heat than is being removed by convection, radiation, and normal evaporation.

The three main factors that affect body comfort (Figure 2-17) are:

❑ Temperature
❑ Relative humidity
❑ Air movement

## Temperature

The **temperature** of an object can be described as that which determines the sensation of warmth or coldness when one comes into contact with it. When two objects are placed together, they are said to be in thermal contact. The object with the higher temperature is cooled while the object with the lower temperature is warmed. At some point in time they will both be the same temperature and no more change will occur. When thermal changes between two objects stop, we say that they are in thermal equilibrium. To our senses, then, both objects would feel the same.

When we say that something is cool or warm, we are speaking in relative terms. For example, consider the following experiment. You will need two pans approximately 7 × 7 × 2 in. (18 × 18 × 5 cm), one pan approximately 9 × 12 × 2 in. (23 × 30 × 5 cm), 9 cups (4.26 liters) tap water, 1 cup (0.47 liter) hot water, and a tray of ice cubes.

### Set Up

1. Place the pans on a level surface with the large pan in the middle and the smaller pans on both sides.
2. Put 2 cups (0.95 liter) of tap water in each of the small pans.
3. Put 5 cups (2.37 liter) of water in the large pan.
4. Allow them to reach thermal equilibrium with the ambient room temperature.

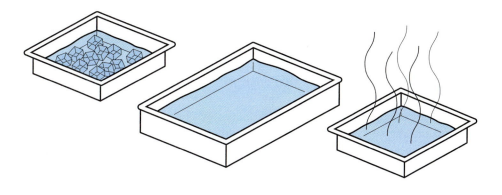

**Figure 2-18** Place ice cubes in the left pan.

5. Put a tray of ice cubes in the pan on the left (Figure 2-18).

6. Add 1 cup (0.47 liter) of hot water to the pan on the right. Water must not be so hot as to cause personal injury.

**The Experiment**

1. Place both hands in the center pan for 10–15 seconds (Figure 2-19). What do you feel? (You should experience a feeling of neither warmth nor cold since the water in this pan is in thermal equilibrium with the room temperature.)

2. Place the left hand in the pan with the ice cubes. What do you feel? (You should experience a sensation of cold since this water is below room temperature.)

3. Next, place the right hand in the pan with warm water. What do youfeel? (You should experience a sensation of warmth since this water is above room temperature. Remember that we are speaking in relative terms; in this case, relative to the ambient temperature.)

4. Remove your left hand from the left pan and place it in the center pan for a few seconds. What do you feel? (The surface temperature of your left hand was lowered, so the water in this pan should now feel warm.)

5. Remove your right hand from the right pan and place it in the center pan for a few seconds. What do you feel? (The surface temperature of your right hand was raised, so the water should now feel cool.)

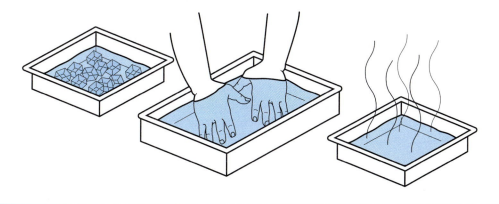

**Figure 2-19** Place both hands in pan for 10–15 seconds.

**Conclusion.** In relative terms, the left hand felt warm because the temperature of the ambient water was higher than the cold water. The right hand felt cool because the temperature of the ambient water was lower than the warm water.

It should now be obvious that the feeling of cold or warm is relative in relation to the temperature of an object or to the ambient environment.

Cool air increases the rate of convection; warm air slows it down. Cool air lowers the temperature of the surrounding surfaces. Therefore, the rate of radiation increases. Since warm air raises the surrounding surface temperature, the radiation rate decreases. In general, cool air increases the rate of evaporation and warm air slows it down. The evaporation rate also depends upon the amount of moisture already in the air and the amount of air movement.

## Humidity

The moisture of air is measured in terms of **relative humidity** (RH). The expression "50 percent relative humidity," for example, means that the air contains half the amount of moisture that it is capable of holding at a given temperature.

A low relative humidity permits heat to be taken away from the body by evaporation. Because low humidity means the air is relatively dry, it can readily absorb moisture. A high relative humidity has the opposite effect. The evaporation process slows down in humid conditions; thus, the speed at which heat can be removed by evaporation decreases. An acceptable comfort range for the human body is 72°F to 80°F (22.2°C to 26.6°C) at 45 percent to 50 percent relative humidity (RH).

In some areas of the country, the average RH is 50 percent or above most of the time. These areas are said to be "**humid**" regions, and dehumidification is generally required to provide an environment ideal for human comfort. In other parts of the country, average RH is less than 50 percent. These regions are said to be "dry" or "**arid**." Humidification is usually required in arid areas to create an ideal environment.

The recommended relative humidity for an occupied area is between 40 percent and 60 percent for a healthy environment. Recent studies show that bacteria, fungi, and viruses are more active below 40 percent RH and above 60 percent RH. The evaporator, that part of an air conditioning system that removes heat from the air, also removes moisture from the air. Some of this moisture, however, tends to cling to the fins and tubes of the evaporator after the system has been turned off. This creates a very high humidity condition within the evaporator, promoting fungi growth from the airborne impurities that were trapped by the moisture. It is not uncommon to hear a complaint of a "musty mildew odor" coming from the automotive air conditioning system when it is first turned on. This odor is caused by the mildew-type fungi that was formed in the evaporator case during the off period of the air conditioning system.

To combat this problem, the blower motor of some systems is turned on for a few minutes after the air conditioner has been turned off for a period of time, generally 30 minutes. There is also a device that can be installed on most vehicles which operates the blower motor some time after the air conditioning system has been turned off. A delay in this process is intended to provide sufficient time for the moisture to run off the tubes and fins of the evaporator and collect in the bottom of the evaporator case. The fan then forces the water out the drain tube and dries off the evaporator coil.

Automotive evaporators may be cleaned of fungi following specific service procedures as given in the appropriate manufacturer's service manual. A typical procedure for correcting this problem may be found in the Shop Manual, Chapter 9, page 332.

**Relative humidity** is the actual moisture content of the air in relation to the total moisture that the air can hold at a given temperature.

**Humid** is another term for damp. It is the feeling of dampness when the dew point of the air is close to the actual ambient air temperature, causing water in the air to condense. The closer the dew point temperature of the air is to the actual ambient air temperature, the more humid it feels.

Some older people are not comfortable in the normal "comfort range" and require special considerations.

**Arid** is another term for dry.

## Air Movement

Another factor that affects the ability of the body to give off heat is the movement of air around the body. As the air movement increases, the following processes occur:

- ❏ The evaporation process of removing body heat speeds up because moisture in the air near the body is carried away at a faster rate.
- ❏ The convection process increases because the layer of warm air surrounding the body is carried away rapidly.
- ❏ The radiation process increases because the heat on the surrounding surfaces is removed at a faster rate. As a result, heat radiates from the body at a faster rate.

As the air movement decreases, the processes of evaporation, convection, and radiation decrease. As the air movement increases so does evaporation, convection, and radiation, a process known as *windchill factor.*

## Windchill Factor

The windchill factor, developed in 1941, is a measure of relative personal discomfort due to combined cold and wind based on physiological studies of the rate of heat loss for various combinations of ambient temperature and wind speed (Table 2-1). The windchill factor is based on the actual air temperature when the wind speed is 4 mph (6.4 km/h) or less. At higher wind speeds, the windchill temperature is lower than the air temperature and measures the increased cold stress and discomfort associated with wind.

The air temperature is not lowered by the windchill factor. Regardless of how strong the wind, the air temperature remains constant. The windchill factor is a measure of how rapidly heat is being removed from a body. If, for example, the air temperature is 40°F (4.4°C) and the wind speed is 20 mph (32 km/h), it feels the same as 19°F (–7°C) with no wind blowing.

A windchill factor near or below 0°F (–17.8°C) is an indication that there is a risk of frostbite or other injury to exposed human flesh. Between 10° and 15°F (–12° and –26°C) there is little danger; between –30° and –70°F (–34° and –57°C) there is danger that human flesh may freeze within one minute of exposure. Below –75°F (–59°C) there is great danger that human flesh may freeze within 30 seconds of exposure,

The effects of wind chill, however, depend on many factors, such as the amount of clothing worn, health, age, gender, and body weight.

## TABLE 2-1   THE EFFECT OF THE WINDCHILL FACTOR

| AIR TEMP (°F) | WIND SPEED (MPH) | | | | | | | |
|---|---|---|---|---|---|---|---|---|
| | 5 | 10 | 15 | 20 | 25 | 30 | 35 | 40* |
| 40 | 37 | 28 | 23 | 19 | 16 | 13 | 12 | 11 |
| 30 | 27 | 16 | 9 | 4 | 1 | –2 | –4 | –5 |
| 20 | 16 | 3 | –5 | –10 | –15 | –18 | –20 | –21 |
| 10 | 6 | –9 | –18 | –24 | –29 | –33 | –35 | –37 |
| 0 | –5 | –22 | –31 | –39 | –44 | –49 | –52 | –53 |
| –10 | –15 | –34 | –45 | –53 | –59 | –64 | –67 | –69 |
| –20 | –26 | –46 | –58 | –67 | –74 | –79 | –82 | –84 |
| –30 | –38 | –58 | –72 | –81 | –88 | –93 | –97 | –100 |
| –40 | –47 | –71 | –85 | –95 | –103 | –109 | –113 | –115 |

*Winds above 40 mph (64 km/h) have little additional effect on windchill factor.

## Cold

We have discussed heat and adding or removing heat, but what about "cold?" Actually, there is no such thing as "cold." Remember the definition "feeling no warmth?"

All matter, everything in nature or everything manufactured, contains heat. Some things contain more heat than others, but all contain heat to some degree.

"Cold," then, refers to an object or matter in which some of its heat has been removed; therefore, an object has more or less of its original heat. In an air conditioning system, we are not really producing cold air. We are simply transferring heat; removing some of the heat from the car's interior where it is not wanted and transferring it to the outside air. The refrigerant in the air conditioning system is the medium that is used for the transfer of this heat. The effect is that the car's interior becomes cool.

Absolute cold is the absence of all heat, or –459.67°F.

## The Industry

Automobile air conditioning, once considered a luxury, has become a necessity. Millions enjoy the benefits it produces. Business people are able to drive to appointments in comfort and arrive fresh and alert. People with allergies are able to travel without the fear of coming into contact with excessive dust and airborne pollen and pollution. Because of the extensive use of the automobile, automobile air conditioning is playing an important role in promoting the comfort, health, and safety of travelers throughout the world.

It is easy to understand how automotive air conditioning has become the industry's most sought-after product. In the South and Southwest, many specialty auto repair shops base their entire trade on selling, installing, and servicing automotive air conditioners throughout the year.

## ASE Certification

The National Institute for Automotive Service Excellence (ASE) has established a certification program for the automotive heating and air conditioning technician (Figure 2-20). This is one of the eight automotive certification areas that lead to certification as a Master Auto Technician

**Figure 2-20** A typical ASE certificate.

**Figure 2-21** A certified Master Auto Technician.

(Figure 2-21). ASE also offers other certification programs in other areas, such as heavy-duty truck, collision repair, school bus, engine machine shop technician, parts specialist, alternate fuels, and advanced engine performance.

ASE's voluntary certification system combines on-the-job experience to confirm that technicians have the necessary skills to work on today's vehicles. The ASE Master Auto Technician status certification is awarded when a technician passes all eight tests that address diagnostic and repair problems in the following areas.

1. Engine Repair
2. Automatic Transmission/transaxle
3. Manual Transmissions and Drive Axles
4. Suspension and Steering
5. Brakes
6. Electrical/Electronic Systems
7. Heating and Air Conditioning
8. Engine Performance (driveability)

After passing at least one ASE-administered exam and providing proof of two years of hands-on work experience, the technician becomes ASE certified in that particular area. The ASE certification is valid for five years. Retesting is necessary every five years to renew certification.

## Work Experience Credit

The technician may be given credit for one of the two years of work experience by substituting relevant formal training in one, or a combination, of the following:

❑ Secondary training: Three years of high school training in automotive repair may be substituted for one year of work experience.

- Postsecondary training: Two full years of training after high school in a public or private trade school, vocational-technical institute, community college, or four-year college may be counted as one year of work experience.
- An apprenticeship program: The completion of a state-approved apprenticeship program may be counted as one year of work experience. Full credit for the experience requirement is given for satisfactorily completing a three- or four-year apprenticeship program.
- Specialty and short courses: For shorter periods of postsecondary training, one may substitute one month of work experience for every two months of training.

## Test Content

The current heating and air conditioning test consists of 50 multiple-choice questions as follows:

| Content Area | Questions | Percent of Test |
|---|---|---|
| A/C system diagnosis and repair | 12 | 24 |
| Refrigeration system components diagnosis and repair | 10 | 20 |
|     Compressor and clutch (5) | | |
|     Evaporator, condenser, and related components (5) | | |
| Heating and engine cooling systems diagnosis and repair | 5 | 10 |
| Operating systems and related controls diagnosis and repair | 16 | 32 |
|     Electrical (7) | | |
|     Vacuum/mechanical (4) | | |
|     Automatic and semiautomatic heating, ventilating, and A/C systems (5) | | |
| Refrigerant recovery, recycling, and handling | 7 | 14 |
| Total | 50 | 100% |

## Additional Questions

The test could contain up to ten additional questions for statistical research purposes and will not affect your score. The five-year recertification test covers the same content areas as those listed above, however, the number of questions in each content area will be reduced by about 50 percent.

## The Questions

The questions are written by a panel of technical service experts, including domestic and import vehicle manufacturers, repair and test equipment and parts manufacturers, working automotive technicians, and automotive instructors. All questions are pretested by a national sample of technicians before they are included in the actual test. Many test questions force the student to choose between two distinct repair methods. Questions similar to the *Technician A, Technician B* format are included in the review questions at the end of each chapter in this text as well as in the Shop Manual.

## Why Certify with ASE?

In a word, "recognition." Being an ASE-certified technician provides credentials that attest to your professional abilities to your peers as well as to your prospective employer. As a matter of practice, although ASE certification is voluntary, many employers ask for certified applicants when advertising for employment, or state "ASE certification preferred." In no small part, certification demonstrates to the employer one's ability to read; an important requirement for technicians of the future.

# EPA Certification

To purchase refrigerant or service air conditioning and refrigeration (ACR) systems, one must be certified under section 608 or 609 of the Clean Air Act (CAA) through an agency approved by the Environmental Protection Agency (EPA). A "609-certified technician" is someone certified by an EPA-approved agency for servicing motor vehicle air conditioning (MVAC) and MVAC-like air conditioning systems. The exam for this certification is open book and is generally available by mail from professional organizations, such as Mobile Air Conditioning Society (MACS), International Mobile Air Conditioning Association (IMACA), National Institute for Automotive Service Excellence (ASE), and others. Testing may also be available in an instructor led classroom setting.

Under the CAA, a 609-certified technician is not permitted to service domestic or commercial air conditioning or refrigeration equipment, even though the equipment may be similar to an automotive air conditioning system. A small domestic air conditioner, for example, contains far less refrigerant than the average MVAC; however, a 609-certified technician cannot legally service it. This service requires a 608-certified technician.

A 608-certified technician is someone certified by an EPA-approved agency for servicing particular types of ACR systems. The exam for this certification, with exception, is closed book and is proctored at an approved test site. There are actually four classes of certification, as follows:

1. Type I: One who services high-pressure ACR systems with a capacity of up to 5 pounds of refrigerant.
2. Type II: One who services high-pressure ACR systems with a capacity over 5 pounds of refrigerant.
3. Type III: One who services low-pressure systems, such as centrifugal systems with up to hundreds of tons of refrigerating capacity.
4. UNIVERSAL: One who is certified in all three types.

The exception to the above is that one may be certified for "small appliances" by taking an open-book exam that is generally administered by mail. This certification, equivalent to Type I, is much more convenient. It is available from trade organizations listed in the Appendix.

For simplicity, some automotive technicians are certified under both sections 608 and 609. For example, one may purchase refrigerant and other supplies at either an automotive parts or refrigeration supply store. When purchasing HFC-134a, for example, the automotive supplier only has cylinders with the "unique" fitting required by EPA. The refrigeration supply store, on the other hand, can supply the cylinder with either fitting: 1/2-in. Acme for automotive use or 1/4-in. SAE for commercial use.

Depending on geographical location, refrigerants may often be less expensive if purchased at a refrigeration supply store. Generally, refrigerant is a "**price leader**" to a refrigeration supply store as engine oil is to an automotive parts store.

**Price leader** is an item that a merchant may sell at cost or near cost to attract customers.

# Cost of Operation

The modern automobile is designed so it will offer less wind resistance with the windows closed.

While the air conditioning system places an extra load on the engine, it seems apparent that the use of an air conditioner will reduce gasoline mileage. This is only true for stop-and-go driving.

At highway speeds, air conditioned cars, with their windows closed and the air conditioning operating, actually average 2–3 percent better mileage than do cars without air conditioning that have their windows down. The aerodynamic design considerations of today's cars are based upon having the windows closed. When the windows are closed, reduced wind resistance offsets the demand load of the air conditioning system on the engine.

# Summary

- ❏ If the surrounding temperature, known as ambient temperature, is above normal body temperature, one is said to feel warm or hot; if it is below, one is said to feel cool or cold.
- ❏ Everything in nature contains heat. This heat is known as specific heat. Some things contain more heat than other things. The absence of heat is cold.
- ❏ Latent heat is hidden heat. It is the heat that is required for a change of state of matter and it cannot be measured with a thermometer.
- ❏ Sensible heat can be measured with a thermometer and can be felt (sensed).
- ❏ Heat flows from a warm surface or object to a less warm surface or object.

## Terms to Know

Absolute zero

Arid

Atom

British thermal unit (Btu)

Chlorofluorocarbon (CFCs)

Conduction

Convection

Deep-tissue (subsurface) temperature

Evaporation

Heat

Humid

Hydrogen

Latent heat

Matter

Molecule

Perspiration

Price leader

Radiation

Relative humidity

Sensible heat

Specific heat

# Review Questions

## Short Answer Essays

1. Explain heat transfer by convection.
2. What is the composition of air we breathe?
3. Describe the molecular movement of matter based on its temperature.
4. How does liquid water become water vapor?
5. What is meant by the term *subsurface temperature*?
6. What is the formula for determining the amount of heat energy required to change the temperature of 1 lb. (0.45 kg) of water ($H_2O$) 1°F?
7. What does the term *relative humidity* mean?
8. Briefly define latent heat.
9. Describe the transfer of heat by conduction.
10. Briefly define *sensible heat*.

## Fill-in-the-Blanks

1. An atom is composed of particles known as _____ , _____ , and electrons.
2. The absence of heat is cold; therefore, _____ is ever present.
3. Moisture in the air is known as _____ .
4. Latent heat is required to cause a change of _____ .
5. One British thermal unit (Btu) contains _____ calories.

6. Moisture becomes vapor by the natural process of _____ .

7. _____ heat cannot be felt or measured with the use of a thermometer.

8. A unit of heat measure is the _____ thermal unit.

9. On the English scale, normal body temperature is _____ .

10. The metric conversion of pounds (weight) is _____ .

## Multiple Choice

1. *Technician A* says that latent heat is hidden heat and cannot be measured on a thermometer.
   *Technician B* says that latent heat is hidden heat that is required for a change of state of matter.
   Who is correct?
   **A.** A only  **C.** Both A and B
   **B.** B only  **D.** Neither A nor B

2. *Technician A* says that heat added to a vapor, causing it to become warmer, is called sensible heat.
   *Technician B* says that heat added to a vapor, causing it to become warmer, is called superheat.
   Who is correct?
   **A.** A only  **C.** Both A and B
   **B.** B only  **D.** Neither A nor B

3. *Technician A* says that a material that transmits heat easily is called an insulator.
   *Technician B* says that blocking the flow of heat is called convection.
   Who is correct?
   **A.** A only  **C.** Both A and B
   **B.** B only  **D.** Neither A nor B

4. *Technician A* says as wind speed increases, air temperature decreases.
   *Technician B* says as air movement increases, so does the process of evaporation and convection.
   Who is correct?
   **A.** A only  **C.** Both A and B
   **B.** B only  **D.** Neither A nor B

5. Heat transfer is being discussed:
   *Technician A* says that heat flows from a hot surface to a surface containing less heat.
   *Technician B* says that heat leaves the body by the process of evaporation.
   Who is correct?
   **A.** A only  **C.** Both A and B
   **B.** B only  **D.** Neither A nor B

6. *Technician A* says that the acceptable comfort range for the human body is 72–80°F.
   *Technician B* says that the acceptable comfort range for the human body is 45–50 percent relative humidity.
   Who is correct?
   **A.** A only  **C.** Both A and B
   **B.** B only  **D.** Neither A nor B

7. *Technician A* says that everything in nature has specific heat.
   *Technician B* says that everything in nature has latent heat.
   Who is correct?
   **A.** A only  **C.** Both A and B
   **B.** B only  **D.** Neither A nor B

8. Heat transfer is being discussed:
   *Technician A* says that heat transfer by radiation does not require air movement.
   *Technician B* says that heat transfer by convection requires air movement.
   Who is correct?
   **A.** A only  **C.** Both A and B
   **B.** B only  **D.** Neither A nor B

9. *Technician A* says as a material increases in temperature the molecules slow down in their motion.
   *Technician B* says it is the latent heat that causes a material to change its state.
   Who is correct?
   **A.** A only  **C.** Both A and B
   **B.** B only  **D.** Neither A nor B

10. The term *heat* is being discussed:
    *Technician A* says that heat is ever present.
    *Technician B* says that heat is the absence of cold.
    Who is correct?
    **A.** A only  **C.** Both A and B
    **B.** B only  **D.** Neither A nor B

# History and Purpose

Upon completion and review of this chapter, you should be able to:

❏ Discuss the historic developments of modern refrigeration.

❏ Discuss the advantages of air conditioning in the automotive industry.

❏ Explain basic air conditioning operation.

❏ Understand basic air conditioning terminology.

❏ Understand basic function of the various air conditioning components.

❏ Know the physical state, pressure, and temperature of the refrigerant in different areas of the refrigerant system.

## Introduction

Automotive air conditioning was first offered as an option by the Packard Motor Car Company in 1940. Cadillac soon followed in 1941. It did not become a popular option until the early 1960s. Since that time, interest in automotive air conditioning has increased annually. Air conditioning is now one of the most popular selections in the entire list of automotive accessories. As a matter of fact, it is now standard equipment on many luxury class automobiles.

Just over 11 percent of all cars sold in 1962 were equipped with air conditioners. This accounted for 756,781 units, including both factory-installed systems and those added after the purchase of the automobile, referred to as "aftermarket." Just five years later, in 1967, the total number had increased an astounding 469 percent—to 3,546,255 units. At the present time, over 93 percent of all automobiles sold in the United States are equipped with air conditioning units. It is expected that this percentage will remain approximately 93 percent. This means, of course, that more than 93 out of every 100 cars on the road will be equipped with a factory- or dealer-installed air conditioning system. Trucks lag behind cars by about ten years in air conditioning. Truck air conditioning became popular in the early 1970s. The percentages of factory- and dealer-installed systems are expected to rise at about the same rate as for cars. The popularity of mobile air conditioning in Europe is just now at about the same level of the late 1970s in the United States. It is expected to increase at about the same rate as in the United States over the next 20 years. When mobile air conditioning was first introduced, it was considered a luxury. Its usefulness, however, soon made it a necessity.

## Air Conditioning Defined

The definition of air conditioning should be reviewed before tracing its history and its application to the automobile. **Air conditioning**, by definition, is the process by which air is:

❏ Cooled
❏ Heated
❏ Cleaned or filtered
❏ Humidified or dehumidified
❏ Circulated or recirculated

In addition, the quantity and quality of the conditioned air are controlled. This means that the temperature, humidity, and volume of air can be controlled at any time in any given situation. Under ideal situations, air conditioning can be expected to accomplish all of these tasks at the same time. It is important to recognize that the air conditioning process includes the process of refrigeration (cooling by removing heat).

**Air conditioning** is the process of adjusting and regulating by heating or refrigerating; the quality, quantity, temperature, humidity, and circulation of air in a space or enclosure; to condition the air.

*Temperature* and *humidity* refer to the quality of the conditioned air.

*Volume* refers to the quantity of the conditioned air.

# Refrigeration

**Refrigeration** is the term given to a process by which heat is removed from matter—solid, liquid, or vapor. It is the process of lowering the temperature of an enclosure or area by natural, chemical, electrical, and/or mechanical means.

# Historical Development of Refrigeration

Refrigeration, as we know it today, is less than one hundred years old. Some of its principles, however, were known as long ago as 10,000 B.C.

The Egyptians developed a method for cooling water. They found that water could be cooled by placing it in porous jugs on the rooftop at sundown (Figure 3-1). The night breeze evaporated the moisture seeping through the jugs and, in turn, cooled the contents. The Greeks and Romans had snow brought down from mountaintops. They preserved it by placing it in cone-shaped pits lined with straw and covered with a thatched roof. Even earlier, the Chinese learned that ice improved the taste of drinks. They cut it from frozen ponds and lakes in the winter, preserved it in straw, and sold it in the summer.

## Domestic Refrigeration

Dr. John Gorrie (1803–1855) of Abbeville, South Carolina, was issued the first U. S. patent for a mechanical refrigeration system in 1851. Gorrie correctly theorized that if air were highly compressed it would be heated by the energy of compression. If this compressed air were then run through metal pipes that were cooled with water, the air could be cooled to the water temperature. If this air was then expanded back to atmospheric pressure, low temperatures of about 26°F (−3.3°C)—low enough to freeze water in pans in a refrigerator box—could be obtained. The

**Figure 3-1** Cooling water ($H_2O$) by evaporating moisture seeping through porous jugs. (Courtesy of Dover Publications)

compressor of this system could be powered by horse, water, wind, or steam. Gorrie's original system was installed in the U. S. Marine Hospital in Apalachicola, Florida, where he used it to treat patients suffering from yellow fever. A replica of his system is on display at the John Gorrie State Museum in Apalachicola.

While Dr. Gorrie's mechanism produced ice in quantities, leakage and irregular performance often impaired its operation. Gorrie's basic principle, however, is the one most often used in today's modern refrigeration: cooling caused by the rapid expansion of gases.

Domestic refrigeration systems first appeared in 1910, although in 1896 the Sears, Roebuck and Company catalog offered several refrigerators (Figure 3-2). Refrigeration, however, was

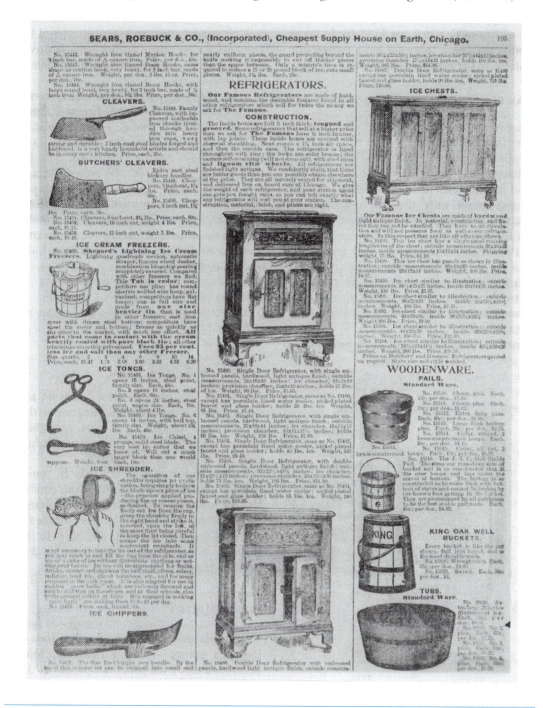

**Figure 3-2** Early "refrigerators," offered by Sears, Roebuck, and Company were actually ice boxes. (Courtesy of Sears, Roebuck, and Company)

provided by ice. The refrigerator held 25 pounds (11.34 kilograms) of ice and was useful only for short-term storage for the preservation of foods.

In 1899, the first household refrigeration patent was awarded to Albert T. Marshall of Brockton, Massachusetts. A manually-operated refrigerator was produced by J. L. Larsen in 1913. The Kelvinator Company produced the first automatic refrigerator in 1918. The acceptance of this new technology was slow. By 1920, only about 200 refrigerators had been sold.

In 1926, the first hermetic (sealed) refrigerator was introduced by General Electric. The following year, Electrolux introduced an automatic absorption unit. A 4-cubic-foot refrigerator was introduced by Sears, Roebuck, and Company in 1931 (Figure 3-3). The refrigerator cabinet and the refrigeration unit were shipped separately and required assembly.

In terms of the cost per cubic foot of refrigeration, the early refrigerator compares favorably to today's modern machines. In terms of the economy, one worked about four times longer to pay for the 4-cubic-foot refrigerator than one works for today's 16-cubic-foot refrigerator, which is four times larger.

Shortly after the beginning of the twentieth century, T. C. Northcott of Luray, Virginia, became the first person known in history to have a home with central heating and air conditioning. A heating and ventilating engineer, Northcott built his house on a hill above the famous Caverns of Luray. Because of his work, he knew that air filtered through limestone was free of dust and pollen. This fact was important because Northcott and his family suffered from hay fever.

Some distance behind his house he drilled a shaft through the ceiling of the cavern and installed a fan to pull cavern air through the shaft. He then constructed a shed over the shaft and a duct system to the house. The duct system was divided into two chambers, one above the other. The upper duct, which carried air from the cavern, was heated by the sun providing air to warm the house on cool days. The lower duct, which was unheated, carried air from the cavern to cool the house on warm days.

Cooling accomplished by humidification is only effective in arid (dry) areas of the country.

The moisture content (humidity) of the air was controlled in a chamber in Northcott's basement. Here, air from both ducts could be mixed. Since it is known that warm air contains more moisture than cool air, Northcott was able to direct conditioned air from the mixing chamber to any or all of the rooms in his house through a network of smaller ducts. During the winter season, auxiliary heat was provided by steam coils located in the base of each of the branch ducts.

## Mobile Air Conditioning

The first automotive air conditioning unit appeared on the market in 1927. True air conditioning was not to appear in cars for another thirteen years. However, air conditioning was advertised as an option in some cars in 1927. At that time, air conditioning meant only that the car could be equipped with a heater, a ventilation system, and a means of filtering the air. In 1938, Nash introduced "air conditioning" heating and ventilation. Fresh outside air was heated and filtered, then circulated around inside the car by fan.

By 1940, heaters and defrosters were standard equipment on many models. That year Packard offered the first method of cooling a car by means of refrigeration. Actually, these first units were belt-driven commercial air conditioners that were adapted for automotive use and were usually located in the trunk. Two years earlier, a few passenger buses had been air conditioned by the same method.

Accurate records were not kept in the early days of automotive air conditioning. However, it is known that before World War II between 3,000 and 4,000 units were installed in Packards. Defense priorities for materials and manufacturing prevented the improvement of automotive air conditioning until the early 1950s. At that time, the demand for air conditioned vehicles began in the Southwest.

**Figure 3-3** An early refrigerator offered by Sears, Roebuck, and Company in 1931. (Courtesy of Sears, Roebuck, and Company)

The first of today's modern automotive air conditioning systems was introduced by Cadillac in 1960. Their bilevel system could cool the top level of the car while heating the lower level. This method provided a means of controlling the in-vehicle humidity.

Many large firms reported increased sales after air conditioning was installed in the cars of their salespeople. Most commercial passenger-carrying vehicles are now air conditioned. Truck lines realize larger profits because drivers who have air conditioned cabs average more miles per day than those who do not.

In 1967, all of the state police cars on the Florida Turnpike were air conditioned. Since that time, most governmental and law enforcement agencies across the nation have added air conditioning to their vehicles.

## Other Applications

Mobile air conditioning is not only found in cars, trucks, and buses. In recent years, mobile air conditioning application has been expanded for use in such farm equipment as tractors, harvesters, and thrashers. Additionally, mobile air conditioning systems have been developed for use in other off-road equipment, such as backhoes, bulldozers, and graders. Air conditioning may be found in almost any kind of domestic, farm, or commercial equipment that has an enclosed cab and requires an onboard operator.

Humidity refers to the amount of moisture in the air.

Early studies of the effectiveness of vehicles equipped with automotive air conditioning proved that sales and production increased significantly.

# Air Conditioning 101

In order to understand how an air conditioning system functions, you must first know all the components that make up that system. You must also learn what role each of these components plays in the system and how each component interrelates with one another.

During the discussion on air conditioning components that follows in this chapter, it may be helpful to refer to Figure 3-18 and Figure 3-19 to understand how the basic components relate to one another.

The remainder of this chapter will discuss the various components in the air conditioning system, the role that each plays in the overall system, as well as the physical state of the refrigerant in various areas of the system. Knowing basic component location and terminology is required of all automotive technicians. Both customers and your peers in the trade expect you to know and use basic trade terminology and have an in-depth knowledge of the systems you are working on. This is all part of being a professional technician. In addition, it will be all but impossible to diagnose and repair a system if you do not grasp the basic operating principles and relationships of the various system components.

## Compressor

The refrigerant compressor (Figure 3-4) is the heart of the refrigerant system. Its purpose is to compress and pump refrigerant through the system. This specially-designed pump raises the pressure of the refrigerant from approximately 20 to 30 psi to approximately 180 to 220 psi. As you may recall from the last chapter, according to the laws of physics when a gas is compressed, its pressure and temperature are increased proportionally. By increasing the refrigerant's pressure, we also increase the temperature at which it will condense.

Figure 3-4 Typical compressors: (A) FS-10; (B) HR-6; (C) TR70 Honda; (D) FS-6.

Compressor designs may use one or more **reciprocating pistons**, rotary vanes, or scroll-type design. They may have a fixed displacement or they may have a variable displacement. There are many compressor designs and styles in use today, and these various designs and styles will be addressed in more detail in Chapter 8. Though many compressors may look alike, they are not interchangeable. Refer to manufacturer specifications for the correct compressor for each application.

The compressor is one of the points in the air conditioning system where there is a separation between high and low pressure. The low side is also referred to as the suction side of the system and connects the compressor inlet to the evaporator side of the system. The high side of the system is also referred to as the discharge side and connects the compressor outlet to the condenser inlet.

The refrigerant leaves the evaporator as a low-pressure gas (vapor) with as much heat as it can transport for its pressure. It goes into the compressor on the low-pressure (suction) side. There it is compressed by compressor action into a high-pressure vapor and is then pumped out of the smaller, outlet (discharge) side of the compressor.

The compressor pumps the low-pressure refrigerant vapor out of the evaporator by suction, raises its pressure, and then pumps it, under high pressure, into the condenser.

Multicylinder compressors have a set of valves for each piston. A set consists of one suction and one discharge valve. The suction and discharge valves operate conversely of each other. Discharge pressure (piston on the upstroke) forces the **suction valve** closed and the **discharge valve** open.

In a two-cylinder compressor, for example, when piston one is on the upstroke, the other piston is on the downstroke. Piston two is then forcing the suction valve open while the high pressure behind the discharge valve is holding it (discharge valve) closed (Figure 3-5).

**Reciprocating piston(s)** move(s) up and down or back and forth in a linear motion.

The compressor increases refrigerant vapor pressure.

**Shop Manual**
Chapter 3,
page 75

The **suction valve** is on the low-side suction port (intake) of the refrigerant compressor. It is a mechanical one-way check valve that only allows refrigerant to flow into the compressor.

The **discharge valve** is on the high-side discharge port (pressure) of the refrigerant compressor. It is a mechanical one-way check valve that only allows refrigerant to flow out of the compressor.

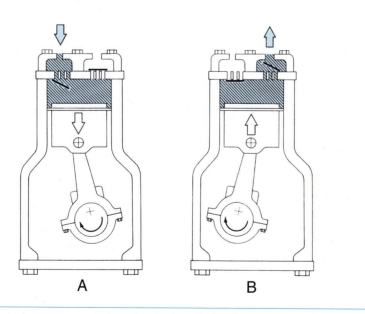

**Figure 3-5** Typical compressor action of a single-cylinder compressor. (A) Piston on downstroke pulls low-pressure refrigerant vapor into the cylinder cavity through the suction valve while (B) piston on the upstroke forces high-pressure refrigerant out through the discharge valve.

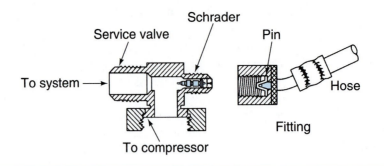

**Figure 3-6** A typical Schrader-type service valve for R-12 systems.

## Service Valves

Some compressors may be equipped with hand shut-off service valves, though most have Schrader-type service valves (Figure 3-6).

In most cases, the system suction and discharge service valves are located on the compressor cylinder heads. The suction and discharge lines or hoses are connected to the compressor at the service valves. If the service valve is not found on the compressor, the suction service valve will be found somewhere between the evaporator outlet and compressor inlet. The discharge service valve will be found somewhere between the compressor outlet and condenser inlet.

## Hand Shut-Off Valve

The hand-type shut-off service valve, once a very popular type, is likely encountered today only on older R-12 mobile air conditioning system applications. It may also be found on some off-road air conditioning systems using the two-cylinder Tecumseh and York compressors. Though no longer found frequently, it is important that the technician be familiar with its operation. Unlike the now-familiar Schrader-type valve, the shut-off service valve has, for all practical purposes, three positions: front seated, back seated, and midpositioned.

**Front Seated.**  When the valve stem is turned clockwise (cw) all the way in, it is said to be front seated (Figure 3-7A). This is not a normal operating position for either hand valve.

The compressor should not be operated with the discharge service valve front seated. To do so will result in serious compressor damage due to excessive high pressure. It may possibly burst, causing personal injury. Do not operate the compressor with service valve(s) in the front-seated position.

**Back Seated.**  When the service valve is turned counterclockwise (ccw) all the way out, it is said to be in the back-seated position. In this position (Figure 3-7B), the gauge port is closed, and the line port and compressor circuit are open. This is the normal operating position for both service valves.

**Midpositioned.**  When the service valve is in midposition (Figure 3-7C), it is said to be cracked. In this position, the line port, gauge port, and compressor are in the circuit. This is not the normal operating position, but it is the position for service when the manifold and gauge set is installed. To midposition a service valve, turn the stem two turns clockwise off its back-seated position. This is sufficient to allow system pressure to the gauge port. Do not front seat, then midposition.

**Shop Manual**
Chapter 3,
page 74

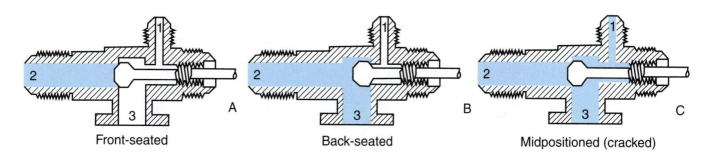

| Front-seated | Back-seated | Midpositioned (cracked) |

**Figure 3-7** (A) Service valve in the front-seated; (B) back-seated; and (C) midposition (cracked).

It should be noted that the hand shut-off type service valve is not to be midpositioned or front seated unless the manifold and gauge set is attached. The compressor should not be operated with the high-side service valve front seated.

## Schrader-Type Valve

The Schrader-type service valve is self-opening when a manifold hose is attached. It operates in much the same manner as a tire valve. Because of its design, the Schrader-type service valve may only be cracked, or back seated.

## Quick-Connect Valve

The service valve used for R-134a systems is a positive-coupled, quick-connect type. There is a Schrader valve similar to the R-12 Schrader access fitting, with the exception that it is recessed further into the fitting (Figure 3-8). The high-side service port, at 16 mm, is larger than the low-side service port, which is 13 mm. Service hoses for automotive air conditioning system use must have unique fittings that attach to the service ports (Figure 3-9) and refrigerant cylinder. This

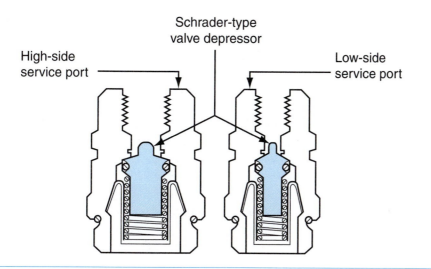

**Figure 3-8** R-134a (HFC-134a) service port details.

**Figure 3-9** Typical R-134a service port adapters.

combination, required by the Environmental Protection Agency (EPA), prevents reversing the hoses as well as introducing the wrong refrigerant.

# Condenser

The **condenser** is a heat exchanger for the superheated refrigerant in the system. Refrigerant containing heat is compressed by the compressor and, in both a high-pressure and high-temperature (**superheated**) gaseous state, flows to the condenser. This super-heated high-pressure vapor enters the top of the condenser. As it passes through the condenser coils, the outside air passing over the coils and fins picks up heat from the refrigerant. This occurs because the outside air at this point has less heat than the refrigerant in the coil. As the heat leaves the refrigerant, the refrigerant condenses, changing from a high-pressure vapor to a high-pressure liquid, which exits at the bottom of the condenser.

The condenser is that part of the air conditioner that removes heat from the refrigerant and dissipates this heat to the outside air. The engine cooling system fan pulls air through the condenser, which is located in front of the radiator. Air passes through the condenser, then through the radiator. Ambient air is also forced through the condenser and radiator by the forward movement of the vehicle. This is known as ram air.

Condenser problems usually result from external clogging, damage, or from leaks. External clogging is caused by dirt, bugs, leaves, or other foreign debris that collects on the condenser fins and restricts air flow. This lessens the condenser's ability to transfer heat, resulting in poor cooling of the car interior.

The condenser and the radiator must be kept clean for best performance. To clean the condenser, use a soft bristle brush (such as a hair brush) and a strong stream of water. Take care not to bend the fins, which would also restrict the flow of air.

Clean the radiator/condenser assembly with clean water directed from the back (engine side) to the front. If air is used, use only low-pressure air to prevent damage to the delicate and fragile fins of the radiator. Do not use a steam cleaner to remove debris from the condenser. To do so may cause an increase in air conditioning system pressure.

Since temperature and pressure are high in the condenser, a leak is not always successfully repaired by soldering. It is generally recommended that the condenser be repaired by a professional or be replaced if it is found to be leaking.

The **condenser** is a heat exchanger located in front of the vehicle radiator. It is the component of the refrigerant system in which refrigerant is changed from a gas to a liquid by the removal of heat.

**Superheated** is the process of adding heat intensity to a liquid above its boiling point without vaporization or to heat a gas above its saturation point so that a drop in temperature will not cause reconversion to liquid.

# Receiver-Drier and Accumulator

The **receiver-drier** and suction line **accumulator** are tank-type devices that have nearly the same external appearance. The functions of the two devices are somewhat different, however.

The function of the receiver-drier is to store a refrigerant reserve to ensure a constant liquid supply to the expansion valve. A strainer and a drying agent (called a desiccant) are found in the receiver-drier to remove moisture and clean the refrigerant.

The function of the accumulator is to catch and trap liquid refrigerant from the evaporator to protect the compressor. The accumulator also contains a strainer and desiccant for refrigerant cleaning and purification.

## Receiver-Drier

From the condenser, the high-pressure liquid refrigerant enters the receiver-drier (Figure 3-10) where it is stored until it is needed by the expansion valve. The receiver-drier performs three functions in the automobile air conditioning system:

❏ The receiver section is the storage tank for excess (reserve) liquid refrigerant that is necessary for proper operation of the air conditioning system.
❏ The drier section collects small droplets of moisture that may have entered the system at the time of installation or repair.
❏ The pickup tube ensures a vapor-free stream of liquid to the expansion valve.

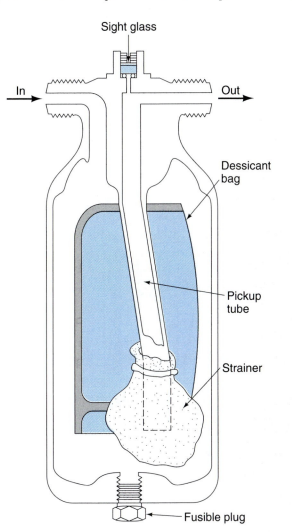

**Figure 3-10** Cutaway of a typical receiver-drier.

The **receiver-drier** is a storage container on the high pressure side of the system between the condenser and the thermostatic expansion valve. It is used to separate out refrigerant vapor from liquid refrigerant allowing only liquefied refrigerant to travel onto the thermostatic expansion valve and contains a drying agent in a desiccant bag inside the container.

The **accumulator** is a storage container on the low-pressure side of the system between the evaporator and the expansion tube, which is often referred to as the fixed orifice tube (FOT). It is used to separate out refrigerant liquid from vaporized refrigerant, allowing only vaporized refrigerant to travel onto the compressor assembly. It contains a drying agent in a desiccant bag inside the container.

The receiver-drier or accumulator contains the drying agent known as desiccant.

A condenser-mounted receiver-drier should be mounted as level as possible, usually by adjusting its bracket or the condenser mounting brackets. The vertical-type drier should be mounted in a position as vertical as possible, with no more than a 15-degree slant off vertical.

Receiver-driers are available in a variety of sizes and have different fittings for different applications. Universal-type receiver-driers are available that may be used if exact replacement units are not available. Driers are also available without the receiver. This type drier is usually used in series with a receiver-drier in a "problem" air conditioning system when a great deal of debris is encountered. It should be noted that receiver-driers and driers are not omnidirectional. They are designed for refrigerant to flow in one direction only. Most driers are marked IN and/or OUT or have an arrow (→) to indicate direction of refrigerant flow. Remember, the refrigerant flow is away from the condenser and toward the evaporator.

## Accumulator

The suction line accumulator (Figure 3-11) is located at the outlet of the evaporator and before the inlet of the compressor. The purpose of the accumulator is to trap excess liquid refrigerant, preventing it from entering the compressor. Liquid refrigerant in the compressor could cause serious damage.

Refrigerant leaving the evaporator enters the accumulator where any liquid (heavier than vapor) falls to the bottom of the tank. A U-shaped pickup tube ensures that only refrigerant vapor leaves the accumulator to the compressor inlet. A metered orifice at the bottom of the U-bend meters a small amount of liquid (when present) into the suction line. This orifice is calibrated to ensure that liquid so metered will vaporize before it reaches the compressor. This orifice also allows small quantities of refrigerant oil to return to the compressor.

The accumulator is used in systems that have a fixed orifice tube as a metering device. Those systems that have a thermostatic expansion valve have liquid-line receivers and not suction accumulators. The system will have either an accumulator or a receiver-drier, not both, depending on system design.

> The system will have either an accumulator or a receiver-drier, not both.

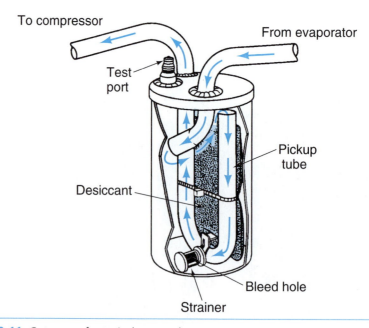

Figure 3-11  Cutaway of a typical accumulator.

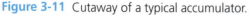

# Metering Devices

At the present time, there are two types of metering devices used in automotive air conditioning systems. The most widely used device is the **thermostatic expansion valve**, more commonly called an expansion valve and often abbreviated TXV.

Another device, originally introduced by General Motors and now found on many car lines, is the expansion tube, more commonly referred to as an orifice tube.

❏ Systems that have an expansion valve will have a receiver-drier in the liquid line *before* the device.

❏ Systems that have an orifice tube will have an accumulator in the suction line *after* the device.

## Expansion Valves

The expansion valves used in automotive air conditioning systems are designed for a specific use and are manufactured as a precision component. No attempt should be made by the inexperienced to disassemble, repair, or adjust the expansion valve. It is possible, however, to clean or replace the inlet screen (strainer) should it become clogged. Some expansion valves may be cleaned, repaired, or adjusted, but this is only accomplished with the proper tools, test equipment, and experience.

The expansion valve (Figure 3-12) controls the amount of refrigerant entering the evaporator under ever-changing heat load conditions. Heat load conditions of the car's interior depend on many factors, such as the number of occupants and heat gain from the sun through windows and the car's body, as well as heat gain from the engine compartment and exhaust system.

The expansion valve is regulated by a sensing bulb that is tightly clamped to the evaporator outlet tube. In operation, the sensing bulb senses the temperature of the refrigerant as it leaves the evaporator coil. If the refrigerant line is warm, the charge of refrigerant (or other volatile liquid) in the sensing bulb expands, putting pressure on the valve bellows through a small capillary tube. The bellows then forces a needle valve off its seat, and the valve opens to allow more refrigerant to enter the evaporator.

As the evaporator outlet tube becomes cooler, the charge of volatile liquid in the sensing bulb will contract and there will be less pressure on the bellows. The needle valve will then close, decreasing the amount of refrigerant that is allowed to enter the evaporator coil.

The **thermostatic expansion valve** is the component in the refrigerant system that regulates the rate of flow of refrigerant into the evaporator core through the use of a variable valve opening as governed by a remote bulb-sensing evaporator temperature. It is located just before the evaporator and after the receiver-dryer. It is one of the points in the air conditioning system where there is a separation between a high and low pressure. A system that uses a thermostatic expansion valve also uses a receiver-dryer assembly.

If the TXV malfunctions, replace it as an assembly.

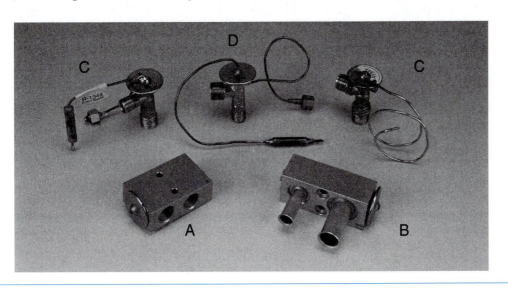

**Figure 3-12** Thermostatic expansion valves: (A) H-valve; (b) block type; (C) internally equalized; (D) externally equalized.

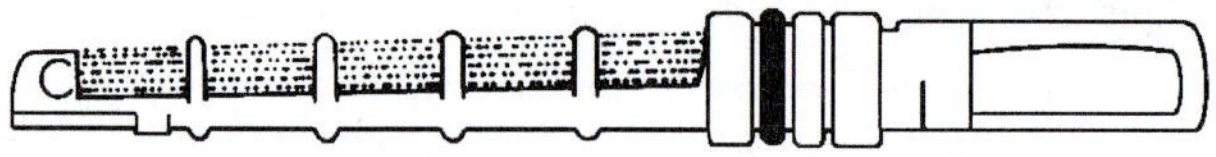

**Figure 3-13** A typical fixed orifice.

If the expansion valve is found to be defective, the sensing bulb may have lost its charge, or the internal parts may be seized due to corrosion or foreign matter. The sensing bulb cannot be recharged. If seized, the valve may be in the fully open or fully closed position. If either is the case, the valve must be replaced as an assembly.

Testing the expansion valve requires special tools and equipment that few technicians have. Hit-and-miss repairs and adjustments may be more expensive in the long run than replacement—even for the experienced technician.

## Expansion Tubes

The **expansion tube**, better known as a fixed orifice tube (FOT), is a nonadjustable device that has a fixed orifice metering element and a fine-mesh strainer. Unlike the expansion valve, the FOT (Figure 3-13), has no remote bulb, no moving parts, and does not vary the amount of refrigerant entering the evaporator in the same manner. The FOT meters the proper amount of refrigerant into the evaporator based on a pressure differential (high side to low side). A pressure differential is known as delta P ($\Delta_p$).

Though FOTs may look the same, except for color, they are not interchangeable. It is the color that identifies their application according to the diameter of their orifice size. Color and orifice size are given in Table 3-1.

Generally the FOT is located in a cavity in the liquid line or at the inlet connection of the evaporator and is easily accessible. Some 1980–1990 Ford lines, however, have an inaccessible FOT located in the liquid line. If found to be defective, the liquid line has to be replaced, or a repair kit may be used to replace only that section of the liquid line that contains the FOT. Procedures for replacing the FOT with the repair kit are found in Chapter 5 of the Shop Manual.

## Variable Orifice Tube

A variable orifice tube, called a variable orifice valve (VOV), is available for aftermarket and retrofit applications. In the late 1990s, engineers from a leading automotive air conditioning parts distributor tested the VOV for inclusion in their line. Their tests determined that although the VOV marginally improved duct temperature as the manufacturer claimed, it also resulted in an increase in high-side pressure. High-side pressure is a major concern when retrofitting a vehicle from CFC-12 to HFC-134a.

**TABLE 3-1  SIZE OF FOT IDENTIFIED BY COLOR**

| COLOR | ORIFICE | |
|---|---|---|
| | INCH | MILLIMETER |
| Blue or black | 0.067 | 1.7 |
| Red | 0.062 | 1.57 |
| Orange | 0.057 | 1.45 |
| Brown | 0.053 | 1.35 |
| Green | 0.047 | 1.19 |

The **expansion tube** is the component in the refrigerant system that regulates the rate of flow of refrigerant into the evaporator core. It is often referred to as the fixed orifice tube (FOT) and is a fixed metering device equipped with a filter screen. It is located between the condenser and the evaporator core. It is one of the points in the air conditioning system where there is a separation between a high and low pressure. A system that uses a fixed orifice tube also uses an accumulator assembly placed between the evaporator and the compressor.

Expansion tubes are often referred to as fixed-orifice tubes.

## Orifice Tube Failure

The primary cause of failure of the FOT is clogging of the metering element orifice and strainer screen. This is often caused by failure of the desiccant inside the accumulator. Cleaning a clogged FOT seldom provides satisfactory results. The time and expense of having to do the repairs a second time far outweigh the cost of a new FOT. For this reason, if the FOT is found to be clogged it should be replaced. Also, if the FOT is clogged, the accumulator should be replaced as well.

# Evaporator

The evaporator is physically located in the air distribution duct work for the passenger compartment comfort heating and cooling system and looks like a small radiator (Figure 3-14). The evaporator is a heat exchanger that *removes heat from the air* flowing across the evaporator cooling fins. The source of the air blown over the evaporator fins and coils may be from outside the passenger compartment or recirculated from inside the passenger compartment when the *MAX* mode or recirculation mode is selected on the heater control panel. Heat in the air is picked up by the fins and coils and transferred to the refrigerant passing through the coil. The refrigerant inside the **evaporator** coil is at a low pressure because it was metered into the coil through the small orifice of the expansion valve or by the orifice tube. Also, the compressor is pulling refrigerant out of the evaporator by a suction action.

The **evaporator** is a heat exchanger that removes heat from the air flowing across the evaporator cooling fins and into the passenger compartment.

**Figure 3-14** A typical evaporator core.

As the low-pressure liquid refrigerant absorbs heat from the evaporator coils and fins, it boils, turning into a vapor. Since heat was taken out of the air inside the car, its temperature is lower (cooler), and the passenger compartment becomes conditioned or more comfortable. As air continues to recirculate over the evaporator coil, more heat is removed and the air continues to cool. Actual temperature control is by the action of a thermostat or a low-pressure control.

The evaporator core contains no moving parts to wear out.

The evaporator coil is that part of the system that removes unwanted heat from the air and transfers it to the refrigerant in the coil. The evaporator consists of tubes (coils), fins, end plates, and return bends, assembled complete with inlet and outlet manifolds and housed in an evaporator case. The evaporator case is fitted with blowers to direct air across the coils and fins.

There are three problems that could occur with the evaporator, resulting in poor cooling:

❑ Leaks
❑ Dirty fins
❑ Blocked or kinked tubes

Humidity is an important factor in the quality and temperature of the air delivered to the interior of the car. The service technician must understand the effect that relative humidity (RH) has on the performance of the system. Relative humidity is the term that is used to denote the amount of moisture in the air. For example, a relative humidity of 80 percent means that the air contains 80 percent of the moisture that it can contain at a given temperature.

When the relative humidity is high, the evaporator has a double function. It must lower the air temperature as well as the temperature of the moisture carried in the air. The process of condensing the moisture in the air transfers a great amount of heat energy in the evaporator. Consequently, the amount of heat that can be absorbed from the air in the evaporator is greatly reduced.

The evaporator capacity required to reduce the amount of moisture in the air is not wasted, however. Lowering the moisture content in the air in the vehicle adds to the comfort of the passengers. The average person is comfortable at a temperature of 78° to 80°F at a relative humidity (RH) of 45 to 50 percent.

# Hoses and Lines

Rust in the system is undesirable and will cause early component failure.

Hoses and lines carry refrigerant, as a liquid or vapor, from one component to another in the system. Hoses are constructed of a special synthetic reinforced rubber. Because of the properties of refrigerants and the high pressure of the system, only this type of hose should be used.

Lines may be constructed of copper (Cu), aluminum (Al), or steel tubing. Any good grade of copper or aluminum tubing may be used, provided it is rated at a working pressure of 400 psig (2,760 kPa) or higher. If steel is used, it must be clean and dry.

Just like the other components of the system, each hose or line is referred to by name. Follow the system layout for identification of the following components (Figure 3-15).

## Suction Line

The suction line is the line connecting the evaporator outlet to the compressor inlet.

The suction line should be cool to the touch.

The suction line is also referred to as the low-pressure line or the low-pressure vapor line. It connects the evaporator outlet to the compressor inlet. This line, which usually has the largest diameter in the system, carries low-pressure refrigerant vapor from the evaporator to the compressor. The suction line is cool to the touch.

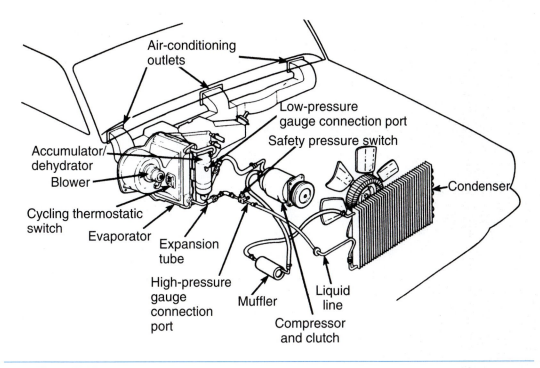

**Figure 3-15** A typical system layout.

## Discharge Line

Also referred to as the high-pressure **discharge line**, the discharge line connects the compressor outlet to the condenser inlet. This line carries high-pressure refrigerant vapor.

In a properly operating system, this line is hot. It may be very hot in an improperly operating system, and care to avoid burns is important in many cases.

## Liquid Line

The **liquid line** is also referred to as the high-pressure liquid line. It connects the condenser outlet to the receiver-drier inlet. It also connects the receiver-drier outlet to the evaporator metering device inlet. This line, which is usually warm, may be hot under certain conditions. This line carries high-pressure liquid/vapor from the condenser to the receiver-drier and high-pressure liquid from the receiver-drier to the metering device.

## Connectors

**Hose.** Early automotive air conditioning systems using CFC-12 refrigerant had hoses constructed of an inner and outer layer of rubber or a synthetic rubber with one or two layers of reinforcing material. Later air conditioning systems using HFC-134a as a refrigerant have hoses known as *barrier hoses*. Barrier hoses are constructed much in the same manner but have a lining and two or more layers of a nonpermeable material, such as nylon.

**Fittings.** Depending on design and application, several types of fittings are used to connect the hoses to the various components of an air conditioning system. Several types, shown in Figure 3-16 and Figure 3-17, include flare (SAE), O-ring, spring lock, barb, and Beadlock fittings.

The **discharge line** is the line connecting the compressor outlet to the condenser inlet.

The **liquid line** connects the condenser to the receiver-dryer inlet and the receiver-dryer outlet with the expansion valve inlet.

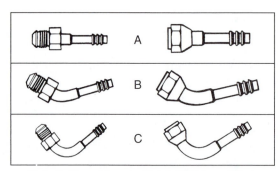

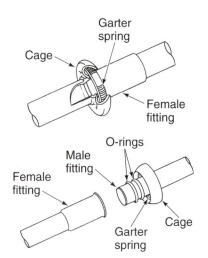

Male (left) and female (right) SAE flare fittings: (A) Straight, (B) 45° elbow, and (C) 90° elbow

Detail of spring lock (garter ) connector

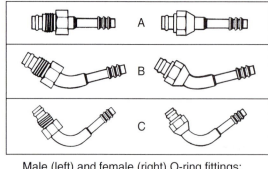

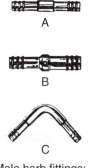

Male (left) and female (right) O-ring fittings: (A) Straight, (B) 45° elbow, and (C) 90° elbow

Male barb fittings: (A) straight, (B) straight reducing, (C) 90° elbow

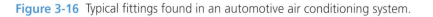

**Figure 3-16** Typical fittings found in an automotive air conditioning system.

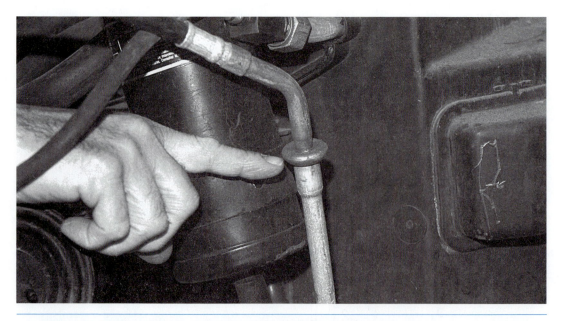

**Figure 3-17** Typical beadlock fittings used with barrier hoses.

# Air Conditioning Circuit

To better understand the function of an automotive air conditioning system, it is helpful to know the physical state of the refrigerant in the various sections of the system. Actually, there are only six such states to be considered:

1. Low-pressure vapor (**A**)
2. Low-pressure liquid (**B**)
3. Low-pressure vapor and liquid (**C**)
4. High-pressure vapor (**D**)
5. High-pressure liquid (**E**)
6. High-pressure liquid and vapor (**F**)

Following is a brief overview of each of these states. For component location, refer to callouts (**A** through **F**) in Figure 3-18 for an expansion valve system or Figure 3-19 for an orifice tube system.

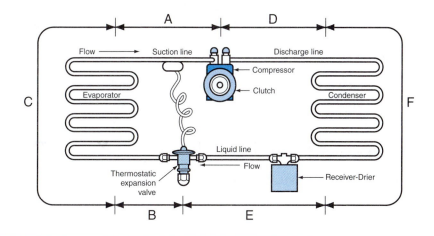

**Figure 3-18** Thermostatic expansion valve system.

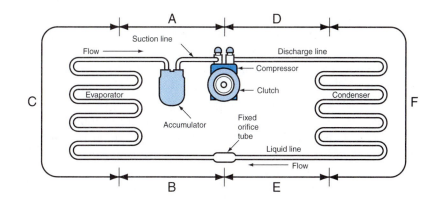

**Figure 3-19** Orifice tube system.

## Low-Pressure Vapor

The refrigerant is a low-pressure vapor in the section of the system from the evaporator outlet to the compressor inlet **(A)**. This includes any devices found in the suction line, such as a suction line drier, muffler, or accumulator.

## Low-Pressure Liquid

Immediately after the metering device, the entrance to the evaporator **(B)** is the only part of the system that may contain low-pressure liquid. Even this section contains vapor, called flash gas, having just passed through the metering device.

## Low-Pressure Vapor and Liquid

In the evaporator **(C)**, low-pressure liquid refrigerant boils as it picks up heat and is changed to low-pressure vapor.

## High-Pressure Vapor

The refrigerant is at high pressure in a vapor state in the line from the compressor outlet to the condenser inlet **(D)**. This includes any devices that may be in the discharge line, such as a muffler.

## High-Pressure Liquid

The high-pressure liquid refrigerant section extends from the condenser outlet to the metering device inlet **(E)**. This includes any devices in the liquid line, such as receiver, drier, and sight glass.

## High-Pressure Liquid and Vapor

In giving up its heat, the high-pressure refrigerant vapor is changed to liquid in the condenser **(F)**.

## System Review

Heat is picked up inside the automobile driver/passenger compartment from the air passing through the coils and fins of the evaporator. This heat is picked up by the liquid refrigerant as it evaporates. The heat-laden refrigerant vapor is then pumped by the compressor into the condenser on the outside of the automobile, usually located in front of the radiator. In the condenser, the refrigerant's heat is given up to the less-hot air passing across the coils and fins as it condenses back to a liquid.

The transfer of heat in an air conditioning system is accomplished by two pressure and two temperature systems: a low-pressure system of 21–35 psig (145–241 kPa) with a low temperature of 21°–38°F (–6.1°–3.3°C), and a high-pressure system of 180–220 psig (1,241–1,517 kPa) with a high temperature of 88°–100°F (31.1°–37.7°C). Any time there is a pressure change, there is a temperature change. During this pressure-temperature change with R-12 and R-134a, there is also a change of state (Figure 3-20). In the low-pressure side, the change is from a liquid to a vapor; in the high-pressure side, the change is from a vapor to a liquid.

It is important that you understand this pressure-temperature relationship as you use the manifold and gauge set as a diagnostic tool. The manifold and gauge set is used as a diagnostic tool to determine many system problems that relate to abnormal gauge pressures.

The pressure of the refrigerant is increased by the compressor. The compressor pumps low-pressure refrigerant vapor from the evaporator to the condenser at a high pressure. The pressure of the refrigerant is decreased by the metering device (expansion valve or orifice tube) at the inlet of the evaporator.

**Shop Manual**
Chapter 3,
page 76

| Temp. °F | Press. psig | Temp. °F | Press. psig | Temp. °F | Press. psig | Temp. °F | Press. psig | Temp. °F | Press. psig |
|---|---|---|---|---|---|---|---|---|---|
| 0 | 9.1 | 35 | 32.5 | 60 | 57.7 | 85 | 91.7 | 110 | 136.0 |
| 2 | 10.1 | 36 | 33.4 | 61 | 58.9 | 86 | 93.2 | 111 | 138.0 |
| 4 | 11.2 | 37 | 34.3 | 62 | 60.0 | 87 | 94.8 | 112 | 140.1 |
| 6 | 12.3 | 38 | 35.1 | 63 | 61.3 | 88 | 96.4 | 113 | 142.1 |
| 8 | 13.4 | 39 | 36.0 | 64 | 62.5 | 89 | 98.0 | 114 | 144.2 |
| 10 | 14.6 | 40 | 36.9 | 65 | 63.7 | 90 | 99.6 | 115 | 146.3 |
| 12 | 15.8 | 41 | 37.9 | 66 | 64.9 | 91 | 101.3 | 116 | 148.4 |
| 14 | 17.1 | 42 | 38.8 | 67 | 66.2 | 92 | 103.0 | 117 | 151.2 |
| 16 | 18.3 | 43 | 39.7 | 68 | 67.5 | 93 | 104.6 | 118 | 152.7 |
| 18 | 19.7 | 44 | 40.7 | 69 | 68.8 | 94 | 106.3 | 119 | 154.9 |
| 20 | 21.0 | 45 | 41.7 | 70 | 70.1 | 95 | 108.1 | 120 | 157.1 |
| 21 | 21.7 | 46 | 42.6 | 71 | 71.4 | 96 | 109.8 | 121 | 159.3 |
| 22 | 22.4 | 47 | 43.6 | 72 | 72.8 | 97 | 111.5 | 122 | 161.5 |
| 23 | 23.1 | 48 | 44.6 | 73 | 74.2 | 98 | 113.3 | 123 | 163.8 |
| 24 | 23.8 | 49 | 45.6 | 74 | 75.5 | 99 | 115.1 | 124 | 166.1 |
| 25 | 24.6 | 50 | 46.6 | 75 | 76.9 | 100 | 116.9 | 125 | 168.4 |
| 26 | 25.3 | 51 | 47.8 | 76 | 78.3 | 101 | 118.8 | 126 | 170.7 |
| 27 | 26.1 | 52 | 48.7 | 77 | 79.2 | 102 | 120.6 | 127 | 173.1 |
| 28 | 26.8 | 53 | 49.8 | 78 | 81.1 | 103 | 122.4 | 128 | 175.4 |
| 29 | 27.6 | 54 | 50.9 | 79 | 82.5 | 104 | 124.3 | 129 | 177.8 |
| 30 | 28.4 | 55 | 52.0 | 80 | 84.0 | 105 | 126.2 | 130 | 182.2 |
| 31 | 29.2 | 56 | 53.1 | 81 | 85.5 | 106 | 128.1 | 131 | 182.6 |
| 32 | 30.0 | 57 | 55.4 | 82 | 87.0 | 107 | 130.0 | 132 | 185.1 |
| 33 | 30.9 | 58 | 56.6 | 83 | 88.5 | 108 | 132.1 | 133 | 187.6 |
| 34 | 31.7 | 59 | 57.1 | 84 | 90.1 | 109 | 135.1 | 134 | 190.1 |

A: English Temp/Pres Fen CFC-12 (R-12)

| Temperature °F | Pressure psig | Temperature °F | Pressure psig |
|---|---|---|---|
| −5 | 4.1 | 39.0 | 34.1 |
| 0 | 6.5 | 40.0 | 35.0 |
| 5.0 | 9.1 | 45.0 | 40.0 |
| 10.0 | 12.0 | 50.0 | 45.4 |
| 15.0 | 15.1 | 55.0 | 51.2 |
| 20.0 | 18.4 | 60.0 | 57.4 |
| 21.0 | 19.1 | 65.0 | 64.0 |
| 22.0 | 19.9 | 70.0 | 71.1 |
| 23.0 | 20.6 | 75.0 | 78.6 |
| 24.0 | 21.4 | 80.0 | 86.7 |
| 25.0 | 22.1 | 85.0 | 95.2 |
| 26.0 | 22.9 | 90.0 | 104.3 |
| 27.0 | 23.7 | 95.0 | 113.9 |
| 28.0 | 24.5 | 100.0 | 124.1 |
| 29.0 | 25.3 | 105.0 | 134.9 |
| 30.0 | 25.3 | 110.0 | 146.3 |
| 31.0 | 27.0 | 115.0 | 158.4 |
| 32.0 | 27.8 | 120.0 | 171.1 |
| 33.0 | 28.7 | 125.0 | 184.5 |
| 34.0 | 29.5 | 130.0 | 198.7 |
| 35.0 | 30.4 | 135.0 | 213.5 |
| 36.0 | 31.3 | 140.0 | 229.2 |
| 37.0 | 32.2 | 145.0 · | 245.6 |
| 38.0 | 33.2 | 150.0 | 262.8 |

B: English Temp/Pres Chart for HFC-134a (R-134a)

| EVAPORATOR TEMPERATURE °C | EVAPORATOR PRESSURE GAUGE READING KILOPASCAL (GAUGE) | (ABSOLUTE) | AMBIENT TEMPERATURE °C | HIGH PRESSURE GAUGE READING KILOPASCAL (GAUGE) |
|---|---|---|---|---|
| −16 | 73.4 | 174.7 | 16 | 737.7 |
| −15 | 81.0 | 182.3 | 17 | 759.8 |
| −14 | 87.8 | 189.1 | 18 | 784.6 |
| −13 | 94.8 | 196.1 | 19 | 810.2 |
| −12 | 100.6 | 201.9 | 20 | 841.2 |
| −11 | 108.9 | 210.2 | 21 | 868.7 |
| −10 | 117.9 | 219.2 | 22 | 901.8 |
| − 9 | 124.5 | 225.8 | 23 | 932.2 |
| − 8 | 133.9 | 235.2 | 24 | 970.8 |
| − 7 | 140.3 | 241.6 | 25 | 1 020.5 |
| − 6 | 149.6 | 250.9 | 26 | 1 075.6 |
| − 5 | 159.2 | 260.5 | 27 | 1 111.5 |
| − 4 | 167.4 | 268.7 | 28 | 1 143.2 |
| − 3 | 183.2 | 268.7 | 29 | 1 174.9 |
| − 2 | 186.9 | 288.2 | 30 | 1 206.6 |
| − 1 | 195.8 | 288.2 | 31 | 1 241.1 |
| 0 | 206.8 | 308.1 | 32 | 1 267.3 |
| 1 | 218.5 | 319.8 | 33 | 1 294.8 |
| 2 | 227.8 | 329.1 | 34 | 1 319.7 |
| 3 | 238.7 | 340.0 | 35 | 1 344.5 |
| 4 | 249.4 | 350.7 | 36 | 1 413.5 |
| 5 | 261.3 | 362.6 | 37 | 1 468.6 |
| 6 | 273.7 | 375.0 | 38 | 1 527.9 |
| 7 | 287.5 | 388.8 | 39 | 1 577.5 |
| 8 | 296.6 | 397.9 | 40 | 1 627.2 |
| 9 | 303.3 | 404.6 | 42 | 1 737.5 |
| 10 | 321.5 | 422.8 | 45 | 1 854.7 |

C: Metric Temp/Pres Chart for CFC-12 (R-12)

| Temperature °C | Pressure kPa | Temperature °C | Pressure kPa |
|---|---|---|---|
| −15.0 | 63 | 5.0 | 247 |
| −12.5 | 83 | 7.5 | 280 |
| −10.0 | 103 | 10.0 | 313 |
| −7.5 | 122 | 12.5 | 345 |
| −5.0 | 142 | 15.0 | 381 |
| −4.5 | 147 | 17.5 | 422 |
| −4.0 | 152 | 20.0 | 465 |
| −3.5 | 157 | 22.5 | 510 |
| −3.0 | 162 | 25.0 | 560 |
| −2.5 | 167 | 27.5 | 616 |
| −2.0 | 172 | 30.0 | 670 |
| −1.5 | 177 | 32.5 | 726 |
| −1.0 | 182 | 35.0 | 785 |
| −0.5 | 187 | 37.5 | 849 |
| 0.0 | 192 | 40.0 | 916 |
| 0.5 | 198 | 42.5 | 990 |
| 1.0 | 203 | 45.0 | 1066 |
| 1.5 | 209 | 47.5 | 1146 |
| 2.0 | 214 | 50.0 | 1230 |
| 2.5 | 220 | 52.5 | 1315 |
| 3.0 | 225 | 55.0 | 1385 |
| 3.5 | 231 | 57.5 | 1480 |
| 4.0 | 236 | 60.0 | 1580 |
| 4.5 | 242 | 65.0 | 1795 |

D: Metric Temp/Pres Chart for HFC-134a (R-134a)

**Figure 3-20** Typical temperature-pressure charts.

The flow of refrigerant is regulated into the evaporator by a metering device such as a thermostatic expansion valve (TXV) or a fixed orifice tube (FOT). Just before entering the metering device, the refrigerant is a high-pressure liquid. Refrigerant is metered into the evaporator through a small orifice, changing it to a low-pressure liquid.

From what we have outlined, it may be concluded that the compressor is the dividing line, low- to high-side, and the metering device is the dividing line, high- to low-side. Whenever necessary, refer to the basic principles previously discussed.

## Summary

- ❏ The colder the matter, the slower the molecular movement.
- ❏ Although the principles were known as long ago as 10,000 B.C., air conditioning and refrigerant is a development of the twentieth century.
- ❏ Automotive air conditioning has played a significant and important role in the comfort, health, and safety of the modern motorist.
- ❏ The air conditioning compressor is the heart of the heating and cooling system. The compressor is one of the points in the air conditioning system where there is a separation between high and low pressure. Its purpose is to pull refrigerant into the compressor through the suction line and compress and pump refrigerant out the discharge (pressure) line.
- ❏ The condenser is a heat exchanger for the superheated refrigerant in the system. It removes the heat energy from the refrigerant that was gained in the evaporator.
- ❏ The evaporator is a heat exchanger that removes heat from the air flowing across the evaporator cooling fins in the passenger compartment duct system to cool the passenger compartment.
- ❏ The accumulator and receiver-drier are storage and distribution components used to clean and dry the refrigerant.
- ❏ Refrigerant lines are of barrier design for R134a refrigerant and are used to transport refrigerant through the system.
- ❏ The air conditioning system is designed to maintain in-car temperature and humidity at a predetermined level.

## Review Questions

### Short Answer Essays

1. What was the initial source for artificial ice?
2. How did the early Egyptians cool water?
3. How was humidity controlled in the Northcotts' home?
4. Define the term *air conditioning*.
5. What is the purpose of the modern air conditioning system?
6. What is the difference between the accumulator and the receiver-drier?
7. Where is the receiver-drier located, and what state is the refrigerant in that flows through it?
8. Where is the accumulator located, and what state is the refrigerant in that flows through it?
9. What is the purpose of a compressor?
10. How does the expansion tube differ from the expansion valve?

## Fill-in-the-Blanks

1. Over _____ percent of all cars produced today are equipped with an air conditioning system.

2. In the late 1920s and early 1930s, an "air conditioning" option meant that the car was equipped with a(n) _____ and _____ system.

3. Once considered a(n) _____ , automotive air conditioning is now considered by many to be a necessity.

4. An air conditioning system that uses a fixed orifice tube has a(n) _____ in the suction line.

5. An air conditioning system that uses a thermostatic expansion valve has a(n) _____ in the liquid line.

6. The _____ is a heat exchanger for the superheated refrigerant in the system.

7. The _____ is one of the points in the air conditioning system where there is a separation between high and low pressure.

8. There is a direct relationship between temperature and _____ in an automotive air conditioning system.

9. The refrigerant changes from a _____ to a _____ in the condenser.

10. Two types of metering devices are the _____ _____ valve and the _____ _____ tube.

## Multiple Choice

1. The popularity of mobile air conditioning is being discussed:
   *Technician A* says that mobile air conditioning became popular for automotive use in the early 1960s.
   *Technician B* says that mobile air conditioning is now found in most any type vehicle.
   Who is correct?
   **A.** A only          **C.** Both A and B
   **B.** B only          **D.** Neither A nor B

2. *Technician A* says that heat added to a vapor, causing it to become warmer, is called sensible heat.
   *Technician B* says that heat added to a vapor, causing it to become warmer, is called superheat.
   Who is correct?
   **A.** A only          **C.** Both A and B
   **B.** B only          **D.** Neither A nor B

3. *Technician A* says that air conditioning is the process where air is cleaned, filtered, and recirculated.
   *Technician B* says that air conditioning is the process of cooling air by removing some of its heat.
   Who is correct?
   **A.** A only          **C.** Both A and B
   **B.** B only          **D.** Neither A nor B

4. *Technician A* says that heating and cooling could be accomplished simultaneously with Cadillac's early bilevel system.
   *Technician B* says the bilevel system provided a method of humidity control.
   Who is correct?
   **A.** A only          **C.** Both A and B
   **B.** B only          **D.** Neither A nor B

5. *Technician A* says that early refrigerators were ice boxes.
   *Technician B* says that early refrigerators were absorption systems.
   Who is correct?
   **A.** A only          **C.** Both A and B
   **B.** B only          **D.** Neither A nor B

6. *Technician A* says the condenser is a heat exchanger for the superheated refrigerant in the system.
   *Technician B* says the accumulator is a heat exchanger that removes heat from the air flowing across the evaporator cooling fins.
   Who is correct?
   **A.** A only          **C.** Both A and B
   **B.** B only          **D.** Neither A nor B

7. *Technician A* says the compressor is one of the points in the air conditioning system where there is a separation between a high and a low pressure. *Technician B* says the metering device is one of the points in the air conditioning system where there is a separation between a high and a low pressure. Who is correct?
   A. A only
   B. B only
   C. Both A and B
   D. Neither A nor B

8. *Technician A* says the compressor changes a low-pressure vapor to a high-pressure vapor. *Technician B* says that the metering device changes high-pressure vapor to a low-pressure vapor. Who is correct?
   A. A only
   B. B only
   C. Both A and B
   D. Neither A nor B

9. *Technician A* says the fixed orifice tube can vary the amount of refrigerant allowed to flow to the evaporator. *Technician B* says the thermostatic expansion valve has fixed opening and cannot vary the amount of refrigerant allowed to flow to the evaporator. Who is correct?
   A. A only
   B. B only
   C. Both A and B
   D. Neither A nor B

10. *Technician A* says that the line or hose that connects the compressor outlet to the condenser inlet is called the discharge line. *Technician B* says that the line or hose that connects the evaporator outlet to the compressor inlet of a TXV system is called a suction line. Who is correct?
   A. A only
   B. B only
   C. Both A and B
   D. Neither A nor B

# Engine Cooling and Comfort Heating Systems

Upon completion and review of this chapter you should be able to:

❏ Explain the engine cooling system and its components.

❏ Recognize the various components of the automotive cooling system.

❏ Identify the different types of radiators.

❏ Explain the operation and function of the coolant (water) pump.

❏ Discuss the requirements for a closed cooling system.

❏ Explain the purpose, advantage, and operation of a thermostat.

❏ Recognize the safety hazards associated with a cooling system service.

❏ Explain the operation of various types of cooling fans.

## Introduction

Normal operation of the automobile engine produces heat that must be carried away. This excessive engine heat, which is a product of combustion, is transferred to the coolant and then dissipated in the radiator. This is accomplished by two heat transfer principles known as conduction and convention. The cooling system, when operating properly, maintains an operational design temperature for the engine and automatic transmission.

The cooling system functions by circulating a liquid coolant through the engine and the radiator. Engine heat is picked up by the coolant by conduction and is given up to the less hot outside air passing through the radiator by convection. Coolant is also circulated through the heater core, which also uses the convection process to supply heated air to the passenger compartment.

**Shop Manual**
Chapter 4,
page 89

## The Cooling System

The purpose of the automotive cooling system is to carry the heat that is generated by the engine during the combustion process away from the engine (Figure 4-1) to maintain a near constant engine operating temperature during varying engine speeds and operating conditions. Due to inefficiencies of the internal combustion engine, as much as 70 percent of the energy from gasoline is converted to heat. The cooling system has a difficult task with internal combustion temperatures, which may exceed 4,500°F (2,482°C). Actually, most of the engine's heat is sent out the exhaust system and is absorbed and dissipated by the cylinder walls, heads, and pistons into the ambient air. The cooling system is designed, therefore, to remove about 35 percent of the total heat produced by the engine.

Another important function of the cooling system is to allow the engine to reach operating temperatures as quickly as possible. When engines are below operating temperature, exhaust emissions are increased, internal components wear faster, and operation is less efficient.

An automobile engine's heat is given up in the radiator by the two heat transfer processes of radiation and convection. The overall surface area of most **radiators** are on the order of about 28 to 35 sq. ft. (2.6 to 3.2 m²), though their physical size does not imply that they have that much cooling area.

Heat, as discussed earlier, is always ready to flow from a hot to a less hot object or area. The heat that is picked up by the coolant in the engine block is given off to the less hot air passing over the fins and coils of the radiator. Air movement across the radiator is created in two ways: (1) by the engine fan, known as forced air, and (2) by the forward motion of the car, known as **ram air**.

A defective cooling system may impair air conditioning performance.

The **radiator** is a coolant-to-air heat exchanger that removes heat from the coolant passing through it.

**Ram air** is air forced through the radiator by the forward movement of the vehicle.

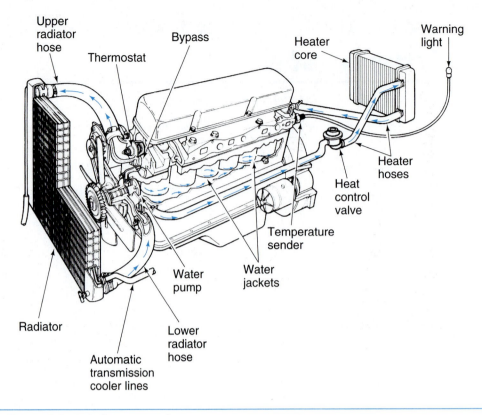

Figure 4-1 Typical engine cooling system.

**Shop Manual**
Chapter 4,
page 90

The **thermostat**
is a temperature-
sensitive device used
to regulate the
cooling system
operating
temperature.

The high-limit properties of engine lubricating oil necessitate proper heat removal to prevent destroying its formulated lubricating characteristics. On the other hand, removing too much heat lowers the thermal efficiency of the engine. To prevent the removal of too much heat, a condition known as overcooling, a **thermostat** is used in the engine outlet water passage. The thermostat, a temperature-sensitive device, controls the flow of coolant from the engine into the radiator.

In addition to hoses required, the closed cooling system (Figure 4-2) consists of the following:

❏ Water pump
❏ Engine water passages
❏ Cooling fan
❏ Radiator
❏ Recovery or expansion tank
❏ Pressure cap
❏ Thermostat
❏ Air baffles and body seals

Each of these components is covered individually in this chapter.

Cooling systems also include a heater core as part of the cooling system circuit. Some car lines may also include a thermostatic vacuum switch (TVS), which is also known as a ported vacuum switch. This vacuum-controlled device advances ignition timing if the engine overheats during prolonged idle periods. Because of modern electronics technology, this component was discontinued on most car lines in the mid to late 1980s, though it was used on some Ford and Jeep car lines through 1991.

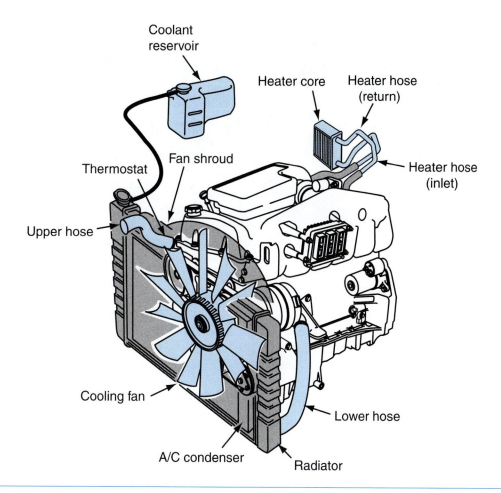

**Figure 4-2** A closed cooling system.

If a vehicle was not equipped with a factory-installed air conditioner, the cooling system is most likely not designed to handle the additional heat load. Under normal circumstances, however, the addition of an aftermarket air conditioning system will cause no problems with the automotive cooling system. This is only true if the cooling system has been well maintained and in good working condition. An aftermarket installation kit often contains a smaller water pump pulley to provide increased coolant flow and a fan system to provide additional airflow.

It is necessary to have a good understanding of the purpose and operation of the cooling system to properly diagnose, troubleshoot, and correct cooling system problems.

## Heat Measurement

Today's technicians use both mechanical and electronic thermometers. High temperature electronic pyrometer probes, which are part of many automotive digital multimeters, are used by touching the surface to be tested or infrared thermometers may be used by simply aiming at the surface or area to be measured (Figure 4-3). The infrared pyrometer is by far the most popular method of determining the temperature of a component. In fact, in some states, they have become a required tool for emission technicians.

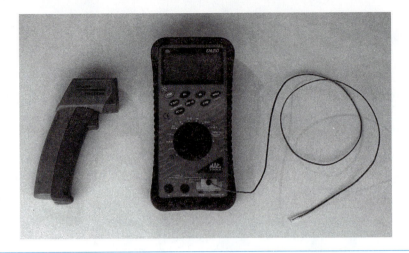

Figure 4-3 Infrared pyrometer and DVOM with temperature probe.

For safety reasons, temperature measurements are usually taken just after turning the engine off. Beware of moving parts, such as the radiator cooling fan, that can start at any time even when the ignition switch is in the OFF position. Specific methods and procedures for taking temperature measurements are covered throughout this manual, as well as in the Shop Manual where applicable.

# Radiator

**Shop Manual**
Chapter 4,
page 91

The terms "vertical flow" and "down flow" for radiators are used interchangeably for the same design. Radiator tanks are also referred to as "headers."

The radiator is a heat exchanger that consists of a core and two tanks. It is used to remove heat from the coolant passing through it. It performs a critical job, and if the radiator fails to remove excess heat, the engine may overheat and extensive damage, such as blown head gaskets or cracked or warped cylinder heads, may result. Excessive heat could also result in scuffed piston skirts and cylinder walls as well as valve stem and guide damage.

There are two basic radiator design types: (1) cross flow tube and fin type, and (2) vertical flow tube and fin type (Figure 4-4). In a cross flow radiator, popular on most late model vehicles,

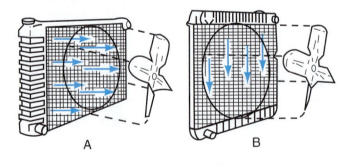

Figure 4-4 Two radiator designs: (A) cross flow and (B) vertical flow.

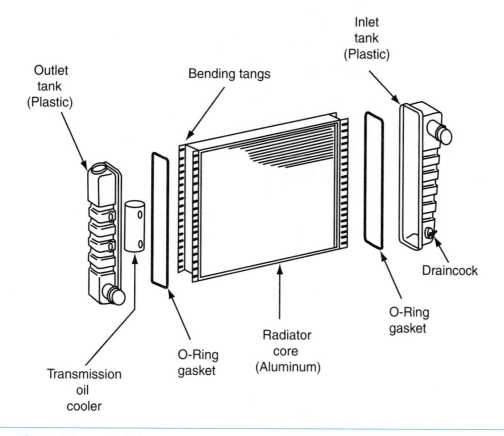

**Figure 4-5** A typical aluminum core/plastic header radiator.

the coolant flows from the inlet tank (generally the upper radiator hose tank) to the outlet tank. In the vertical flow design, coolant flow is from the top tank to the bottom tank. This design is not as popular today.

Radiators are generally constructed of an aluminum (Al) core and high-temperature, nylon-reinforced plastic tanks and are used on most late-model vehicles or with copper (Cu) core with brass tanks on early radiators through the late 1980s and early 1990s. On the aluminum core radiator, the high-temperature plastic tanks are held in place by clinch tabs, which are part of the aluminum header at each end of the core, and a special high-temperature rubber gasket seal between the core header and tank flange edge to prevent leakage (Figure 4-5). There are, however, occasional variations in how these four materials are combined.

In our discussion, we refer to the first tank as the inlet tank since it receives hot coolant after it passes through the engine and distributes it to the radiator core. The second tank will be referred to as the outlet tank since it collects the less-hot coolant after it has passed through the many tubes in the radiator core. The outlet tank also contains a drain cock to aid in the removal of coolant.

The inlet tank usually contains a baffle plate to aid in the even distribution of coolant through the passages of the core. The outlet tank may also be considered a storage tank for the coolant after it has given up much of its heat after passing through the core. From the outlet tank, coolant is directed to the water pump inlet via a radiator hose (lower).

The outlet tank often contains an internal coil used as automatic transmission oil cooler (Figure 4-6). Transmission fluid is pumped from the transmission through the coil and back to the transmission. This transmission fluid has no other connection with the engine coolant. Though not common, the transmission oil cooler sometimes develops a leak. Since transmission oil pressure is usually greater than cooling system pressure, the oil will leak into the cooling system, cre-

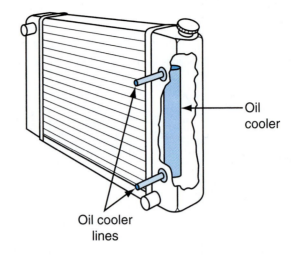

Figure 4-6 Transmission oil cooler details.

The cellular core is often called a honeycomb.

The **expansion tank** is a pressurized auxiliary tank that is usually connected to the inlet tank on a radiator to provide additional storage space for heated coolant. It is often called a coolant **recovery tank** or an overflow tank when not pressurized and under atmospheric pressure.

ating an oily, strawberry-colored foam in the cooling system. There could, on the other hand, be a coolant leakage into the transmission depending on pressure differential ($\Delta p$). Some vehicles equipped with a trailer-towing package may also have an external transmission cooler.

Two common designs for cores are the tubular core (B) and the cellular core (A) (Figure 4-7). The tubular core has a series of long, narrow, oblong tubes that connect the inlet and outlet tanks. There are fins around the outside of the tubes to improve heat transfer from the coolant flowing in the tubes. The fins on the core absorb heat from the coolant passing through the tubes and release it to the ambient air passing through the core and across the fins and tubes, thus carrying off heat and cooling the coolant (Figure 4-8). A process of soldering together thin, preformed sheets of metal fabricates the cellular core, usually made of aluminum, copper, or brass.

During engine operation, the coolant heats up and expands. As the coolant expands, it is displaced into the **recovery** or **expansion** tank. In addition, as the coolant circulates, air bubbles are allowed to escape. The advantage to allowing air bubbles to escape is that coolant without bubbles absorbs heat much better than if they were allowed to flow through the system.

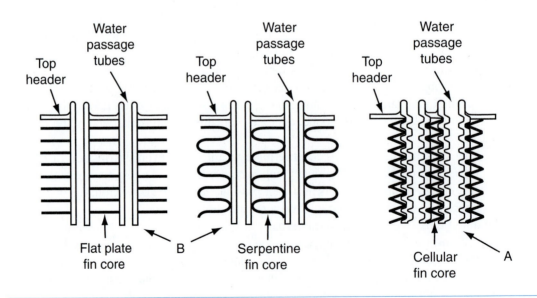

Figure 4-7 Two types of radiator core designs: (A) cellular and (B) tubular.

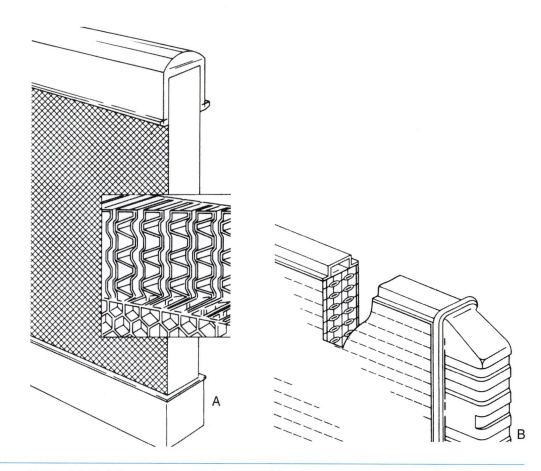

**Figure 4-8** Cellular core (A) and tubular core (B) radiator details.

Under certain applications, there may be a need to increase the cooling capacity of the system by recommending the upgrade to a heavy duty or performance radiator. Vehicles that could benefit from an upgrade include those used for towing, carrying heavy loads, off-roading, and other uses that would put increased demand on the cooling system. These radiators will have additional rows of tubes, added thickness, and may have a more efficient design.

The walls of either type of core are not much thicker than the paper you are now reading. Their passages are about the size of a pencil lead. This should give some idea of how fragile radiators are and the care that must be taken to avoid costly damage.

The cooling system should also be checked for signs of **electrolysis**. Electrolysis occurs when an electrical component is not properly grounded and routes itself through the cooling system in search of one. Likely sources are electrical accessories that are bolted to the engine and components in the cooling system, such as the starter motor or engine block to the battery ground connection. The destructive effect of electrolysis may be in the form of recurring pinholes in the coolant tube of the heater and radiator core or where mounting brackets are attached. Increases in the current draw of poorly grounded accessories will increase the destructiveness of electrolysis. Small amounts of voltage may be measurable in a cooling system that has become slightly acidic, and the coolant reacts with the metal in the system but should never exceed a tenth of a volt (0.10V) in engines with aluminum cylinder heads or blocks. Using a digital DC voltmeter may test for this. Connect the negative lead to the battery negative post and place the positive lead into the coolant at the filler neck, make sure not to touch any metal, and note the reading as accessories are turned on, including the starter. If higher voltage is found, determine the source to avoid damage to the cooling system. Cooling system electrolysis is becoming a more frequent problem in today's cars and should not be overlooked.

**Electrolysis** is the decomposition of an electrolyte (coolant in this case) by the action of an electric current passing through it.

The primary cause of a radiator's failure is that they develop leaks or become clogged. Whenever a failure occurs, the radiator must be repaired or replaced. It is common practice to perform an off-vehicle radiator leak test by pressurizing the radiator to 20 psig (138 kPa) and submerging it in a test tank. If you are performing a leak test on an aluminum core radiator, however, do not use a tank that has been used for brass/copper radiators. The flux, acids, and caustic cleaner residue in the tank will attack the aluminum and cause early radiator failure. On-vehicle leak testing of an aluminum radiator is performed in the same manner as for a brass/copper radiator cooling system. Due to the high cost of labor, it is generally less expensive to replace a radiator than to have it repaired. Radiator repairs should be attempted only by those with the proper tools, equipment, and knowledge.

# Pressure Cap

## Concentration

The **pressure cap** increases the pressure of the cooling system and allows higher operating temperatures.

The **pressure cap** both seals and pressurizes the cooling system. One of the functions of the pressure cap is to allow pressure to build up in the cooling system. It is known that water boils at 212°F (100°C) at sea level atmospheric pressure—14.69 psia (101.3 kPa) (Figure 4-9). As pres-

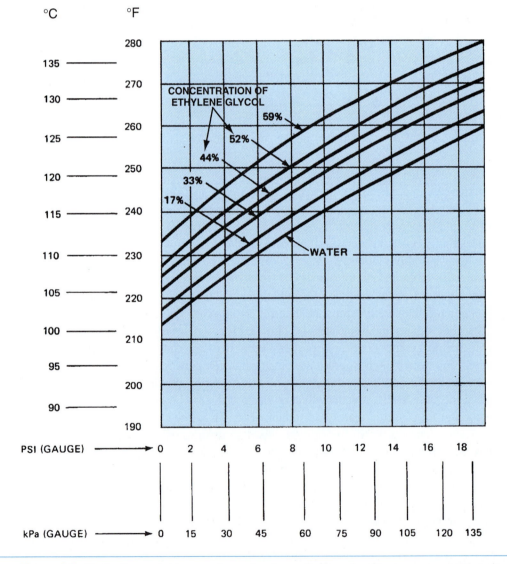

**Figure 4-9** The boiling-point temperature of various ethylene glycol/water concentrations is increased by increasing its pressure.

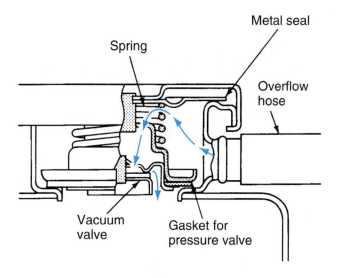

Spring
Metal seal
Overflow hose
Vacuum valve
Gasket for pressure valve

**Figure 4-10** Pressure and vacuum valve details of a pressure cap.

sure builds up in the cooling system, the boiling point of the coolant also goes up. For each pound of pressure (6.9 kPa), the boiling point of the coolant (water) is increased about 3°F (1.7°C). For example, if an 8 psig (55.2 kPa) pressure cap is used, the boiling point of coolant will be raised to 236°F (113.3°C). This allows the cooling system to be safely run at temperatures far above the boiling point of coolant at atmospheric pressure. This enables the engine to reach operating temperature sooner and adds to the overall efficiency of the engine.

Today's vehicle cooling systems are closed systems, with coolant being displaced to or drawn from a recovery tank (as cooling system pressure increases or decreases) connected to the radiator by a hose connected at the radiator filler neck (Figure 4-10). The pressure cap contains an external seal and two spring-loaded valves; the larger valve is called the pressure valve and the smaller one is called the vacuum valve. The pressure valve contains a spring of a predetermined strength, which is indicated by a pressure rating on the top of the cap. This spring holds the valve closed against its seat. As the coolant heats up, it begins to expand, increasing the internal cooling system pressure. When pressure exceeds the rated value (i.e., 15 psig) on the cap, the pressure valve lifts off its seat to relieve excess pressure in order to maintain correct system pressure and protect the cooling system from overpressurization (Figure 4-11B). The vacuum valve is also held against its seat by a calibrated spring. When the engine is stopped, the cooling systems cool down, the system pressure begins to drop from a positive pressure to a negative pressure, and a vacuum develops inside the cooling system. At a predetermined point, the vacuum valve opens to draw coolant back out of the expansion tank and into the radiator to equalize internal pressure with atmospheric pressure, thereby preventing the radiator and other cooling system components from collapsing (Figure 4-11A).

A vacuum valve that fails to open to release negative pressure in the cooling system may cause system damage. A collapsed upper radiator hose generally notes this condition as the system cools or during heavy acceleration. Components likely to be damaged by a defective vacuum valve are the radiator and **heater core** tanks, which may collapse, as well as sealing surfaces.

Remember that there are three gasket-sealing surfaces that are part of the pressure cap assembly. If the gasket-sealing surface of the pressure valve fails, the system will not become properly pressurized. The outer gasket between the cap top and the radiator neck both seals coolant from leaking out the top of the radiator neck and keeps air from leaking into the system as it cools down. If this seal allows air to leak past during the cool-down process, the coolant in the expansion tank will not be drawn back into the cooling system, and a low coolant level in

**Shop Manual**
Chapter 4,
page 94

The pressure valve is also referred to as the blow-off valve, while the vacuum valve may be referred to as the atmospheric valve. Never exceed the OEM specifications for a pressure cap.

Due to heat soak, the temperature of the coolant in the engine will increase several degrees a few minutes after the engine is stopped.

The **heater core** is a heat exchanger used to transfer heat from the engine coolant to the air passing through it. It is used in the comfort heating system to heat the passenger compartment.

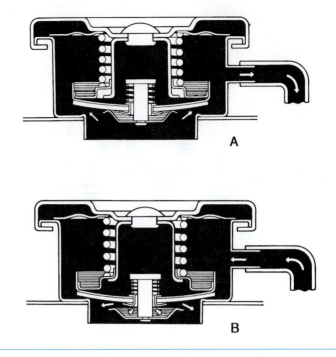

**Figure 4-11** Radiator cap details: (A) pressure operation and (B) vacuum operation.

The pressure valve is also referred to as the blow-off valve while the vacuum valve may be referred to as the atmospheric valve. Never exceed the OEM specifications for a pressure cap.

the cooling system will result. The vacuum valve-sealing surface must also be inspected. Gaskets should be checked for distortion or damage, and the radiator neck-mounting surface must be clean and undamaged. If a good seal is not maintained, overheating and coolant loss will result.

A pressure cap rated at a higher pressure or a lower pressure than the one designed for the system should not be used. A cap with a higher pressure rating could cause the radiator or other cooling system element to rupture or leak. Using a cap of a lower rated value could cause the engine to overheat to a point that could damage internal components. If in doubt about the proper rating for the replacement cap, check the manufacturer's specifications and replace with one of equal design and rating. Radiator caps range from 4 psig (27.6 kPa) to 18 psig (241 kPa). Always remove the radiator cap slowly. Removing the radiator cap on a hot cooling system can cause serious burns as steam and coolant escape. Extreme caution should be used when working on closed systems.

Most cooling system test kits include adapters for both pressurizing the cooling system as well as pressure testing the pressure cap. The pressure cap should be tested annually or any time service is performed to the cooling system. It is an inexpensive repair that will avoid costly system failures. If the pressure cap fails the test, it should be replaced with one of equal pressure ratings. It should also be noted that special aluminum caps are required on aluminum radiators.

## Coolant Recovery System

Coolant recovery systems have been standard equipment on most cars since 1969. Coolant expands by about 10 percent of its original volume when it reaches operating temperature. There can be air and vapor present in every cooling system that can cause serious problems if not removed. Coolant without air bubbles trapped in it absorbs heat better than coolant with air bubbles. Air is the leading contributor to the formation of rust and corrosion that causes early cooling system component failure as well as increasing the formation of sludge in the system by breaking down the coolant additives. Air that becomes trapped in the cooling system may create an air lock blocking the flow of coolant. This is especially common on systems that have been

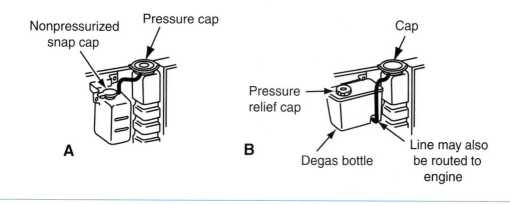

Figure 4-12 Nonpressurized (A) and pressurized (B) coolant recovery tanks.

recently filled after service. This trapped air and vapor can cause pump cavitation, which inhibits the pump's ability to move the coolant and create hot spots in the coolant galleys. To eliminate this problem, systems use either a non-pressurized **overflow tank** or a pressurized expansion tank (Figure 4-12). These systems, when properly maintained, prevent air from entering the cooling system and ensure proper coolant capacity. In addition, many systems today also have a manual air bleed valve, which is often placed on top of the thermostat housing (Figure 4-13).

An **overflow tank** (or catch tank) is a nonpressurized coolant recovery tank.

## Recovery Tank

A nonpressurized recovery tank, usually of 1/2 to 1 gal. (1.9 to 3.8 L) capacity, is connected to the pressurized cooling system through the overflow fitting at the filler cap. It is used to capture and store vented coolant and vapor from the radiator as it is being heated to operating temperature. Heating causes expansion, and the excess coolant is expelled through the pressure valve of

Figure 4-13 Manual air bleed on thermostat housing.

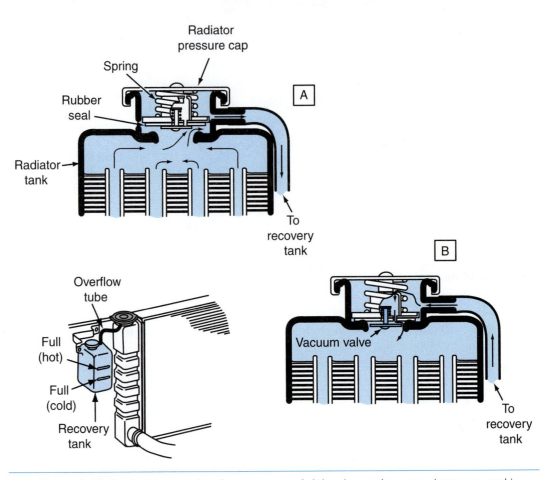

**Figure 4-14** Coolant is vented to the recovery tank (A) as internal pressure increases, and is returned to the radiator (B) as pressure in the cooling system decreases.

the radiator cap to the recovery tank (Figure 4-14A). When the coolant cools, it retracts, and the vacuum valve of the radiator cap opens, allowing the same vented coolant to be metered back into the cooling system from the recovery tank (Figure 4-14B). Any vapor is vented to the atmosphere and is not returned to the cooling system as long as the proper level of coolant is maintained in the recovery tank.

The coolant level of the cooling system is easily determined by noting the coolant level in the recovery tank. It is not necessary to remove the radiator cap to check or add coolant. If a low coolant condition is noted, it should be filled to either the hot or cold mark on the side of the recovery tank, depending on engine temperature (Figure 4-15). Unlike the pressurized system, the cap on the recovery tank can be removed at any time for service.

The small hose that connects the recovery tank to the filler neck provisions of the radiator is an important link in the proper performance of the system. Its purpose is to allow coolant to flow back and forth between the recovery tank and the radiator filler neck. If it is clogged or kinked, coolant cannot be transferred from the recovery tank to the radiator. If it is disconnected or leaking, coolant will be lost and/or ambient air will be drawn into the system. This condition will result in poor performance and early failure of the cooling system.

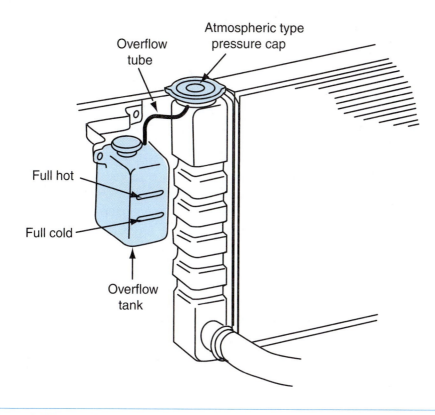

Figure 4-15 A coolant recovery system tank.

## Expansion Tank

Some manufacturers have addressed the problem of trapped air by using a pressurized expansion tank or surge tank placed at the high point in the cooling system to allow air and vapor to rise and be purged out of the cooling system. It is usually mounted on the inner fender (Figure 4-16). It is an integral part of the cooling system and continuously separates and removes air from the

Figure 4-16 Closed system coolant recovery tank.

system's coolant. When the engine coolant thermostat is open, coolant flows from the top of the radiator outlet tank through a small hose to the expansion tank. The pressurized system recovery tank should have 17 to 34 oz. (0.5-1.0 L) of air when the coolant is cold to allow space for coolant expansion. Unlike the nonpressurized recovery tank, the pressurized expansion tank cap must not be removed for service when the coolant is hot, or serious injury could result.

Some expansion tanks on European vehicles use a weighted vacuum relief valve (sometimes referred to as a pressure vent type cap), which is normally open. The vacuum valve on this style cap hangs freely on the pressure valve and is calibrated with a small weight. Under normal operation, this system operates at atmospheric pressure. If rapid expansion takes place, such as under heavy acceleration, the vacuum valve is closed by the escaping pressure or steam and the pressure valve comes into play. The cap operates in the same way a constant pressure cap operates. As pressure subsides, the weight causes the valve to open, returning the system to atmospheric pressure.

## Engine Block and Cylinder Head Coolant Passages

Water jackets are a collection of passages molded into the engine block and cylinder heads. The passages of the water jackets in the cylinder block and head(s) are designed to control coolant flow and circulation to provide proper cooling around the hot spots of the engine. The water jackets in the cylinder block completely surround the cylinders to dissipate the heat generated during the combustion process. The cylinder head contains water jackets that surround the combustion chamber and contain passages around the valve seats in order to cool them off (Figure 4-17). If the vehicle overheats and the coolant boils, gas pockets may form in the cylinder block and/or cylinder head causing hot spots due to the poor heat transfer characteristics of a gas.

In most systems, coolant flows through the water pump to the engine block, around the cylinder wall, and then back to the radiator. The flow then proceeds to the cylinder heads. On the **reverse flow** cooling system, coolant first flows to the hotter cylinder head and around the valves and combustion chamber where most of the heat is centralized. The coolant then flows to the less hot engine block and cylinder walls. This process of coolant flow results in more even engine temperatures, reduces wear, and increases horsepower and fuel economy.

**Reverse flow** cooling systems first flow coolant through cylinder head(s) then through the engine block for more even heat transfer.

**Figure 4-17** Cutaway of cylinder head water jackets.

## Expansion Plugs

Expansion plugs are small steel plugs that are pressed into casting holes located in engine blocks and cylinder heads to produce a watertight seal. The casting holes are the result of the casting process. Expansion plugs that fail are a source of external coolant leaks and need to be inspected for signs of leakage, especially if a system is loosing coolant. Their failure is generally due to corrosion from inadequate maintenance of the cooling system, specifically not flushing the coolant at the recommended intervals.

# Coolant Pump

Coolant is circulated through the cooling system by a **centrifugal impeller**-type pump (Figure 4-18), which is usually driven by a belt off the engine crankshaft pulley. This pump may turn as fast as 5,000 revolutions per minute and carry coolant as fast as 10,000 gal./hr. (631L/min.). At an average road speed, the coolant may be circulated as much as 160 to 170 gal. (605 to 643 L) per minute.

The pump consists of a housing with an inlet and outlet, an impeller blade, nonserviceable sealed bearing(s), and seals. The impeller is the internal rotating part of the pump that moves coolant through the cooling system. The impeller consists of a flat plate with a series of flat or curved blades or vanes and is mounted to a shaft that passes through the pump casting. This shaft, which is generally stainless steel to prevent rust, is equipped with one or more sealed bearing assemblies, and an internal and external seal to support the shaft. As the impeller rotates, coolant is drawn in from the center and is forced outward to the passage entering the engine block by centrifugal force. A belt pulley is mounted on the shaft end opposite the impeller. On vehicles equipped with an engine-mounted cooling fan, the fan is also attached. A defective coolant pump is not generally rebuilt because of the special tools required and are replaced as an assembly.

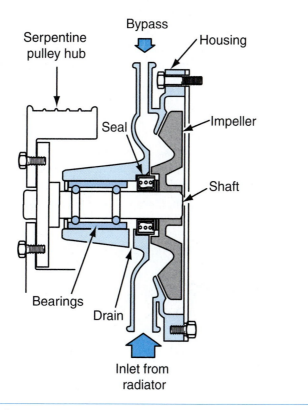

**Figure 4-18** Parts of a water pump.

Expansion core plugs are also referred to as freeze plugs. Though they may pop out if the coolant freezes, their purpose is not to protect the engine from damage caused by coolant that freezes.

A **centrifugal impeller**-type pump uses rotational force to pull coolant from the center of the pump to the outside coolant passage connected to the engine.

Coolant pumps are generally referred to as water pumps.

**Shop Manual**
Chapter 4,
page 93

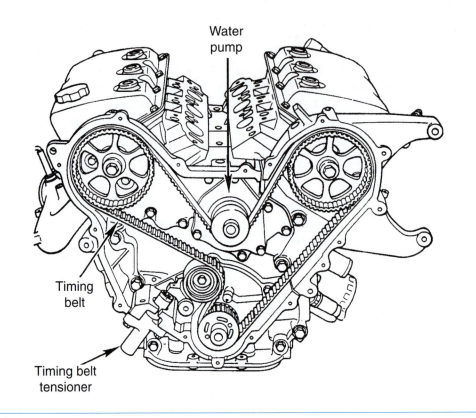

Figure 4-19 A typical timing-belt-driven water pump.

Some vehicles may have a coolant pump that is driven by the timing belt (Figure 4-19). This coolant pump is generally replaced when the timing belt is serviced as preventative maintenance to avoid a future repair since most timing belts are serviced at 90,000 miles and the pump has been in service for millions of rotations (Figure 4-20).

On most engines, the coolant pump inlet is connected to the bottom of the radiator with a rubber hose. This hose is preformed to fit a particular year and model engine, and it generally contains a spiral wire to prevent it from collapsing due to the suction action of the coolant pump impeller when the engine is revved up. The coolant pump outlet is through passages behind the impeller, which pushes the coolant through the engine block. After the coolant has passed through the engine block, it is returned to the radiator through the thermostat housing and upper radiator hose. A centrifugal water pump is a variable-displacement pump. Restricting the flow of coolant does not harm the pump. When the thermostat is closed, restricting coolant flow, coolant circulates though the engine via a **bypass** passage below the thermostat leading from the engine block to the water pump. When the thermostat is open, coolant flow is through the cooling system.

The **bypass** redirects coolant away from the thermostat and back to the water pump to enable coolant circulation in the engine block during the warm-up cycle.

The thermostat outlet hosing is sometimes referred to as the gooseneck.

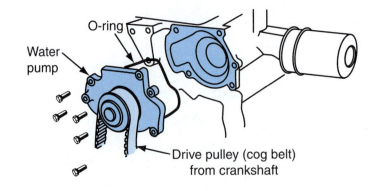

Figure 4-20 Details of a typical timing-belt-driven water pump.

The most frequent cause of coolant pump failure is leaks, which are often the result of bearing failure. Industry studies have linked these leaks and bearing failures to improper cooling system maintenance and service as antifreeze additives are depleted or contaminated. We will discuss proper service under the antifreeze section.

# Fan Shrouds, Air Baffles, and Seals

Airflow can make up to a 30 percent difference in cooling system capacity. There are several air deflectors used in the cooling system to improve overall cooling and air conditioner condenser performance. These include fan shrouds, deflectors, air baffles, and air seals. The radiator fan shroud directs all the air handled by the fan through the radiator, thereby improving the efficiency of the fan. Air deflectors are installed under the vehicle to redirect airflow through the radiator to increase flow. Air baffles are also used to direct airflow through the radiator. Air seals, which are mounted to seal the hood to the body, prevent air from bypassing the radiator and air conditioning condenser. In addition, the air seals help to prevent recirculation of air from under the hood to improve hot weather cooling.

Air deflectors are commonly damaged by curb impacts. If damaged, they should be repaired or replaced, not discarded.

# Thermostat

The thermostat is the automatic temperature control component that controls coolant flow in the cooling system and is necessary for efficient engine operation, improving both performance and economy. The primary purpose of the thermostat is to ensure that the minimum operating temperature of the engine is reached as soon as possible. This improves fuel economy and vehicle emissions, as well as preventing the formation of sludge in the engine crankcase. The water pump begins to circulate the coolant the moment the engine is started. The thermostat restricts the circulation of coolant from entering the radiator until the engine has warmed up in order to provide hot coolant to the heater core and improve passenger comfort during the warm-up cycle. This is particularly important for cars driven only a short distance. When the thermostat is closed, a bypass passage in the water pump or coolant passage allows coolant to circulate through the engine. The thermostat also provides a restriction in the cooling system both before and after it has opened. The purpose of this restriction is to provide a pressure difference for the water pump in order to prevent pump cavitation, and it aids in forcing the coolant through the passages in the engine block. Under no circumstances should the thermostat be left out of the system.

The rating of the thermostat is the temperature at which it is designed to begin to open and is usually stamped on the thermostat body. Different engines use thermostats with different temperature ratings, though the most common rating today is 195°F (91°C). Engines are designed to operate at a minimum coolant temperature of 140 to 195°F (60 to 91°C). When coolant temperature is below its rated value, the thermostat remains closed. Engine coolant temperature is sensed by a temperature-sensitive element within the thermostat. This causes the normally closed (NC) thermostat to open at a predetermined rating. A typical 195°F (91°C) thermostat will start to open at this rated temperature and be fully open at 220°F (105°C). This restricts initial circulation to allow for proper engine warm up. A thermostat's opening and closing are gradual as the temperature of the coolant increases or decreases (Figure 4-21). While the thermostat is closed, coolant flows through the bypass passage in the water jackets. For example, if a thermostat rated at 195°F (91°C) is used, the coolant will not circulate through the cooling system and the radiator until the engine coolant has reached this temperature, and circulation to the radiator will increase as the temperature of the coolant rises. The purpose of a thermostat, then, is to protect against engine **overcooling**.

**Overcooling** is a condition where the engine never reaches operating temperature due to a thermostat that is opening before the engine reaches operating temperature.

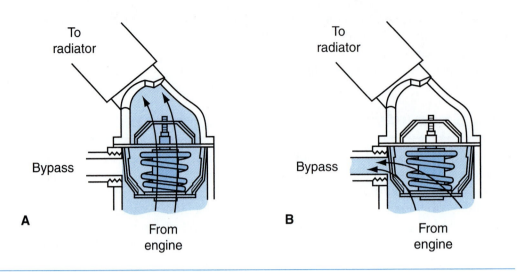

**Figure 4-21** A thermostat opening (A) and closing (B).

The engine should take between 5 and 15 minutes to warm up, depending on ambient air temperature. If the engine requires long warm ups or if the engine always runs hot, you will need to remove and test the thermostat operation by suspending it in a water bath and heating the water to boiling. You will need to note the temperature at which the thermostat begins to open and the temperature at which the thermostat is fully open and compare this to its rated value.

Unless it is defective, a thermostat will not cause overheating. A thermostat rated at 180°F (82°C) is wide open at 205°F (96°C), and full coolant flow is provided through the cooling system. A thermostat rated at 195°F (91°C) is wide open at 220°F (105°C), and full coolant flow is provided through the cooling system. The 195°F (91°C) thermostat provides neither more nor less coolant flow than the 180°F (82°C) thermostat, but it does change the operating temperature of the engine and the amount of heat the passenger compartment heater can produce.

The cooling system thermostat (Figure 4-22) is located between the engine and the radiator. It is housed at the outlet of the engine coolant passage under a return hose flange called a ther-

A thermostat usually starts to open at its rated value and is fully open with a 25°F (14°C) temperature rise.

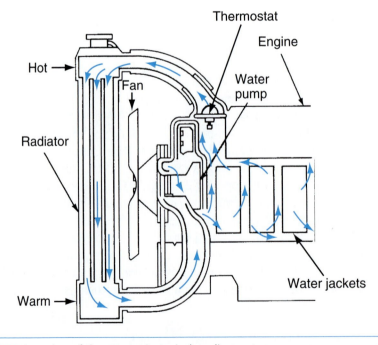

**Figure 4-22** Location of thermostat in typical cooling system.

mostat housing and, in most cases, is bolted onto the cylinder head or intake manifold. There is a gasket or O-ring seal between the thermostat housing and mounting surface that must be torqued to specifications to avoid leaks. Thermostats may have either a bleed notch or a jiggle pin that is designed to let trapped air out of the system after refilling in order to eliminate hot spots in the coolant passages during engine warm up. Many closed cooling systems today require air pockets to be bled out of the system after servicing using a bleed-off valve for air which may be part of the thermostat housing; see Figure 4-13.

Some manufacturers have chosen to locate the thermostat at the engine inlet. This reduces the risk of thermal shock that may result as cold coolant enters the engine block when the thermostat opens. Inlet thermostats slowly bleed cold coolant into the engine until the entire cooling system comes up to operating temperature.

Six important facts regarding thermostats should be noted.

1. Thermostats are a design component of the engine cooling system and should not be omitted.
2. The design temperature of a thermostat should not be altered.
3. A thermostat will cause engine overheating if stuck closed.
4. A thermostat will cause engine overcooling if stuck open.
5. A vehicle may fail an emissions test due to an improperly functioning thermostat.
6. An improperly functioning thermostat will affect passenger compartment heater efficiency.

There are three basic design types of thermostats. They are: (1) solid expansion, (2) bimetallic, and (3) bellows-type. A brief description of each follows.

## Solid Expansion Thermostat

The solid expansion thermostat (Figure 4-23) is a heat motor that utilizes a thermally-responsive wax pellet sealed in a heat-conducting copper cup containing a flexible rubber diaphragm and piston. This is, by far, the most popular style thermostat used today. Heat causes expansion of the now liquid wax compound exerting pressure on the diaphragm and pushing a stainless steel piston plunger up to open a valve. As the element cools, the compound contracts, and a spring is allowed to push the thermostat valve closed.

**Shop Manual**
Chapter 4,
page 95

Thermostats are a design consideration of the cooling system and should not be permanently removed or changed to one of a different rating.

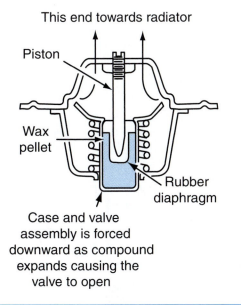

**Figure 4-23** A typical solid expansion thermostat.

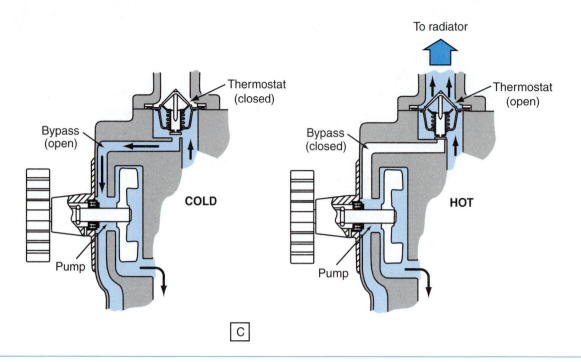

COLD

HOT

C

**Figure 4-24** Three-way thermostat.

There are currently three popular variations of the solid expansion type; the balanced sleeve, the reverse poppet, and the three-way thermostat (Figure 4-24). These styles function similarly but with some design differences. The balanced-sleeve thermostat allows pressurized coolant to flow around all of its moving parts while the reverse-flow thermostat opens against the direction of coolant flow and water pump pressure. In this manner, it is able to use water pump pressure to hold it closed when it is cool. The reverse-poppet thermostat is engineered with a self-cleaning, self-aligning stainless steel valve and offers improved coolant flow. The three-way thermostat has a bypass passage located directly below it. When the engine is cold, the thermostat restricts flow to the radiator and allows coolant to flow through the bypass passage. As the thermostat opens allowing coolant to flow to the radiator, it also closes off the bypass passage.

Corrosion and age will cause a calibration change in this type of thermostat. If the thermostat is found to be defective or inoperative, a new one of equal design and rating should be installed.

The solid expansion thermostat is also known as the "pellet" type, so called because of the wax pellet used.

## Bimetallic Thermostat

The bimetallic thermostat (Figure 4-25) uses a bimetallic strip of two dissimilar metals fused together to form a coil. One metal expands faster than the other when heated, causing the coil to unwind, and opening a butterfly valve.

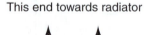

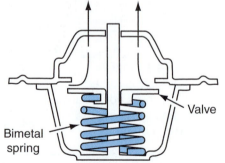

**Figure 4-25** A typical bimetal thermostat.

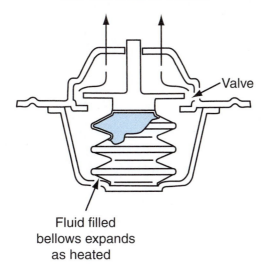

This end towards radiator

Valve

Fluid filled
bellows expands
as heated

**Figure 4-26** A typical bellows-type thermostat.

Again, corrosion and age will cause a calibration change in this type of thermostat. It must be replaced if found to be defective or inoperative.

## Bellows-type Thermostat

The bellows-type thermostat (Figure 4-26) is made up of a thin metal bellows assembly filled with a low-boiling point fluid, usually alcohol, and is sealed under a vacuum. They were popular before the advent of the pressurized cooling system. When increased coolant temperature causes the fluid to boil, the bellows expands. This expansion opens the thermostat, allowing engine coolant to circulate through the cooling system. As the volatile fluid cools, the bellows retracts, restricting the flow of engine coolant. The pressurized cooling system made this style obsolete. Pressure in the cooling system would prevent the bellows from opening at the correct temperature.

## Thermostat Service

Thermostats fail and can cause excessive engine wear and waste fuel. If failure occurs while the thermostat is in the closed position, severe engine overheating will result. An extremely hot engine and a cool-to-warm radiator may be noted. If failure occurs while the thermostat is in the open position, a longer-than-normal warm-up period may be noted by the temperature gauge, or poor passenger compartment heating may be noted. Often, a thermostat that is stuck open will go undetected in warmer months, but lack of heater performance reveals this condition during cooler months.

It should be noted that a defective thermostat could have an adverse effect on the computer's engine control system. A thermostat that is stuck open or opens prematurely may cause the closed-loop status to be delayed, resulting in erratic or fast idle and/or richer-than-normal fuel conditions which may result in an engine service indicator light illuminating. It is, therefore, important that the engine coolant thermostat be replaced with the correct temperature range thermostat if it is found to be defective. Thermostats should also be replaced as part of any cooling system repair service.

Thermostats generally fail in the closed position.

**Shop Manual**
Chapter 4,
page 95

**AUTHOR'S NOTE:** If a vehicle comes into your shop overheating, do not add coolant or water to the system until it has completely cooled down. The cool-down process is necessary to avoid thermal shock to the engine and cooling system components. Thermal shock could cause components to crack and gaskets to fail, making a bad situation worse.

**Shop Manual**
Chapter 4,
page 97

There are several different sizes of both types of belts.

The **pitch** of a belt is the degree or slope of the V shape of the belt.

# Pulley and Belt

Two types of belt systems are used to drive the air conditioning compressor and many water pumps, as well as other accessories: the serpentine belt (Figure 4-27) and the V belt (Figure 4-28). The serpentine belt system is found on most late model vehicles. This is often a single-belt system whereby one belt drives all the accessories (Figure 4-29).

The **pitch** and width of belts in the V belt system are important in that they must match those of the drive (engine crank shaft) and driven (engine accessories) pulleys (Figure 4-30). If the compressor and/or alternator are driven with two V belts, they should be replaced as a pair with a matched set. This is true even though only one of the pair may appear to be damaged.

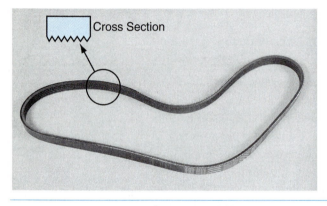

**Figure 4-27** A typical serpentine belt.

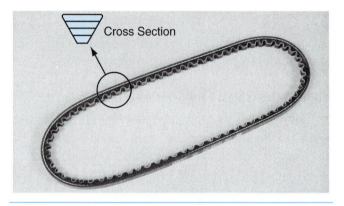

**Figure 4-28** A typical V belt.

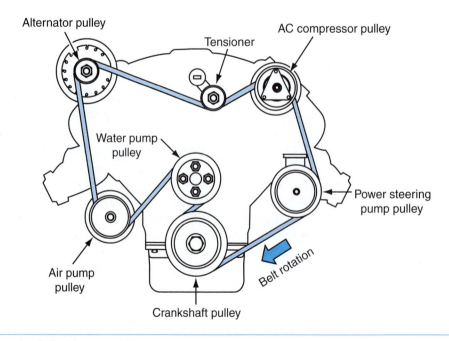

**Figure 4-29** A serpentine belt drive system.

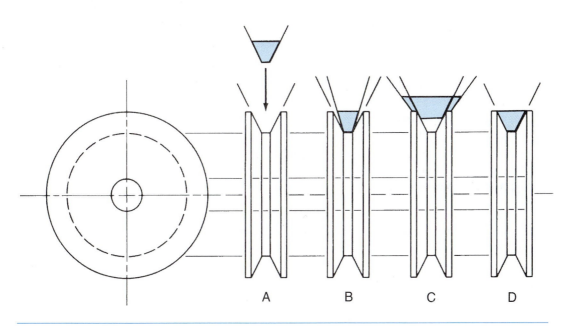

**Figure 4-30** The belt should fit the pulley snugly as shown in A and D. The belt in pulley B is too narrow and has an improper pitch. The belt in pulley C (exaggerated) is too wide and has an improper pitch.

Belts should be tensioned in foot-pounds (ft.-lb.) or Newton meters (Nm), according to manufactures' specifications. It is recommended that the belt be retensioned after a "run-in" period of a few hundred miles (kilometers) to ensure proper belt tensioning.

Belts must be replaced with exact duplicates. Their length, width, and groove characteristics are important to ensure proper fit and alignment. Manual belt tension should be set to 1/2 inch deflection per 12 inches of distance spanned between pulleys. The serpentine system may have a spring-loaded idler pulley used as a belt tensioner. It is, therefore, not necessary to manually tension this type of belt tension system. If the belt will not remain tight, the tensioner must be replaced.

It should be noted that some coolant pump pulleys turn in the opposite direction from others (Figure 4-31). Therefore, it is possible that the same engine in two different vehicles with either different drive belt styles (V belt versus serpentine belt) or belt routing due to bolt on belt-driven accessories (one system with A/C and one without), will require two different water pumps and two different mechanical cooling fans. Water pump rotation may be either clockwise or counterclockwise based on drive belt routing.

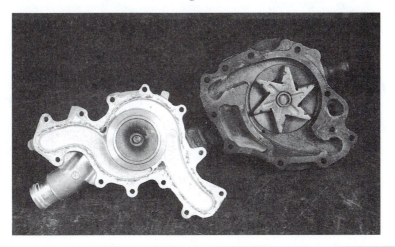

**Figure 4-31** Some coolant pumps turn in opposite directions.

# Fans

The fan is used in the cooling system to increase airflow across the radiator in order to improve the efficiency of the cooling system. Engine coolant fans are essential for idle and low-speed driving to pull sufficient air through the condenser, radiator, and the engine to affect adequate cooling. At road speeds, ram air is sufficient for this purpose. To satisfy the needs for low-speed cooling and to reduce the engine load at high speed, a fan clutch or flexible fan is often used. An electric fan, which replaces the coolant pump-mounted fan, is found on most late-model vehicles.

## Engine-Mounted Fan

**Shop Manual**
Chapter 4,
page 102

The engine-driven cooling fan is mounted onto the water pump shaft in front of the pulley (Figure 4-32). Five- or six-blade fans (Figure 4-33) are found on air conditioned vehicles, and four-blade fans are found on vehicles without air conditioning. Fans are made of steel, nylon, fiberglass, or a combination of materials. They are precisely balanced to prevent noise, vibration, coolant pump bearing failure, and/or seal damage.

It must be noted that engine-driven fans are designed to turn either clockwise or counterclockwise, depending on pulley rotation. For proper airflow, it is important that the replacement fan be suitable for the design. An improper fan will result in little (or no) air circulation and will cause engine overheating.

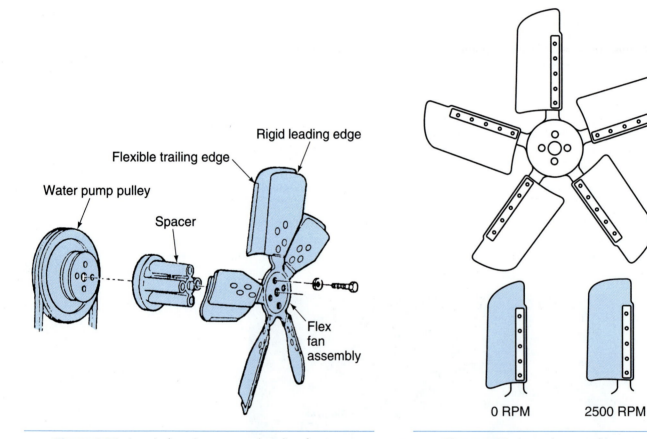

**Figure 4-32** A typical engine-mounted cooling fan.

**Figure 4-33** As engine speed increases, the pitch of the blade decreases, this reduces loan on the engine.

**Declutching Fan**

The declutching fan is used on some rear-wheel-drive vehicles with air conditioning and consists of a fan blade assembly attached to a special clutch. The clutch is attached to the water pump shaft. There are two types of fan clutches: one that is sensitive to engine speed, known as a centrifugal clutch, and one that is sensitive to temperature, often referred to as a thermostatic clutch, which is designed with an internal bimetallic control valve. Either type of fan clutch uses a silicone fluid to engage and disengage the fan blades (Figure 4-34). Either method causes the clutch to be sensitive to engine speed and under-the-hood temperature.

The declutching fan is used as a method of solving a problem of increased air needs at low speed and, at the same time, of eliminating air noise problems during high speed. A smaller fan pulley allows for higher fan speed at low engine speed and, at the same time, provides for increased coolant circulation. The increased air and coolant flow is important when the forward motion of the automobile is not sufficient to produce a strong ram air effect.

The centrifugal clutch is engaged at low engine speed and disengaged at high engine speed. As engine speed is increased, the fluid coupling of the fan clutch increases until the fan reaches its maximum speed. The fan clutch allows the fan to turn at coolant pump speeds up to about 800 rpm. Thereafter, there is slippage that limits the fan speed to between 1,100–1,350 rpm when the engine is cold and between 1,500–1,750 rpm when the engine is hot. The maximum speed of the fan is limited to about 2,00 rpm regardless of engine speed. At maximum speed, the fan will not turn any faster, regardless of how much the engine speed is increased.

The thermostatic clutch has a fluid coupling partially filled with silicone oil. When the temperature is above 160°F (71°C), a bimetal coil spring uncoils or expands. As it expands, it allows additional oil to enter the fluid coupling, causing less slippage and enabling the fan to turn at about the same speed as the coolant pump up to a maximum of about 2,000 rpm. Minimum fan speed should be between 1,500–2,000 rpm. When the under-hood temperature is below about 160°F (71°C), the opposite will occur; the bimetal coil contracts and fluid is bled off the fluid coupling, causing increased slippage and slowing the fan speed. It now turns at less than coolant-pump speed. Slower fan speeds when additional cooling is not required saves fuel, lowers engine noise, and increases engine power.

The coolant pump pulley generally turns faster than the crankshaft pulley. The ratio varies from vehicle model to model. For example, if the ratio is determined to be 1.25:1, the coolant pump will turn 1,000 rpm at an engine speed of 800 rpm.

**Shop Manual**
Chapter 4,
page 103

A fan clutch limits the terminal (top) speed of the fan.

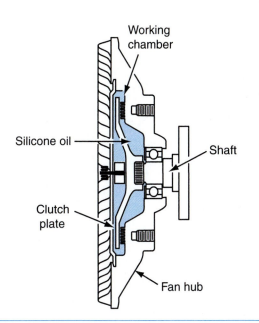

**Figure 4-34** Sectional view of a fluid-coupled declutching fan clutch.

Failure of a fan clutch is usually due to lockup of the clutch or a leak of the silicone fluid, which allows "free-wheeling" of the fan blade. A lockup is generally noted by excessive noise when the engine is revved up and may reduce engine power due to increased drag on the engine. It should be noted, however, that some noise is to be expected during initial cold engine startup. A fluid leak is most noticeable by a tacky residue substance at the shaft area of the clutch bearing. It is possible for a neglected fan clutch assembly to become detached from the shaft and cause serious damage to the radiator. Also, a defective fan clutch can cause vibrations in the coolant pump shaft, leading to its early failure. The fan clutch is not repairable and, if found to be defective, must be replaced. Many technicians are injured each year by defective fans. Fan blades have been known to come off the hub assembly. Before working under the hood of a vehicle, particularly if looking to locate a noise problem, inspect the fan assembly before starting the engine. Check for loose, bent, or damaged blades.

### Flexible Fans

Flexible, or flex, fans (Figure 4-35) have blades that are made of a material (metal, plastic, fiberglass, or nylon) that will flex, or change pitch, based on engine speed. As engine speed increases, the pitch of the blade decreases. The extreme pitch at low speeds provides maximum airflow to cool the engine and coolant.

At higher engine speeds, the vehicle is moving faster and the need for forced air is provided by ram air provided by the forward motion of the vehicle. The flex blades feather reducing pitch, which in turn saves engine power and reduces the noise level.

## Electric Fans

Most late-model vehicles use one or more electric-driven coolant fan motors (Figure 4-36) that are often controlled by the **power train control module (PCM)**, which have replaced the belt-driven fans. The electric motor and fan assembly are generally mounted to the radiator shroud (Figure 4-37) and are not connected mechanically or physically to the engine coolant pump. Either or both of the following two input methods electronically controls the 12V motor-driven fan:

❏ Engine coolant temperature switch (thermostat) or sensor
❏ Air conditioner select switch

There are many variations of electric cooling fan operation. Some provide a cool-down period whereby the fan continues to operate after the engine has been stopped even with the ignition switch in the OFF position. The fan stops only when the engine coolant temperature falls to a

The **power train control module (PCM)** is the microprocessor (computer) that monitors input sensors related to engine and transmission operation, interprets this data, and sends commands to output devices.

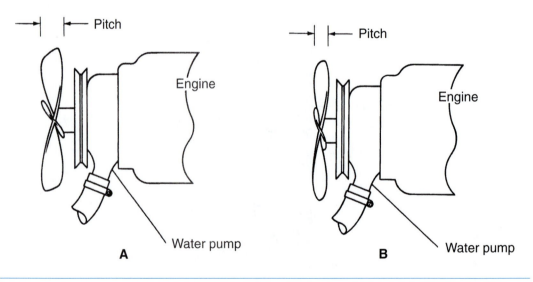

**Figure 4-35** Extreme pitch at low speed (A); reduced pitch at high speed (B).

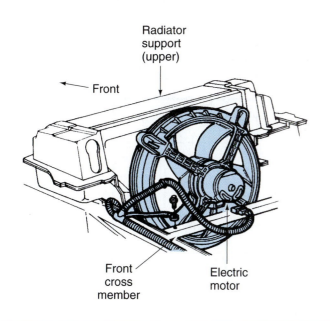

Figure 4-36 An electrically driven engine cooling fan.

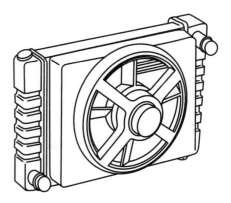

Figure 4-37 A typical electric cooling fan and radiator shroud assembly.

predetermined safe value, usually 210°F (99°C). In addition, some air conditioned vehicles will have two electric cooling fans working independently of each other, depending on temperature conditions.

Because of the many variations of electric fan systems, manufacturers' specifications must be consulted for troubleshooting and repairing any particular year and/or model vehicle. For example, the computerized engine management system also often plays an important part in controlling the electrically operated engine-cooling fan, and in many systems the PCM determines when to energize the fan relay control coil. Electric cooling fans may start without warning, even with the ignition in the OFF position. Many technicians are injured each year by defective fans.

There are several methods of controlling fan operation. In the wiring schematic in Figure 4-38, the fan is controlled by both a coolant temperature sensor and the air conditioner selection switch. The cooling fan motor is connected to the 12V battery supply through a normally open

**Shop Manual**
Chapter 4,
page 104

The temperature of the coolant in the engine will increase several degrees a few minutes after the engine is stopped.

Dual fan systems often operate independently of each other; either or both may start without warning.

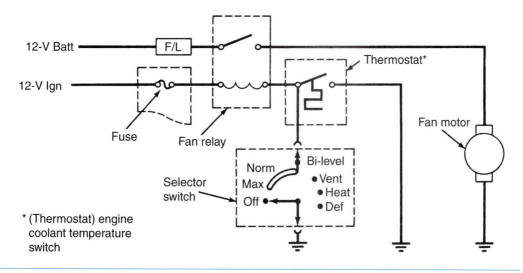

Figure 4-38 A typical cooling fan schematic.

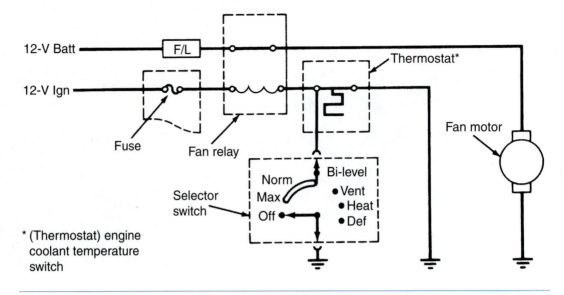

Figure 4-39 The cooling fan switch closes at a predetermined high temperature.

set of contacts (points) in the cooling fan relay. A fusible link provides protection for this circuit. During normal operation, with the air conditioner off and the engine coolant below a predetermined temperature of approximately 215°F (102°C), the relay contacts are open and the fan motor does not operate. If the coolant temperature exceeds approximately 230°F (110°C), the engine coolant temperature switch will close (Figure 4-39) to energize the fan relay coil. This action, in turn, will create an electromagnet to close the relay contact, assuming that the ignition switch is in the run position.

The 12V supply for the relay coil circuit is independent of the 12V supply for the fan motor circuit. The coil circuit is from the run terminal of the ignition switch, through a fuse in the fuse panel, and to ground through the relay coil control device.

In some systems, if the air conditioner select switch is turned to any cool position (Figure 4-40), regardless of engine coolant temperature, a circuit will be completed through the relay coil to ground (–) through the selection switch. This action closes the relay contacts to provide 12 volts to the fan motor. The fan then operates as long as both the air conditioner and ignition switches are on.

In other systems, the fan does not start when the air conditioner select switch is turned on unless the air conditioning system high-side pressure is above a predetermined high pressure value. Although, if the air conditioning high-side pressure level is below the predetermined pressure but the engine coolant temperature is above a predetermined level, usually 230°F (110°C), the cooling fan will still come on.

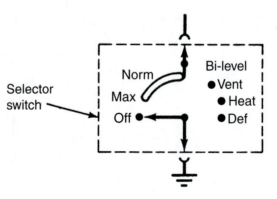

Figure 4-40 The cooling fan will run if the A/C switch is turned to any COOL position.

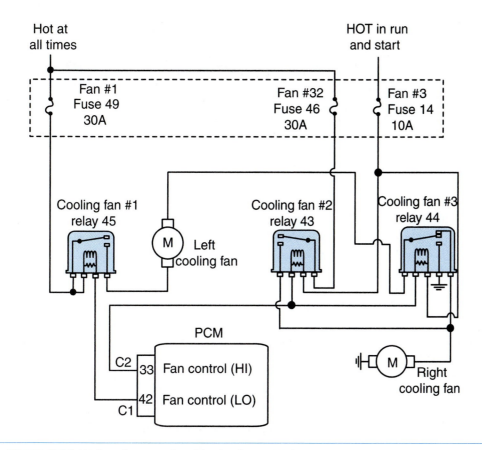

**Figure 4-41** Wiring diagram of multi-relay fan control.

Many fan control systems are ultimately controlled by the power train control module (PCM) which supplies a ground path to the fan relay coil if it is determined that the fan operation is required. There are several inputs that the PCM may look at in order to determine the need to engage the fan. These inputs include, but are not limited to the:

❏ coolant temperature sensor
❏ air conditioning selection switch
❏ air conditioning high pressure switch
❏ vehicle speed

Some PCM systems also have the ability to vary the fan speed based on cooling requirements. This is usually accomplished through an arrangement of relays arranged in a series/parallel configuration (Figure 4-41), allowing the fan(s) to be operated at low or high speeds.

# Hoses and Clamps

Radiators usually have two hoses: an inlet (upper) hose and an outlet (lower) hose. Radiator hoses are constructed of an ozone- and oil-resistant reinforced synthetic rubber. They must be the proper length to allow for engine movement on the motor mounts. Preformed hoses (Figure 4-42A) often have a spiral tempered steel wire installed in the lower radiator hose to prevent collapse due to the suction action of the coolant pump impeller. Upper hoses, not subject to this condition, usually do not have this wire. If the original hose has a wire, make sure the replacement hose also has one.

**Shop Manual**
Chapter 4,
page 107

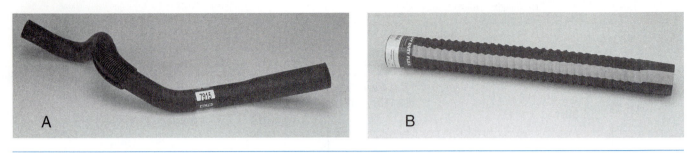

Figure 4-42 Preformed (A) cooling system hoses and (B) flexible.

Aside from the radiator hoses, the cooling system also contains heater hoses, a bypass hose in some applications, and may also contain steel piping. These hoses are smaller and somewhat more flexible. For high heat applications, silicone rubber hoses are available. They are usually identified by a green coloration of the hose and are often found on fleet application vehicles, such as police cruisers.

Universal flexible hoses (Figure 4-42B) have wire inserts available for use when preformed hoses are not available. Because of body and engine parts, hoses must often be critically routed. The universal flexible hoses, however, are not always easily routed. Also, it has been determined that the use of a flexible hose may place an unwanted stress on the radiator connecting flange, resulting in early failure of the radiator due to stress cracks. Preformed hoses designed for the specific vehicle application should always be used whenever possible.

Many types of hose clamp styles are available in several sizes. A popular replacement type is the worm-gear clamp, which has a carbon steel screw and stainless steel band (Figure 4-43). Hose clamp sizes are given by number or letter designations, which are stamped on the side of the clamp. The important consideration is that the clamp is properly positioned and not over-tightened, which could cut into the hose. Worm-gear clamp tension should be rechecked period-ically to avoid a source of coolant leakage. Many manufacturers have chosen to use constant tension spring clamps (Figure 4-44) because of their ability to maintain consistent clamping pres-sure as components and hoses expand and contract due to thermal cycling, thereby eliminating temperature-related leaks. Some vehicles today use quick-connect couplings on smaller hose connections at the heater core and intake manifold connections. Quick-connect couplings may require special tools to disconnect them, and special care should be exercised when servicing them.

If one hose is found to be defective, all should be replaced.

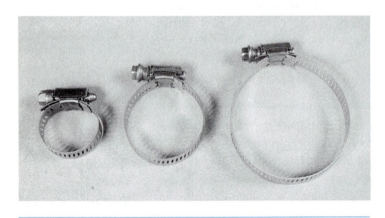

Figure 4-43 A worm-gear clamp.

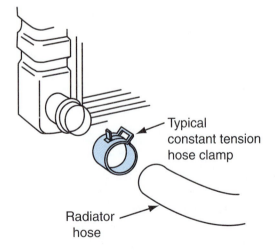

Typical constant tension hose clamp

Radiator hose

Figure 4-44 A typical constant tension hose clamp.

Figure 4-45 A hose that is defective on the inside.

Engine coolant hoses and clamps should be replaced every four years as a preventative maintenance item. One of the major reasons for a vehicle's breaking down today is a poor cooling system maintenance service schedule. Avoid damaging components by first loosening the clamp and sliding it out of the way. Then make a small slice lengthwise so the hose may be peeled off.

Hoses should be inspected on a regular basis for defects or contamination. Oil contamination may cause the rubber to soften or swell, while heat will cause the hoses to become hard and brittle. Hoses should be checked by squeezing them near the clamp or connection and in the middle, feeling for any differences. Soft spots, cracks, and channels can often be detected in this manner.

Failure of cooling system hoses may also be due to electrochemical degradation (Figure 4-45) or electrolysis. As the coolant ages and the additives break down or are depleted, the coolant, engine, and radiator actually form a galvanic cell, a type of battery. As was noted under the Radiator section, electrolysis occurs when an electrical component is not properly grounded and routes itself through the cooling system in search of a ground.

This electrochemical action causes microscopic cracks on the inside of the hose that allow coolant to reach and weaken the reinforcement material. This action is accelerated by high heat and flexing and continues until the hose develops a leak or ruptures. Damage is generally more severe within an inch or two of the end of the hose where it is attached to a metal component. A sign that the interior of the hose is damaged is indicated by a green residue on the reinforcement fibers at the end of the hose where the coolant was wicked out.

# Heater System

The automotive heater system consists of two parts in addition to the hoses and clamps. They are the heater core and the coolant flow **control valve** on some vehicles. The heater housing and duct are part of the passenger compartment's air distribution system.

The **control valve** is a mechanical valve that regulates coolant flow through the heater core assembly.

## Heater Core

The automobile heater and heater core is actually a part of the engine cooling system, though it does not provide the removal of heat from the engine as a normal function. The heater is meant to provide in-car passenger comfort during the cold winter months. The heater core is mounted

Figure 4-46 A typical heater core.

in the air distribution duct system and is usually under the dash area of the front passenger side of the vehicle. The heater core (Figure 4-46) resembles a small radiator and also functions as a heat exchanger with the engine coolant flowing from the top of the engine through the heater core and back to the water pump in most designs. Engine heat is picked up by the coolant through the process of conduction and is transferred by convection to the less hot outside air passing through the heater core to the vehicle's interior. An electric blower motor is used to force the air through the heater core. This provides a ready source of heated air to be used to improve passenger comfort when needed. In some systems, the engine coolant is constantly flowing through the heater core any time the engine is running, while in other systems, a control valve is used to stop the flow of coolant when heat is not required.

Heater cores may be of tubular or cellular construction similar to the construction of radiators. The tanks on the heater core serve to direct coolant flow through the core. They may be constructed of brass and copper or of plastic and aluminum (Figure 4-47).

Figure 4-47 A typical plastic heater core.

If a vehicle is running hot, a temporary solution that it is sometimes effective is to turn the vehicle passenger heater on the maximum hot position to use the heater core as an additional heat exchanger in order to keep a vehicle from overheating.

Leaks are the most common cause of heater core problems. Leaks in a heater core are detected by an obvious loss of engine coolant that is leaking at the firewall or engine compartment ductwork. Other signs that a heater core is leaking may be steam on the windshield when the defroster is on, or the passenger floor carpets could be wet with coolant. A slight leak can also be indicated by a sweet smell coming from the passenger compartment vents. If heater cores are found to be leaking, they are replaced as an assembly and not generally repaired. The replacement heater core should be physically matched to the original to ensure proper fit. In addition, some heater cores are placed higher than the radiator cap in the system. Air can become trapped in these systems, so it is critical to follow manufacturer's recommendations on proper bleeding procedures.

Occasionally, a heater core may become plugged due to poor cooling system maintenance. If this occurs, little or no coolant will flow through the heater core, resulting in no heated air being available for the passenger compartment. A quick method of determining this is by comparing the temperature of the inlet with the outlet hose at the heater core. If the core is blocked or severely restricted, there will be a large temperature difference between the two hoses.

Procedures for replacing the heater core vary with the year, make, and model of the vehicle. It is therefore necessary to consult the manufacturer's repair manual for the proper procedure for replacement.

## Control Valve

The heater control valve regulates the flow of coolant through the heater core to control core temperature by opening and closing a passage to increase or decrease flow. The heater control valve may be located in the inlet or outlet line to the heater core. When the control valve is open, a portion of the heated engine coolant circulates through the heater core. This provides a means of providing warm air to the passenger compartment when desired. The heater control valve may be cable operated, vacuum operated, or operated by a bidirectional electric solenoid or motor (Figure 4-48). The control valve, depending on the valve position selected, meters the amount of heated coolant that is allowed to enter the heater core, from full off to full flow. The HVAC control panel temperature selector regulates the operation of most heater control valves,

**Figure 4-48** Various types of control valves.

whether actuated by a Bowden cable, vacuum diaphragm, or electrically energized. Some heater core assemblies have a mechanical heater control valve integrated into them to regulate coolant flow through the core.

## Additives

Using additives is not recommended as a matter of practice.

Many additives, inhibitors, and "remedies" are available for use in the automotive cooling system. These include, but are not limited to, stop-leak, water pump lubricant, engine flush, and acid neutralizers. Extreme caution should be exercised when using any additive in the cooling system. Read the label directions and precautions to know what the end results of using any additive may be. For example, caustic solutions should not be used in aluminum radiators; alcohol-based "remedies" should not be used in any cooling system.

If a cooling system is maintained in good order by a program of preventative maintenance, additives and inhibitors should not be necessary. Only manufacturer-recommended ethylene glycol-based antifreeze and additives should be added to the cooling system.

## Antifreeze

**Antifreeze** is a generic term used to refer to engine coolant mixtures, whether they be ethylene glycol- or propylene glycol-based, used to raise the boiling temperature and lower the freezing temperature of an engine coolant mixture.

There are four key areas of engine protection. They are freeze protection, heating (boil over) protection, corrosion prevention, and adequate heat transfer.

The coolant in an automotive cooling system is the medium used to transport engine heat to the radiator. A 50/50 mixture of water ($H_2O$) and ethylene glycol ($C_2H_4[OH]_2$), an **antifreeze**, is the recommended coolant formula generally considered best for the engine. This solution is capable of quickly absorbing and giving up large amounts of heat.

**Ethylene glycol** ($HOCH_2CH_2OH$) is the base stock used for most automotive antifreezes and is a colorless, viscous liquid in its pure form.

Ethylene glycol, a main ingredient of antifreeze, is poisonous. When ingested, ethylene glycol converts to oxalic acid, $(COOH)_2$, which damages the kidneys and may result in kidney failure and death. Just 2 oz. (59 mL) of ethylene antifreeze can kill a dog; 1 tsp. (4.93 mL) can be lethal to a cat; and 2 tbsp. (29.6 mL) can be hazardous to a child.

Most automobile manufacturers recommend a 50/50 percent mixture of antifreeze and water for adequate year-round cooling system protection. Also, most manufacturers warn against the use of an alcohol-based antifreeze solution or the use of straight water. Instead, they recommend a mixture of **ethylene glycol** (Figure 4-49) or propylene glycol (Figure 4-50) with distilled water (Figure 4-51). Either mixture in the cooling system is sufficient to:

**Figure 4-49** Ethylene glycol antifreeze.

**Figure 4-50** Propylene glycol antifreeze.

**Figure 4-51** Distilled water.

❑ lower the freezing temperature point of the coolant,
❑ raise the boiling temperature point of the coolant,
❑ help maintain the proper engine temperature,
❑ provide water pump lubrication,
❑ inhibit rust and corrosion, and
❑ allow coolant-immersed sensors and switches to operate properly.

## A BIT OF HISTORY

Prior to 1930, methyl alcohol was the most commonly used engine antifreeze and required constant maintenance to ensure proper freeze protection. Ethylene glycol was first introduced by Prestone in 1927, but it did not become a standard year-round factory fill until the early 1960s.

The freezing temperature of water as a coolant, at ambient sea-level atmospheric pressure, is 32°F (0°C) and the boiling point of 212°F (100°C). Water in a radiator with a 15-psi cap will boil at 250°F (121°C). Water should never be used straight as a coolant in an engine because it offers no corrosion protection, lubricating properties, or other necessary additives that are available in antifreezes.

Standard ethylene glycol is generally green or yellow in color, but can also be red (Toyota), blue, or pink. The recommended mixture of 50/50 percent ethylene glycol and water (Figure 4-52) has a freeze point of −34°F (−36.7°C) and a boiling point of 265°F (129.4°C) in a radiator with a 15-psi cap. If the percentage of ethylene glycol-to-water is increased to 70/30 percent, the freeze point is decreased to -84°F (−64.4°C) and the boiling point is increased to 276°F (135.6°C). It is not recommended that the mixture be increase beyond 70 percent ethylene glycol. The ability of the coolant to carry away heat decreases as the percentage of ethylene glycol increases. Straight ethylene glycol only provides freeze protection down to −2°F (−18.9°C) but has a boiling point of 276°F (135.6°C). A straight mixture of ethylene glycol should never be used because ethylene glycol is 15 percent less efficient than water at removing heat and could cause hot spots to develop, resulting in severe engine damage.

The protection level selected should be to the lowest temperature expected. In warmer climate zones, such as southern Florida and southern California, protection is required for the antirust and anticorrosion inhibitors, as well as for anti-boiling protection. In any climate zone, antifreeze is essential for this protection, as well as coolant pump lubrication. The coolant should contain no less than 30 percent antifreeze, which will provide protection to −5°F (−15°C).

A safer alternative to ethylene glycol coolant is antifreeze formulated with **propylene glycol**. Unlike ethylene glycol, propylene glycol is essentially nontoxic and safer for animal life, children, and the environment. Also, propylene glycol is classified "Generally Recognized as Safe" by the U.S. Food and Drug Administration (USFDA). Low toxicity does not mean that it is safe to drink, but the risk of poisoning is a greatly reduced.

Propylene glycol is available on the aftermarket, and not currently used as factory-fill antifreeze. Popular brands are Prestone "Low Tox" and Safe Brands "Sierra." Propylene glycol has similar thermal characteristics as ethylene glycol. A 50/50 mixture of Propylene glycol and water has a freeze point of −26°F (−32.2°C) and a boiling point of 256°F (124.4°C) in a radiator with a 15-psi cap, while a 100 percent mixture has a freeze point of −70°F (−56.7°C) and a boiling point of 370°F (187.8°C) in a radiator with a 15-psi cap.

**Propylene glycol**
($C_3H_8O_2$) is the base stock used for most automotive antifreezes and is a colorless, viscous liquid in its pure form, has a low toxicity, and is considered an environmentally-friendly alternative to ethylene glycol.

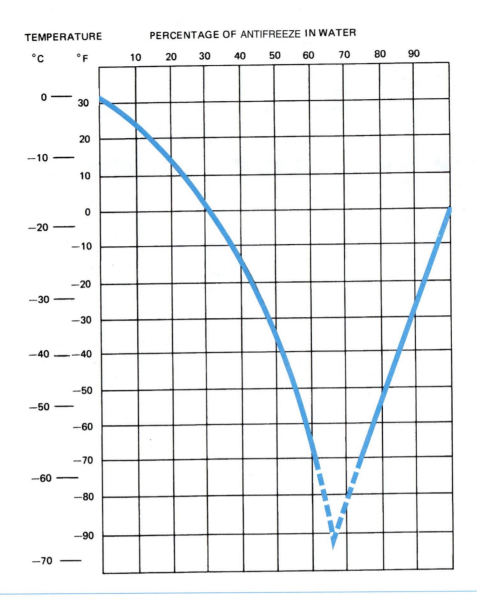

**Figure 4-52** A coolant percentage/protection chart.

Propylene glycol and ethylene glycol are compatible antifreezes and can be mixed, but mixing the two antifreezes eliminates the low toxicity characteristics of propylene glycol and makes it impossible to test the coolant's strength using a hydrometer. This is due to the differences in the specific gravities of the two coolants.

Antifreezes contain many additives to improve their performance in the cooling system, about 2 to 3 percent of the total volume in pure coolant. Corrosion inhibitors protect metal surfaces from rust, corrosion, and electrolysis. This is particularly important for thin, lightweight aluminum radiators and heater cores. Most ethylene glycol formulated in North America contains inorganic salts of borate, phosphate, and silicate to prevent rust and corrosion of metal components. The additives produce an alkaline mixture with a pH range of 7.5–11.0, depending on the manufacturer. The silicates in the mixture form a protective coating on the surface of metal components and are especially effective at protecting aluminum.

The additive package usually offers enough protection for at least two years or 30,000 miles in most vehicles, or longer if mixed with **distilled water**. The ability of a coolant to neutralize acids is referred to as the coolant's reserve alkalinity and varies among manufacturers. Time, heat,

**Distilled water** is pure water produced by distillation. It is available at grocery stores and pharmacies.

dissolved oxygen, and minerals contained in water as well as glycol degradation will eventually deplete these protective additives, and acids will form. Once the pH level drops to 7.0 or lower, corrosion and electrostatic discharge accelerates, leading to radiator, heater core, water pump, and hose failure. Chemical test strips can be used to check the pH level of the cooling system.

Electrolytic corrosion, as was discussed under Hoses, is of special concern with today's bimetal engines. The different metals contained in radiator cylinder blocks and heads can create an electrochemical action (battery) that promotes corrosion. One metal becomes the anode (aluminum), while the other becomes the cathode (iron), and the coolant is the electrolyte. The higher the percentage of dissolved impurities in the coolant, the greater its ability to conduct electricity, which increases the rate of electrolysis. Aluminum and thin metal components, such as the radiator and heater core, are generally the first to suffer damage.

Other failures can also accelerate the depletion of coolant additives. Air pockets from low coolant levels or improper bleeding during service, exhaust gases leaking into the cooling system due to leaky head gaskets, or cracks in the combustion chamber all lead to rapid coolant failure.

Some European vehicle manufacturers recommend the use of phosphate-free coolants because phosphates can react with calcium and magnesium contained in some water to form sediment and scale, while Asian vehicle manufacturers may recommend using coolants containing phosphates but low or no silicate additives. Regardless of the coolant chosen, under no circumstances should softened water be used in a cooling system. Domestic water softeners use salt (sodium), which is very corrosive to all metals and could lead to serious damage to the cooling system and engine components.

The latest coolant to be developed is the extended-life coolant. General Motors first introduced it in 1995 under the name of Dex-Cool (Texico/Havoline) and, by 1996, was using it in most of their vehicle platforms as the factory fill. It uses a corrosion-inhibiting package referred to as **Organic Acid Technology** (OAT). It contains organic salts of mono and dicarboxylic acids such as sebasic and octanoic acids plus tolytriazole, and is less alkaline than standard coolants with a pH of 8.3. Extended-life coolant offers protection for five years or 150,000 miles and is still an ethylene glycol-based coolant. As such, extended-life coolants are compatible with standard coolants but, if combined, will only offer the corrosion protection of the conventional coolant. If the system becomes contaminated or is to be converted to an extended-life coolant, it must be thoroughly drained and flushed to remove all traces of the conventional coolant in order to gain the benefits of the longer-lasting antifreeze formula.

The percent of antifreeze concentrations in a cooling system mixture can be determined by several methods, which will indicate the freeze point of the mixture and its specific gravity. Common methods for determining the freeze point are the coolant hydrometer, test strips, and the refractometer. A separate hydrometer for propylene glycol and ethylene glycol is required since they have different specific gravities. The most accurate methods for determining the concentration of antifreeze in the mixture are with the use of a refractometer. A refractometer can measure the specific gravity of propylene glycol, ethylene glycol, and battery electrolyte. It does this by analyzing the way the light bends as it passes though the liquid. Ethylene glycol never wears as additives do; however, and none of these methods will indicate the condition of the coolant additives.

Standard Propylene glycol and ethylene glycol offer full protection for two years of normal driving. To determine the amount of antifreeze to add to the cooling system after flushing with water, refer to the manufacturer's specifications for total cooling system volume, and divide by 2. Example: If the total cooling system volume is 16 quarts (15 liters), you will need to add 8 quarts (7.5 liters) of pure antifreeze, and then finish filling the system with water. Remember that after flushing the system with water, some of the water may still remain in the water jackets.

Although propylene glycol is much less hazardous than ethylene glycol antifreeze, it still should be considered hazardous. At the present time, the Environmental Protection Agency (EPA) has no restrictions on the disposal of antifreeze unless it is contaminated with lead (Pb). Lead, a byproduct of the material used to solder the seams and joints of the radiator, is considered hazardous in any quantity. State and local governments, however, may have requirements for safe

**Organic acid technology** is used in extended-life antifreeze based on carboxylates of organic acids and does not contain silicates, phosphates, borates, amines, or nitrates.

disposal, reclamation, or recycling. To protect animal life and the environment, follow these simple rules:

❏ Do not mix different types of antifreezes.
❏ Wipe up and/or wash away spills.
❏ Keep stored antifreeze off the floor and away from animals.
❏ Keep antifreeze in its original container, or use a container that is specifically labeled for the product it contains.
❏ Store used antifreeze before recycling or reclamation, in a sealed container that is properly labeled with it contents (i.e., used ethylene glycol).
❏ Ensure that the vehicle's cooling system has no leaks.

## Preventive Maintenance

The cooling system, which is often neglected, is one of the most important systems of the car. If it is kept in good shape and provided with routine preventive maintenance, the cooling system should give years of troublefree service. The cost of maintenance every 12,000–15,000 miles (19,308–24,135 km) is more than offset by the cost of breakdown and consequent repairs. These repairs, incidentally, often result in expensive engine service.

Replace belts that are frayed, glazed, or obviously damaged. Replace any hoses that are found to be brittle, soft, or otherwise deteriorated (Figure 4-53).

Mineral-free distilled water is preferred over tap water for maximum cooling system performance and integrity.

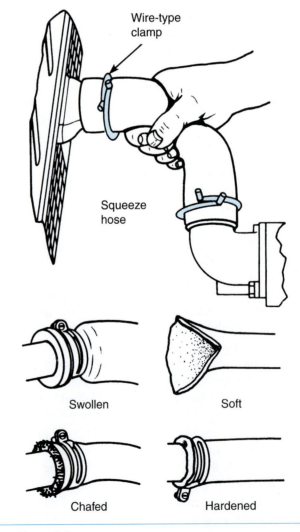

Figure 4-53 Typical hose defects.

The design consideration of a cooling system is to provide for a minimum sustained road speed operation of 90 mph (144.8 km/h) at an ambient temperature of 125°F (52°C). Another criteria is for 30 minutes of driving in congested stop-and-go traffic in an ambient temperature of 115°F (46°C) without experiencing any overheating problems. These design considerations exceed the conditions that one is likely to encounter in regular day-to-day driving.

If the engine overheats, the problem should be found and corrected. The life of an engine or a transmission that is habitually allowed to overheat is greatly reduced. The high-limit properties of lubricating oil require adequate and proper heat removal to preserve formulated lubricating characteristics.

## Summary

The preventive maintenance (PM) program should include the following procedures:

- ❏ Test and/or replace the thermostat
- ❏ Test and/or replace the pressure cap
- ❏ Inspect and/or replace the radiator hose(s)
- ❏ Inspect and/or replace the heater hoses
- ❏ Pressure test the cooling system
- ❏ Test and/or replace the antifreeze solution
- ❏ Visually inspect the coolant pump, heater, control valve, and belt(s)

## Review Questions

### Short Answer Essays

1. How is heat removed from the cooling system?
2. What are the two types of radiator core that are found in the automotive cooling system?
3. What method(s) is used to increase the boiling point temperature of the coolant in an automotive cooling system?
4. Describe the operation of a typical cooling system thermostat.
5. What precaution should be observed when replacing coolant pumps and engine-driven fan blades?
6. Describe an advantage of a declutching engine-driven cooling fan.
7. Describe an advantage of an electric-motor-driven cooling fan.
8. Briefly, what is the purpose of the coolant recovery tank?
9. When (Why) is hot coolant allowed to circulate through the heater core when COOL is selected?
10. What are the advantages of a 50/50 mix of antifreeze and water?

## Fill-in-the-Blanks

1. Radiators are constructed of _____ , _____ , and/or plastic.

2. A frequent coolant pump failure is due to _____ often caused by worn _____ .

3. If the gasket or sealing surfaces of a pressure cap are damaged, the cooling system cannot be _____ .

4. A thermostat failing in the _____ position will result in engine _____ .

5. Engine-driven fans are balanced to prevent _____ , _____ , coolant pump _____ failure, and/or seal damage.

6. Most vehicles now have a _____ -controlled _____ motor-driven cooling fan.

7. Electric cooling fans will _____ and _____ without notice.

8. Heater core leaks are detected by a loss of _____ and a wet _____ _____ .

9. An antifreeze solution _____ the freezing temperature and _____ the boiling temperature of the coolant.

10. PM is the acronym given to _____ _____ .

## Multiple Choice

1. *Technician A* says that a defective thermostat will cause overheating.
   *Technician B* says that a defective thermostat will result in overcooling.
   Who is correct?
   **A.** A only          **C.** Both A and B
   **B.** B only          **D.** Neither A nor B

2. *Technician A* says that extended-life coolant is rated to last 3 years or 100,000 miles.
   *Technician B* says that it is okay to mix standard ethylene glycol coolant with extended-life coolant without affecting the benefits of the extended-life coolant.
   Who is correct?
   **A.** A only          **C.** Both A and B
   **B.** B only          **D.** Neither A nor B

3. *Technician A* says that antifreeze lowers the boiling point of the coolant.
   *Technician B* says that antifreeze lowers the freezing point of the coolant.
   Who is correct?
   **A.** A only          **C.** Both A and B
   **B.** B only          **D.** Neither A nor B

4. *Technician A* says that additives and inhibitors should not have to be added to a cooling system if a good preventive maintenance (PM) program is in place.
   *Technician B* says that antifreeze must be changed every two years, even with a good PM program.
   Who is correct?
   **A.** A only          **C.** Both A and B
   **B.** B only          **D.** Neither A nor B

5. *Technician A* says that the heater core is generally a part of the cooling system.
   *Technician B* says that a heater core is not essential and may be eliminated without affecting the cooling system performance.
   Who is correct?
   **A.** A only
   **B.** B only
   **C.** Both A and B
   **D.** Neither A nor B

6. A leaking external transmission oil cooler is being discussed:
   *Technician A* says that transmission oil may be noted in the coolant.
   *Technician B* says that coolant may be noted in the transmission.
   Who is correct?
   **A.** A only
   **B.** B only
   **C.** Both A and B
   **D.** Neither A nor B

7. Centrifugal pumps are being discussed:
   *Technician A* says that they are driven by pulleys and belts off the engine crankshaft.
   *Technician B* says that some are driven by an electric motor.
   Who is correct?
   **A.** A only
   **B.** B only
   **C.** Both A and B
   **D.** Neither A nor B

8. The cooling system is being discussed:
   *Technician A* says that the pressure cap releases excess coolant to the recovery tank.
   *Technician B* says that the pressure cap allows coolant to return to the radiator from the recovery tank.
   Who is correct?
   **A.** A only
   **B.** B only
   **C.** Both A and B
   **D.** Neither A nor B

9. *Technician A* says that new serpentine belts generally require retensioning after a brief "run-in" period.
   *Technician B* says that V belts are pretensioned and do not have to be retensioned after a "run-in" period.
   Who is correct?
   **A.** A only
   **B.** B only
   **C.** Both A and B
   **D.** Neither A nor B

10. *Technician A* says that a cooling system must be vented to the atmosphere.
    *Technician B* says that the recovery tank is vented to the atmosphere.
    Who is correct?
    **A.** A only
    **B.** B only
    **C.** Both A and B
    **D.** Neither A nor B

# System Components

Upon completion and review of this chapter, you should be able to:

❏ Explain the purpose and operation of an automotive air conditioner compressor.

❏ Identify and compare the state of the refrigerant in each section of the automotive air conditioning system.

❏ Discuss the **change of state** of the refrigerant:
  **a.** In the evaporator
  **b.** In the condenser

❏ Explain the purpose of:
  **a.** The receiver-drier
  **b.** The accumulator

❏ Compare the function of the thermostatic expansion valve (TXV) to the fixed orifice tube (FOT).

## Introduction

In the following discussion, the purpose and function of each component of the basic automotive air conditioning system are discussed. The sizes of the system refrigerant hoses are given, as are the states of the refrigerant in each of them. The state of the refrigerant in each of the components is also discussed (Figure 5-1). Although hose sizes may vary slightly from vehicle to vehicle, the state of the refrigerant at various points in all systems is basically the same.

For the purpose of this discussion of the air conditioning cycle, we will start with the compressor. It is the compressor's function to circulate the refrigerant throughout the system.

## The Refrigeration Cycle

The entire refrigeration cycle exhibits several processes as the refrigerant changes state, from liquid to vapor and from vapor to liquid. When the pressure of the refrigerant drops in the evaporator, the refrigerant boils and, while boiling, picks up heat. The compressor raises the temperature and pressure of the refrigerant so that it will condense in the condenser. In the condenser, the refrigerant gives up the same heat (in Btu) that was picked up in the evaporator.

The thermostatic expansion valve (TXV) or fixed orifice tube (FOT) controls the flow of refrigerant into the evaporator and thereby separates the high side of the system from the low side. The compressor increases gas pressure and thereby separates the low side of the system from the high side. This is the basic air conditioning circuit from which all of the other automotive refrigeration circuits are patterned. A good understanding of the basic circuit makes an understanding of the other circuits much easier.

### A BIT OF HISTORY

Recovery of R-134a became mandatory on November 15, 1995, and the recycling of R-134a became mandatory on January 29, 1998.

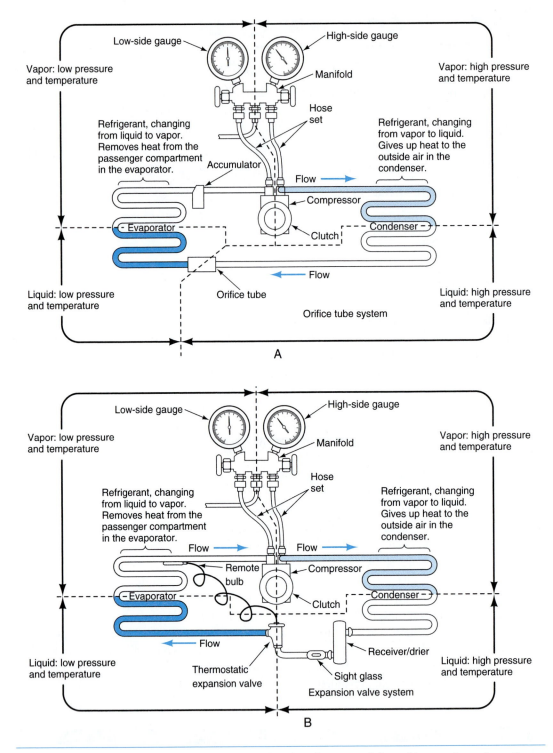

**Figure 5-1** Typical air conditioning circuit showing the state of the refrigerant in each section: (A) orifice tube system, (B) expansion valve system.

# Compressor

The compressor (Figure 5-2) in an air conditioning system is a pump especially designed to raise the pressure of the refrigerant and circulate it through the system. According to the laws of physics, when the pressure of a gas or vapor is increased, its temperature is also increased. When pressure and temperature are increased, refrigerant condenses more rapidly in the next component, the condenser.

With some exceptions, automotive air conditioning compressors are of the same design, **reciprocating** piston. This means that the pistons move in a linear motion, back and forth or up and down. The only exceptions are the rotary vane (RV) and scroll compressors, which are both increasing in popularity.

The automotive air conditioning system uses a fixed- or variable-displacement compressor to move the refrigerant and to compress low-pressure, low-temperature refrigerant vapor from the evaporator into a high-pressure, high-temperature vapor to the condenser.

A label is generally found on the compressor to identify the type of refrigerant for which it is designed. This is a requirement to comply with the rules of the Environmental Protection Agency (EPA).

Compressors are belt driven from the engine crankshaft through an **electromagnetic** clutch pulley (Figure 5-3). When not energized, the compressor clutch pulley rotates freely without turning

There are three basic types of compressors: reciprocating, rotary, and scroll.

**Shop Manual**
Chapter 5, page 153

**Reciprocating** motion is to move to and fro, fore and aft, or up and down.

**Electromagnetic** is a temporary magnet created by passing electrical current through a coil of wire. A clutch coil is a good example of an electromagnet.

**Figure 5-2** A typical air conditioning compressor.

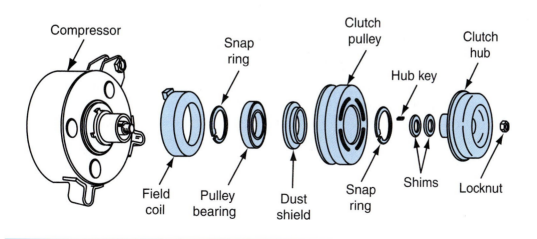

Compressor · Snap ring · Clutch pulley · Hub key · Clutch hub · Field coil · Pulley bearing · Dust shield · Snap ring · Shims · Locknut

**Figure 5-3** A typical compressor showing clutch details.

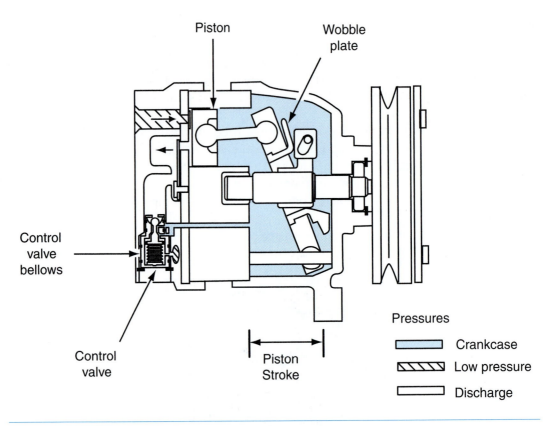

Figure 5-4 Cutaway of a typical swashplate compressor.

The intake stroke of the compressor is also called the suction stroke.

The compression stroke of the compressor is also called the discharge stroke.

**Reed valve** are the leaves of steel located on the valve plate of a compressor that allow refrigerant to enter or leave the compressor.

**Stroke** is the distance a piston travels from its lowest point to its highest point.

the compressor shaft. When voltage is applied, the electromagnetic clutch coil is energized, and the pulley engages with a clutch plate, often referred to as an armature, mounted on the compressor shaft. The magnetic field locks the clutch plate and pulley together as one unit to drive the compressor shaft.

Some compressors cannot be repaired and, if defective or damaged, must be replaced. Many rebuilt replacement compressors contain lubricant that must be drained and replaced with the proper type and amount. Most new compressors, on the other hand, are supplied without lubricant. Fill the rebuilt or new compressor with the same amount and type lubricant as removed from the defective compressor or as recommended in the manufacturer's service manual.

Piston motion is caused by action of a crankshaft or a swashplate, often referred to as a wobble plate. Some swashplate compressors have double-ended pistons, such as General Motors DA-6, while others have single-ended pistons, such as Sanden's SD-5 (Figure 5-4). A more detailed explanation of compressors is given in Chapter 8 of this Manual, with troubleshooting and repair procedures given in Chapter 8 of the Shop Manual. The following brief description is of the operation of the pistons and valves of a typical reciprocating compressor.

## Operation

Each piston in a compressor has a set of **reed valves** and valve plates—one suction and one discharge valve. Assume a simple two-cylinder compressor for the following description of operation (Figure 5-5). While one piston is on the suction (intake) **stroke**, the other piston is on the

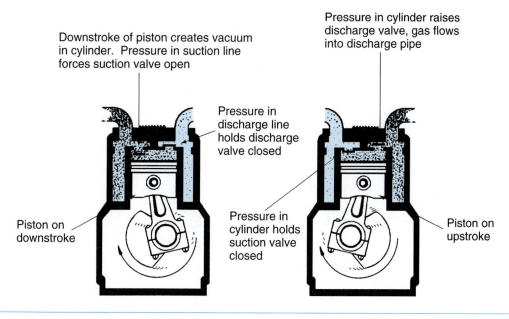

Figure 5-5 Typical operation of a single-cylinder compressor.

discharge (**compression**) stroke. The piston draws refrigerant into the compressor through the suction valve and forces it out of the compressor through the discharge valve. When the piston is on the suction (or intake) stroke, the discharge valve is held closed by the higher pressure above it. At the same time, the suction valve is opened to allow low-pressure refrigerant vapor to enter. When the piston is on the compression (or discharge) stroke, refrigerant vapor is forced through the discharge valve; the suction valve is held closed by this same pressure.

The compressor separates the low side from the high side of the system (Figure 5-6). Refrigerant entering the compressor is a low-pressure, slightly superheated, vapor. When the refrigerant leaves the compressor, it is a high-pressure, highly superheated vapor.

The compressor in some air conditioning systems has service valves that are used to access the air conditioning system. The manifold and gauge set is connected into the system at the service valve ports. All service procedures—such as recovering, evacuating, and charging the system—are performed with the use of a manifold and gauge set and the proper recovery and charging equipment.

**Compression** is the act of reducing volume by pressure.

**Shop Manual**
Chapter 5, page 153

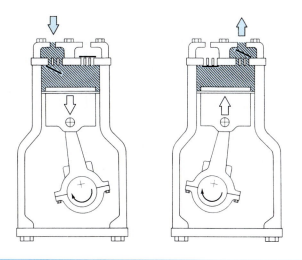

Figure 5-6 Refrigerant entering the compressor is low-pressure vapor and is high-pressure vapor when leaving.

Refrigeration lubricant, most often referred to as oil, is stored in the compressor and is essential in keeping the internal parts of the compressor lubricated. A small amount of this lubricant circulates with the refrigerant through the system. The velocity of the refrigerant through the tubes and hoses, however, allows this lubricant to return to the compressor. Chapter 7 will provide greater detail on the various oils used in refrigerant systems.

## Hoses and Lines

Refrigerant fluid and vapor lines may be made of aluminum, copper, or steel. Hoses are usually made of synthetic rubber covered with nylon braid for strength and have an inner lining of nylon to ensure integrity and to form a barrier wall to prevent refrigerant leakage. This hose design is classified as a barrier hose and is found on all R-134a refrigerant systems. Older R-12 systems used hoses with inner liners typically made of Buna "N," a synthetic rubber. Buna "N," which is not affected by R-12, is not acceptable for R-134a systems. Barrier hoses with a nylon lining are compatible with both R-134a and R12 systems.

Special consideration must be given for hoses and other components used in an R-134a air conditioning system. Many materials that were compatible for an R-12 system, such as nitrile or epichlorohydrin, cannot be used for R-134a service. For example, O-rings used with fittings in an R-12 system, such as nitrile, and those used in an R-134a system, such as neoprene, are not interchangeable.

Standard hose sizes are given a number designation, such as #6, #8, #10, and #12. Size #6 is usually used for the liquid line, #8 or #10 as the hot gas discharge line, and #10 or #12 as the suction line. Figure 5-7 gives the inside diameter (ID) and outside diameter (OD) of two types of hoses used in automotive air conditioning service.

Most early R-12 hoses were not barrier hoses, which have a nylon liner inside the hose designed to stop the leakage of the smaller particles of R-134a refrigerants. Though not of a barrier design, the old hoses used in R-12 systems are oil soaked on the inside with the mineral oil lubricant used in these systems. The idea is that R-134a is not compatible with mineral oil and will not go through it. Although true in most cases, the constant refrigerant pressure eventually opens a path and allows the refrigerant to escape to the atmosphere. Most original equipment manufacturer (OEM) retrofit procedures, as far back as 1984, do not require replacing hoses. Many feel, however, that if a retrofit is to be done properly, all nonbarrier hoses should be replaced with barrier hoses (Figure 5-8). The EPA does not require replacement of hoses or seals during the retrofit of a vehicle from R-12 to R-134a. Always refer to manufacturer recommenda-

Most early R-12 (CFC-12) hoses are not compatible with R-134a (HFC-134a) refrigerant.

**Shop Manual**
Chapter 5, page 141

| Hose Size | Inside Diameter | | Outside Diameter (OD) | | | |
| --- | --- | --- | --- | --- | --- | --- |
| | | | Rubber Hose | | Nylon Hose | |
| | English | Metric | English | Metric | English | Metric |
| #6 | 5/16 in | 7.94 mm | 3/4 in | 19.05 mm | 15/32 in[1] | 11.9 mm[3] |
| #8 | 13/32 in | 10.32 mm | 59/64 in[1] | 23.42 mm[3] | 35/64 in[1] | 13.89 mm[3] |
| #10 | 1/2 in | 12.7 mm | 1-1/32 in[2] | 25.8 mm[4] | 11/16 in[1] | 17.46 mm[3] |
| #12 | 5/8 in | 15.87 mm | 1-5/32 in[2] | 29.37 mm[4] | NA | NA |

[1] ± 1/64 inch
[2] ± 1/32 inch
[3] ± 0.4 mm
[4] ± 0.8 mm

**Figure 5-7** Inside and outside diameter of hoses used for air conditioning service.

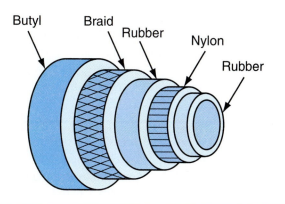

Figure 5-8 Barrier hose details.

tions. Figure 5-9 is a comparison table of R-134a and R-12 refrigerants. As the table indicates, barrier hoses are an option for the R-12 system. The best practice is to always follow the manufacturer's procedures and recommendations when retrofitting an air conditioning system.

The hose type is generally distinguished by the crimp style used on the fitting (Figure 5-10). Either the finger style crimp, used with a nonbarrier hose having a barb fitting, or the bubble

When refrigerant changes from vapor to liquid, it gives up heat.

When refrigerant changes from liquid to vapor, it takes on heat.

*Do not mix refrigerants.*

| | R-134a System | R-12 System |
|---|---|---|
| Chemical Name | Tetrafluoroethane | Dichlorodifluoromethane |
| Refrigerant Container Identification | Labeled R-134a Sky Blue Container | Labeled R-12 White Container |
| Refrigerant Container Fitting | ½" x 16 ACME | ⁷⁄₁₆" x 20, ¼" Flare |
| Boiling Point at Sea Level | −15.07°F (−26.15°C) | −21.62°F (−29.79°C) |
| Desiccant | XH7, XH9 | XH5, XH7, XH9 |
| Hose Construction | Barrier Nylon Liner Required | Barrier Nylon Liner Optional |
| Valve Core | M6 Thread, O-ring Seal | TV Thread, Teflon Seal |
| Refrigerant Oil | Polyalkylene Glycol (PAG) or Polyol Ester (Ester) | Mineral Based |
| Refrigerant Oil Hygroscopicity | 2.3%–5.6% by weight | 0.005% by weight |
| Condenser | Improved Heat Transfer Design | Standard |

Figure 5-9 R-134a/R-12 comparison table.

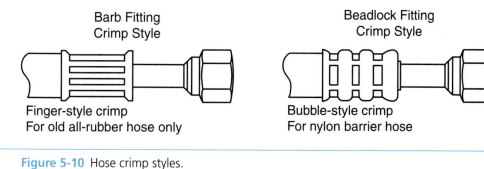

Barb Fitting Crimp Style

Beadlock Fitting Crimp Style

Finger-style crimp
For old all-rubber hose only

Bubble-style crimp
For nylon barrier hose

Figure 5-10 Hose crimp styles.

style beadlock crimp, used specifically with a nylon barrier hose, will generally be found. Also, fittings with worm gear hose clamps are used with nonbarrier type hoses. A worm gear hose clamp should never be used with nylon barrier hose fittings.

# Discharge Line

The hose leaving the compressor contains high-pressure refrigerant vapor. This hose, which is made of synthetic rubber, generally has a nylon **barrier** lining. It typically has a 13/32-in. (10.3-mm) inside diameter and often has extended preformed metal (steel or aluminum) ends with fittings. It is known as the hot gas discharge line and connects the outlet of the compressor to the inlet of the condenser.

Under normal operating conditions, this line is very warm. During certain system malfunctions, however, it is very hot. Because of the refrigerant temperature and pressure in this line, it is generally the most susceptible to leaks.

# Condenser

The condenser, which is located in front of the engine cooling radiator, is a heat exchanger made up of cooling fins and tubes that carry refrigerant. The condenser provides a rapid transfer of heat from the refrigerant passing through the tubes to the air passing through the fins and across the tubes. Part of a preventive maintenance service is to ensure that the condenser is clean and free of all debris. If found to be bent, a fin comb may be used to straighten the condenser fins.

Heat-laden refrigerant in the vapor state liquifies or condenses in the condenser. To do so, the refrigerant must give up its heat. As cooler air passing over the condenser carries its heat away, the vapor condenses. Heat that is removed from the refrigerant in the condenser as it changes from a vapor to a liquid is the same heat that was absorbed in the evaporator as it changed from a liquid to a vapor.

The refrigerant from the compressor is almost 100 percent vapor as it enters the condenser. On certain occasions, a very small amount of vapor may condense in the hot gas discharge line. The amount is so small, however, that it is not considered in the overall operation of the system.

The refrigerant is not always 100 percent liquid when it leaves the condenser, however. Only a certain amount of heat can be dissipated by the condenser at any given time. A small percentage of refrigerant, then, may leave the condenser in the vapor state. This condition does not affect overall system performance since the next component is a long liquid line or a receiver-drier.

The refrigerant in the condenser is a combination of liquid and vapor under high pressure. To avoid personal injury, extreme care must be exercised when servicing the condenser.

The inlet of the condenser must be at the top so the refrigerant vapor, as it condenses, will collect at the outlet at the bottom of the condenser. To ensure that all of the refrigerant vapor has condensed to a liquid when leaving the condenser, some systems are equipped with a small, second (auxiliary) condenser. This auxiliary condenser, called a subcondenser, provides the additional heat transfer surface required in some air conditioning systems for the refrigerant to condense to a liquid.

The outlet of a condenser in a thermostatic expansion valve (TXV) system is connected to the receiver-drier, then to the metering device, by the liquid line. In a fixed orifice tube (FOT) system, the outlet of the condenser is connected by a liquid line to the metering device.

The condenser for an R-134a system has a larger capacity and is designed for increased heat transfer compared to the standard R-12 system. This is necessary due to the differences in heat transfer characteristic of R-134a. The volume of gas entering the condenser is about 1,000 times the volume of the condensed liquid leaving the condenser. The efficiency of the condenser affects the overall performance of the refrigerant system.

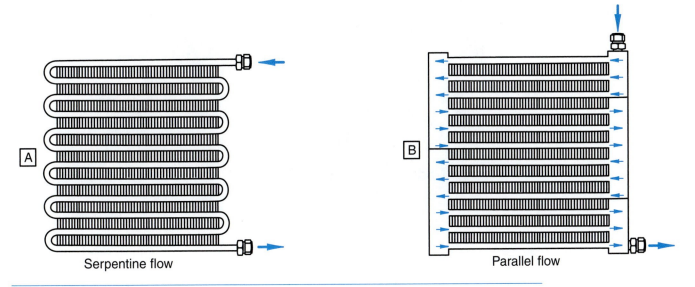

**Figure 5-11** Two common flow paths through air conditioning condensers are (A) serpentine flow, and (B) parallel flow.

There are several condenser designs and flow paths in use today. The two flow paths for refrigerant through the condenser's tubing is either parallel cross flow or a serpentine path flowing back and forth (Figure 5-11). The condenser may be a tube and fin with older designs using 3/8" tubing and newer designs using a 6 mm tube. They have similar heat transfer characteristics of the serpentine design and 15 percent better heat transfer than older 3/8" designs. Condenser tubes may also be extruded aluminum tubing with honeycomb serpentine passages for increased surface area and airflow for improved heat transfer (Figure 5-12). This design is physically smaller for the same level of heat transfer, making them popular for compact car designs. All aluminum parallel flow condensers with tubes and fins are currently popular with original equipment manufacturers (OEM) where limited space and airflow is a concern.

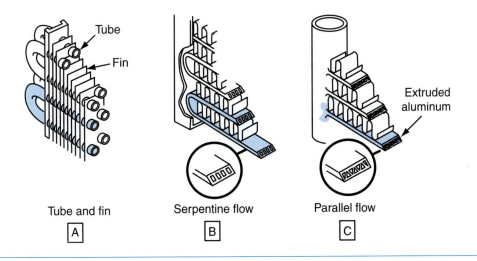

**Figure 5-12** Condensers may be (A) tube and fin, extruder aluminum (B) serpentine or (C) parallel flow.

Figure 5-13 Typical receiver-drier assembly.

# Receiver-Drier

**Shop Manual**

Chapter 5, page 158

The receiver-drier (Figure 5-13) is used in systems that have a thermostatic expansion valve (TXV) as a metering device. The receiver-drier stores reserve refrigerant and ensures a vapor-free liquid column to the thermostatic expansion valve (TXV). The receiver-drier, often referred to simply as a drier, is located in the high-pressure side of the air conditioning system between the condenser outlet and the metering device inlet. Construction of the drier is such that refrigerant vapor and liquid are separated to ensure that 100 percent liquid is available at the metering device, the thermostatic expansion valve (TXV).

The receiver-drier is often called a "receiver" or "drier."

## Receiver Section

The receiver section of the receiver-drier is a tanklike storage compartment. This section holds the proper amount of reserve refrigerant required to ensure proper performance of the air conditioning system under variable operating conditions. The receiver also ensures that a steady flow of liquid refrigerant can be supplied to the thermostatic expansion valve.

## Drier Section

**Desiccant** is a drying agent used to remove excess moisture in refrigeration systems. The desiccant is located in a bag in the receiver-drier or accumulator.

The drier section of the receiver-drier is generally nothing more than a fabric bag filled with **desiccant**, which is a chemical drying agent that can absorb and hold a small quantity of moisture to prevent it from circulating through the system. The desiccant used in an R-12 receiver-drier may not be compatible with R-134a refrigerant. The desiccants are classified XH5, XH7, and XH9. Only XH7 and XH9 are acceptable for use on R-134a systems. Therefore, to ensure that the desiccant will be compatible with the refrigerant and refrigeration lubricant in the system, use only replacement components that are designated for a particular application. The receiver-drier should be changed any time a major component of the air conditioning system has been replaced. Most vendors will not honor warranty claims on a new or rebuilt replacement compressor if the receiver-drier is not replaced at the time the system is serviced.

## Screen/Strainer

A screen and/or strainer is included inside the receiver-drier. This is intended to prevent the circulation of any debris throughout the system that may have entered during careless service procedures. This screen cannot be serviced as a component; the receiver-drier must be replaced as an assembly if the screen is found to be restricted.

# Liquid Line

High-pressure liquid refrigerant moves from the condenser or receiver-drier through a hose or tube called the liquid line to the evaporator metering device. The liquid line, which is usually made of aluminum, is generally 1/4-in. to 5/16-in. (6.3-mm to 7.9-mm) inside diameter. In some installations, such as a dual evaporator system, the inside diameter of the liquid line may be as large as 3/8 in. (9.5 mm). This line is sized so the refrigerant flow is not restricted yet maintains a constant pressure that is required to ensure proper metering of the refrigerant into the evaporator.

The liquid line may also be made of copper, steel, or a combination of rubber or nylon and copper, steel, or aluminum. As its name implies, the state of refrigerant in the liquid line is liquid under high pressure.

The liquid line is usually identified as the smallest line in the system.

# Thermostatic Expansion Valve

The thermostatic expansion valve, or TXV (Figure 5-14), located at the inlet side of the evaporator, is the metering device for the system. The TXV separates the high side of the system from the low side of the system. A small variable **orifice** in the valve allows only a small amount of liquid refrigerant to enter the evaporator. The amount of refrigerant passing through the valve is governed by the evaporator temperature. A tapered pin is raised or lowered in an orifice to change the size of the opening up to 0.008-in. (0.2-mm) diameter when the valve is wide open (Figure 5-15).

Refrigerant, as it passes through the thermostatic expansion valve and immediately after it, is 100 percent liquid. A very small amount of liquid refrigerant, known as flash gas, vaporizes immediately after passing through the valve due to the severe pressure drop. All of the liquid refrigerant soon changes state; as the pressure drops, the liquid refrigerant begins to boil. All liquid should boil off before reaching the outlet of the evaporator. As it boils, it must absorb heat from the air passing over the coils and fins of the evaporator. The air, then, feels cool; heat is being removed from the air, cold air is not being created.

At the point of total evaporation, the refrigerant is said to be saturated. The saturated vapor continues to pick up heat in the evaporator and in the suction line until it reaches the compressor. The refrigerant is then said to be superheated.

The two types of TXV are internal equalized and external equalized. They are not interchangeable.

**Orifice** is a small hole of calibrated dimensions for metering fluid or gas in exact proportions.

**Shop Manual**
Chapter 5, page 146

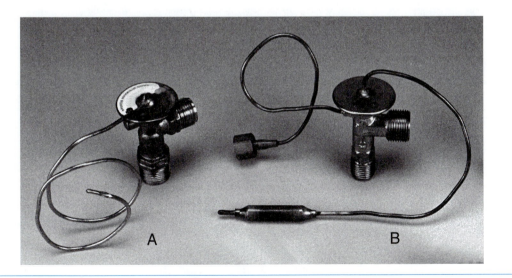

**Figure 5-14** Typical thermostatic expansion valves: (A) internal equalized; (B) external equalized.

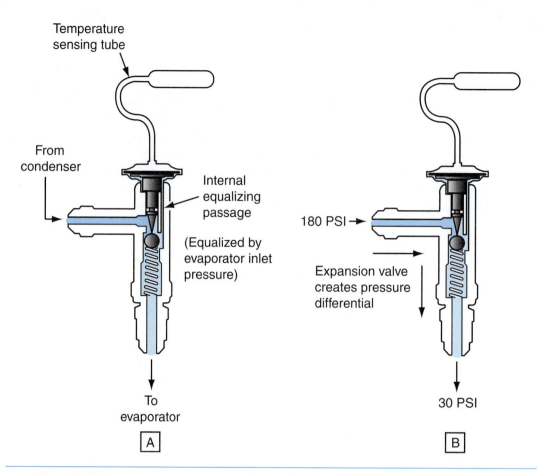

Temperature
sensing tube

From
condenser

Internal
equalizing
passage

(Equalized by
evaporator inlet
pressure)

To
evaporator

A

180 PSI →

Expansion valve
creates pressure
differential

30 PSI

B

**Figure 5-15** Expansion valves are internally equalized (A), and provide a variable restriction (B) to refrigerant flow.

Many Chrysler car lines now use an orifice tube for a metering device.

The expansion valve has a sensing element called a remote bulb attached to a power unit by a capillary tube (Figure 5-16). This bulb, which is attached to the evaporator tailpipe, senses outlet temperature. In this manner, the valve regulates itself.

**Figure 5-16** The (H-Block) thermostatic expansion valve showing the remote bulb attached to the outlet of the evaporator.

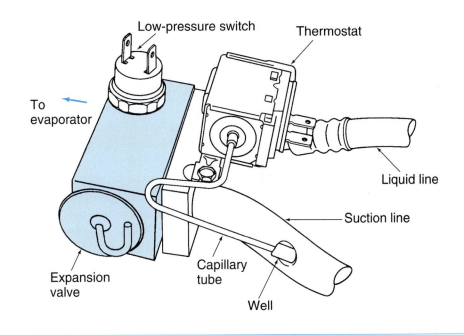

Figure 5-17 A typical H-valve, also known as a block valve.

# H-Valve

The **H-valve** (Figure 5-17), often called a block valve, is used on many Chrysler car lines. It was also used on Mercury through 1988, Golf and Jetta through 1986, as well as Mercedes-Benz and BMW through 1984. The most common block-type expansion valve is internally regulated (Figure 5-18). The refrigerant enters the valve through the high-pressure liquid line and passes

**H-valve** is an expansion valve with all parts contained within that are used on some Chrysler and Ford lines.

The H-valve is internally equalized.

Block valve: Another term for H-valve.

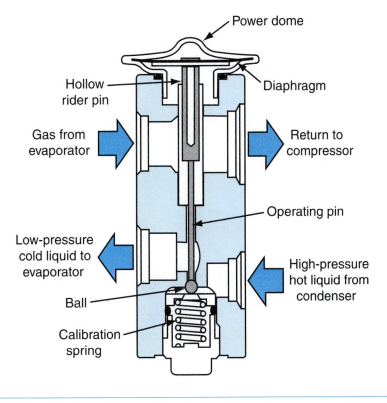

Figure 5-18 Details of H-block style expansion valve.

through a variable restriction that regulates the pressure to the evaporator. As the refrigerant leaves the evaporator, it travels back through the H-valve's upper outlet port and passes over the temperature sensing sleeve (internal sensing bulb) contained in the passage, transferring some heat to the refrigerant contained in the power dome diaphragm. This causes the refrigerant contained in the power dome to expand and contract based on the temperature of the refrigerant leaving the evaporator. The expansion and contraction exerts pressure on the sensing cavity diaphragm causing the valve pin to move up and down and, in turn, regulates the flow of refrigerant through the evaporator core, thus regulating core temperature. Its purpose, like the standard TXV, is to sense suction line refrigerant temperature. Operation and function of the H-valve, or block valve, are essentially the same as for the thermostatic expansion valve (TXV).

The equalizing passage, whether it is internal or external, is a direct passage to the low side of the system to the opposite side of the power dome diaphragm that the sensing bulb connects to. The equalizing pressure ensures smooth, consistent opening and closing of the expansion valve. It allows for fine adjustments, thus reducing broad temperature fluctuations of the evaporator core, and more consistent temperature levels are maintained within an acceptable operating range.

# The Orifice Tube

The orifice tube (Figure 5-19) is a calibrated restrictor used as a means of metering liquid refrigerant into the evaporator. Its purpose is to meter high-pressure liquid refrigerant into the evaporator as a low-pressure liquid. The orifice tube establishes a pressure differential at the restriction, with the high-pressure liquid line and condenser on one side and the low-pressure liquid line and evaporator on the other side.

The amount of refrigerant entering the evaporator with an orifice tube system is dependent on the size of the orifice, subcooling of the refrigerant, and the pressure difference ($\Delta p$) between the inlet and outlet of the orifice device. It is frequently referred to as a fixed orifice tube (FOT) because of its fixed orifice and tubular shape. The orifice tube is available in sizes ranging from 0.047 in. (1.19 mm) to 0.072 in. (1.83 mm), depending on application and are generally color coded.

Fine-mesh filter screens protect the inlet and outlet of the orifice tube. If foreign matter blocks or partially blocks the orifice, the air conditioning system will not function to full efficiency. If the blockage is severe enough, the system may not function at all.

The fixed orifice tube, with few exceptions, is located in a cavity in the liquid line or at the inlet connection of the evaporator and is easily accessible. Exceptions are that some vehicles have an inaccessible FOT located inside the liquid line. If found to be defective, the liquid line

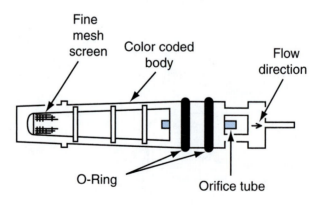

**Figure 5-19** A typical fixed orifice tube (FOT).

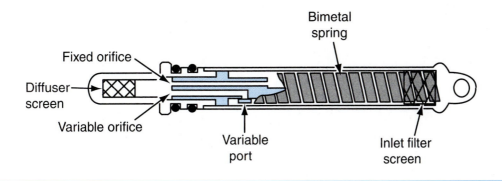

**Figure 5-20** Details of a variable orifice tube.

either has to be replaced, or a repair kit must be used to replace a section of the liquid line containing the FOT. Procedures for replacing the FOT are found in Chapter 5 of the Shop Manual.

Some "aftermarket engineers" replace the standard original equipment manufacturers (OEM) fixed orifice tube with an aftermarket Smart variable orifice valve (VOV). The Smart VOV utilizes system pressure to move a metering piston relative to a fixed opening in the sleeve. This is claimed to compensate for reduced compressor output at idle speeds and increase the cooling performance. The Smart VOV manufacturer claims that it is a "drop in" replacement for ineffective OEM orifice tubes and that it can offer a "dramatic improvement on factory R-134a systems." Before making any changes to an automotive air conditioning system, it is strongly suggested that manufacturer's recommendations be followed.

The factory-installed air conditioning system in some Jeep models, beginning in 1999, are equipped with a variable orifice tube. The Jeep design, however, is slightly different from aftermarket VOVs. There are two parallel paths for refrigerant to flow through the variable orifice valve (Figure 5-20). One is a fixed orifice opening, and the other is a variable orifice opening. As the temperature of the refrigerant flowing though the VOV changes, a bimetal coil opens or closes the variable port. High temperatures cause the port to close. The opening through the fixed orifice tube is normally 0.047 in. (1.1938 mm), and the variable orifice tube opening ranges from 0–0.015 in. (0–0.381 mm). The advantage of the variable orifice tube is improved air conditioning cooling during high heat load conditions, such as in stop-and-go traffic or extremely hot days.

On General Motors orifice tube systems, two methods of temperature control are used. One method, called a **cycling clutch** orifice tube (CCOT) system, uses a fixed displacement compressor. A pressure- or temperature-actuated cycling switch is used to turn the compressor's electromagnetic clutch on and off. This action starts and stops the compressor to maintain the desired in-car temperature.

The other orifice tube system used by General Motors has a **variable displacement** (VD) compressor. This regulates the quantity of refrigerant that flows through the system to maintain the selected in-car temperature. This system, called the variable displacement orifice tube (VDOT) system, eliminates the need to cycle the clutch on and off for temperature control.

Many Ford Motor Company car lines use the cycling clutch method of temperature control on their orifice tube systems. Either a temperature- or pressure-actuated control may be used to cycle the clutch on and off to maintain selected in-car temperature. Their system is called a fixed orifice tube/cycling clutch (FOTCC) system.

All orifice tube air conditioning systems have an accumulator located at the evaporator outlet (Figure 5-21). The accumulator prevents unwanted quantities of liquid refrigerant and/or oil from returning to the compressor at any one time.

**Shop Manual**
Chapter 5, page 148

**Cycling clutch** systems turn the compressor clutch on and off to control evaporator temperature.

The orifice tube, if clogged, may be cleaned.

**Variable displacement** changes the displacement of the compressor by changing the stoke of the piston(s).

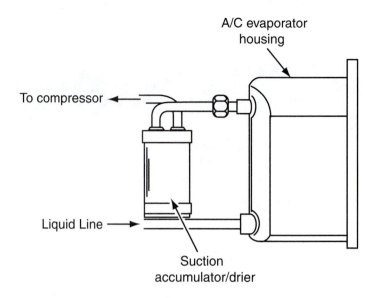

To compressor

A/C evaporator housing

Liquid Line

Suction accumulator/drier

Figure 5-21 A typical accumulator, located at the outlet of the evaporator.

**Shop Manual**
Chapter 5, page 154

**Heat load** is the load imposed on an air conditioner due to ambient temperature, humidity, and other factors that may produce unwanted heat.

**Flooded** refers to a condition whereby too much refrigerant is metered into the evaporator.

**Starved** refers to a condition whereby too little refrigerant is metered into the evaporator.

Automotive air conditioning compressors are not designed to "pump" liquid.

# Evaporator

The evaporator's purpose is to cool and dehumidify the incoming air when the air conditioning system is operating. The evaporator (Figure 5-22) is that part of the air conditioning system where the refrigerant vaporizes as it picks up heat. Air is forced through and past the fins and tubes of the evaporator as heat from the air is picked up by the boiling refrigerant. Important considerations in the design of evaporators are:

❏ Size and length of the tubing
❏ Number and size of the fins
❏ Number of return bends
❏ Amount of air passing through and past the fins
❏ The **heat load** (**NOTE**: Heat load refers to the amount of heat, in Btu, to be removed.)

Refrigerant, as it leaves the evaporator, should be a low-pressure, slightly superheated vapor. If too much refrigerant is metered into the evaporator, it is said to be **flooded**. As a result, a flooded evaporator will not cool well because the pressure of the refrigerant in the evaporator is high, and it does not boil away as rapidly. When the evaporator is full of liquid refrigerant, there is no room for expansion. In this case, the refrigerant cannot vaporize properly, which is necessary if the refrigerant is to take on heat. A flooded evaporator also allows an excess of liquid refrigerant to leave the evaporator. The result is that serious damage can be done to the compressor. An accumulator is included in a fixed orifice tube (FOT) system to prevent liquid slugging of the compressor. There is no superheat if the evaporator is flooded.

If too little refrigerant is metered into the evaporator, the system is said to be **starved**. Again, the unit does not cool because the refrigerant boils off too rapidly, long before it passes through the evaporator. Under this condition, the superheat is very high.

Under ideal conditions, the refrigerant should boil off about two-thirds to three-quarters of the way through the evaporator. At this point, the refrigerant is said to be saturated. It has picked up all of the latent heat required to change from a liquid to a vapor without undergoing a temperature change.

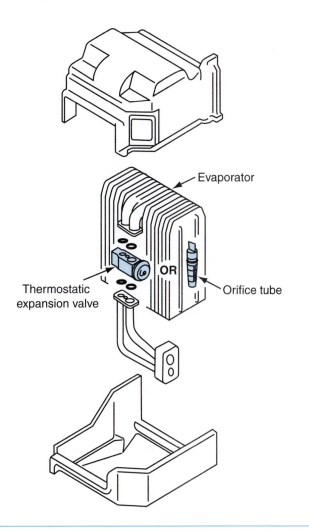

Evaporator

Thermostatic
expansion valve

OR

Orifice tube

**Figure 5-22** A typical evaporator core.

From this point, the vaporized refrigerant will pick up additional heat before leaving the evaporator. The refrigerant will also pick up underhood heat in the suction line before reaching the compressor. This superheat is sensible heat that is added to a vapor, raising its temperature without increasing its pressure. The ideal superheat for an air conditioning system is between 10–20°F (5.6–11.1°C). In humid regions of the country, it is the addition of superheat that often causes the suction line to sweat and, in some cases, ice over.

During normal system operation, moisture collects on the surface of the evaporator and collects in the HVAC housing. This moisture then drains out a vent in the bottom of the case assembly. It is normal to see a puddle of water forming under a vehicle while the air conditioning is operating; this indicates that the drain vent is not blocked. A blocked vent can lead to moisture building up in the case, causing bacterial growth and odor as well as water dripping into the passenger compartment.

> **AUTHOR'S NOTE:** While on a summer vacation with my family, my daughter noticed a large puddle of water forming on the passenger side floor. Shortly after she noticed the puddle, water mist began to blow out of the dash vents. After arriving at our destination and recovering from the laughter that this incident had generated, I crawled under the vehicle and, with a piece of coat hanger, carefully cleaned out the case vent tube drain. No less than a gallon of water drained from the HVAC case, and another 2 gallons of water had to be wet/dry vacuumed off the passenger compartment floor. This was one vacation that was not soon forgotten.

Latent heat cannot be measured with a thermometer.

The accumulator may be considered a liquid trap.

# Accumulator

The accumulator, a tanklike vessel, is located at the outlet of the evaporator (Figure 5-23). It is an essential part of an orifice tube air conditioning system. The orifice tube, under certain conditions, may meter more liquid refrigerant into the evaporator than can be evaporated. If it were not for the accumulator, excess liquid refrigerant leaving the evaporator would enter the compressor, causing damage.

To prevent this problem, all refrigerant and oil leaving the evaporator must enter the accumulator. The accumulator allows the refrigerant vapor to pass on to the compressor and traps the liquid refrigerant and oil. The accumulator includes a calibrated orifice, known as an "oil bleed hole," not to be confused with the orifice tube. It is found in the outlet provisions of the accumulator to allow small amounts of liquid refrigerant and/or oil to return to the compressor with the vapor.

Another important function of the accumulator is that it contains the desiccant, a chemical drying agent. The desiccant attracts, absorbs, and holds moisture that may have entered the system due to improper or inadequate service procedures. The desiccant is not serviced as a component of the accumulator. If desiccant replacement is indicated, the accumulator must be replaced as an assembly. The desiccant used in R-12 accumulators may not be compatible in an R-134a system. The desiccants are classified XH5, XH7 and XH9. Only XH7 and XH9 are acceptable for use on R-134a systems. To be sure of system compatibility, use only replacement components specifically designated for a particular application.

A fine-mesh screen is placed in the accumulator to catch and prevent the circulation of any debris that may be in the system. This screen cannot be serviced; if it is clogged, the entire unit must be replaced as an assembly.

The accumulator should be replaced any time a major component of the air conditioning system is replaced or repaired. Most vendors will not honor the warranty on new or rebuilt compressors unless the accumulator is replaced at the time of service.

**AUTHOR'S NOTE:** In general, students have difficulty in the beginning distinguishing what type of system they are dealing with, whether orifice tube or expansion valve. First, find the lines entering and leaving the evaporator. Follow the outlet line which leads to the compressor. If there is a metal canister attached to this line you have found the accumulator and you are dealing with an orifice tube system. If no canister is found you are dealing with an expansion valve system.

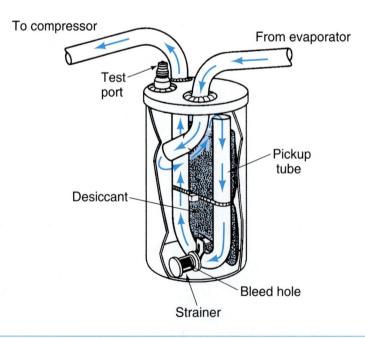

**Figure 5-23** Construction details of the accumulator.

# What Type System

There are basically two methods of temperature control for automotive air conditioning systems:

- ❏ Cycling clutch
- ❏ Noncycling clutch

## Cycling Clutch

The cycling clutch system relies on two methods for temperature control:

1. Temperature cycling switch. The temperature cycling switch is a temperature-sensitive switch that cycles the compressor clutch on and off at **predetermined** temperature levels.
2. Pressure cycling switch. The pressure cycling switch, as its name implies, is sensitive to system pressure and turns the compressor clutch on and off at predetermined pressure levels.

**Predetermined** is a set of fixed values or parameters that have been programmed or otherwise fixed into an operating system.

## Noncycling Clutch

The noncycling clutch system relies on a variable displacement (VD) compressor to control the in-car temperature. The amount of refrigerant permitted to flow through the system is controlled by the compressor's ability to alter the stroke of the pistons as required by varying system conditions.

The only purpose of the clutch in a noncycling system, then, is to disengage the compressor when the air conditioner is not in use and to engage the compressor when the driver calls for cooling.

# What Type Refrigerant

Several refrigerants have been approved by the Environmental Protection Agency (EPA) for use in automotive air conditioning systems. Only two types, however, are approved by the automotive industry for use. The use of a refrigerant not approved by industry may void manufacturer's warranties on the system as well as on replacement components.

Use the proper refrigerant.

The two industry approved refrigerants are:

1. R-12 (CFC-12)
2. R-134a (HFC-134a)

Other refrigerants approved by the EPA for automotive use include:

- ❏ FRIGC FR-12
- ❏ Freeze-12
- ❏ Free Zone (also, RB-276)
- ❏ GHG-HP
- ❏ GHG-X4 (also, Autofrost and Chill-It)
- ❏ GHG-X5
- ❏ Hot Shot (also, Kar Kool)
- ❏ Ikon-12
- ❏ R-406A (also, GHG)

## Refrigerant R-12 (CFC-12)

A refrigerant, known as R-12 or CFC-12, was used in automotive air conditioning systems through the early 1990s. Because of environmental concerns, its production and use has been phased out. Certain system changes, however, have to be made in order to use the new refrigerant. There is no drop-in refrigerant available that is approved for automotive use.

## Refrigerant R-134a (HFC-134a)

Refrigerant-134a (HFC-134a) is at present the automotive industry's refrigerant of choice to replace R-12 in automotive service. It is not, however, a drop-in replacement. Certain system modifications must be made before the new refrigerant can be used in an old system. This new refrigerant was first used in automotive applications in the early 1990s. By 1995, all new cars manufactured contained the new refrigerant.

## Other Refrigerants

Do not contaminate recovery system equipment or cylinders.

In 1994, the EPA established the Significant New Alternatives Policy (SNAP) Program to review alternatives to ozone-depleting substances. Under authority of the 1990 Clean Air Act (CAA), the EPA also examines potential substitute refrigerants as to their flammability, effects on global warming, and toxicity. As of this writing, the agency has determined that ten "new" refrigerants, including R-134a, are acceptable for use as an R-12 replacement in motor vehicle air conditioning systems. They are all, however, "acceptable subject to use conditions." All alternate refrigerants, except R-134a, are "blends," which means that they contain more than one component in their composition.

"Acceptable subject to use conditions" indicates that the EPA believes these refrigerants, when used in accordance with the use conditions, to be safer for human health and for the environment than the R-12 they are meant to replace. This designation, however, is not intended to imply that the refrigerant will work as satisfactorily as R-12 in any specific system. Also, it is not intended to imply that the refrigerant is perfectly safe regardless of how it may be used.

The EPA does not test refrigerants and, therefore, does not specifically approve or endorse any one refrigerant over any others. The agency reviews all of the information about a refrigerant submitted by its manufacturer and independent testing laboratories. The EPA does not determine what effect, if any, a "new" refrigerant may have on vehicle warranty.

Some refrigerant manufacturers use the term *drop-in* to imply that their refrigerant will perform identically to R-12 and that no modification is required for its use. The term also implies that the alternate refrigerant can be used alone or mixed with R-12. The EPA believes the term *drop-in* confuses and obscures at least two important regulatory points:

1. Charging one refrigerant into a system before extracting the old refrigerant is a violation of the SNAP use conditions and is, therefore, illegal.
2. Certain components may be required by law, such as hoses and compressor shutoff switches. If these components are not present, they must be installed. Five blends, for example, contain HCFC-22 and require barrier hoses.

**Contaminated** is a term generally used when referring to a refrigerant cylinder or system that fails a purity test and is known to contain foreign substances such as other incompatible or hazardous refrigerants.

It may also be noted that system performance is affected by such variables as outside temperature, relative humidity, and driving conditions. Therefore, it is not possible to ensure equal performance of any refrigerant under all of these conditions.

The service facility must have service and recovery equipment specifically designed for each type of refrigerant that is to be serviced. This means that at least two systems are required: one for R-12, and one for R-134a. A third set is required if **contaminated** systems are to be serviced, and a fourth set is required if a blend refrigerant is to be used.

Each new alternate refrigerant must be used with a unique set of fittings attached on the service ports, all recovery and recycling equipment, on can taps and other charging equipment, and on all refrigerant containers. A unique label must be affixed over the original label to identify the type refrigerant, as well as lubricant used in the air conditioning system.

# Summary

❏ The compressor is the prime mover of the refrigerant. Its purpose is to pump refrigerant throughout the air conditioning system.

❏ Each piston in a multipiston compressor has one suction and one discharge valve. Several valves may be found in one valve plate, depending on compressor design.

❏ Refrigerant changes state: vapor to liquid in the condenser, and liquid to vapor in the evaporator.

❏ The receiver-drier ensures a gas-free liquid supply to the metering device.

❏ The accumulator ensures that no liquid refrigerant is returned to the compressor.

❏ A thermostatic expansion valve (TXV), H-valve, or orifice tube (OT) is essential to meter the proper amount of refrigerant into the evaporator. These restrictive devices establish a pressure differential between the high side and the low side in the system.

❏ There are two types of refrigerant used in the automotive air conditioning system: R-12 (CFC-12) and R-134a (HFC-134a). The two refrigerants are not compatible; they must not be mixed.

# Review Questions

## Short Answer Essays

1. How does compressor action increase the condensation rate of refrigerant?

2. Briefly, how does a compressor "pump" refrigerant?

3. Why is it important that the inlet of the condenser be at the top?

4. What are two purposes of the receiver-drier?

5. Explain the term *flash gas* and what causes it.

6. What two factors determine how much refrigerant enters the evaporator in an FOT system?

7. Briefly describe the state of the refrigerant as it leaves the evaporator in a properly operating system.

8. What is the primary purpose of an accumulator?

9. Briefly describe the refrigeration cycle.

10. Describe the manner in which the two refrigerants approved for automotive service may be mixed in the system.

## Fill-in-the-Blanks

1. The compressor's function is to _____ _____ throughout the system.

2. Refrigeration oil keeps the _____, _____ _____, and other internal parts lubricated.

3. Heat-laden refrigerant gives up its heat in the _____ as it changes from a _____ to a _____.

4. High-pressure liquid refrigerant moves through a hose called a _____ _____.

5. The point of total evaporation of refrigerant is called its _____ point. As it picks up additional heat, it is said to be _____.

6. All orifice tube systems have a(n) _____ at the _____ of the evaporator.

7. The evaporator is said to be _____ if too little refrigerant is metered into it and _____ if too much refrigerant is metered into it.

8. The _____, a drying agent, is found in the _____ or _____ _____.

9. The compressor separates the _____ side of the system from the _____ side of the system; the metering device separates the _____ side from the _____ side of the system.

10. There are two types of refrigerant used in the automotive air conditioning system: _____-_____ and _____-_____.

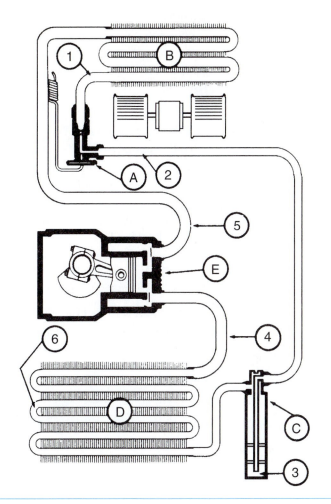

**Figure 5-24** The automotive air conditioning system.

## Multiple Choice

Refer to Figure 5-24 to answer questions 1 through 7.

1. *Technician A* says that the component identified by D is a receiver-drier.
   *Technician B* says that the component identified by D is an accumulator.
   Who is correct?
   **A.** A only (if the illustration depicts a thermostatic expansion valve [TXV] system)
   **B.** B only (if the illustration depicts an orifice tube [OT] system)
   **C.** Either A or B (depending on the system type)
   **D.** Neither A nor B

2. *Technician A* says that the component identified by B is an evaporator.
   *Technician B* says that the component identified by A is a condenser.
   Who is correct?
   **A.** A only (if the refrigerant flow through the receiver is left to right)
   **B.** B only (if the refrigerant flow through the receiver is right to left)
   **C.** Both A and B (depending on the direction of flow of the refrigerant)
   **D.** Neither A nor B

3. What component is shown as C?
   *Technician A* says that it is an accumulator.
   *Technician B* says that it is a receiver-drier.
   Who is correct?
   **A.** A only      **C.** Both A and B
   **B.** B only      **D.** Neither A nor B

4. What is the state of the refrigerant in line 4?
   *Technician A* says that it is high-pressure vapor.
   *Technician B* says that it is high-pressure liquid.
   Who is correct?
   **A.** A only      **C.** Both A and B
   **B.** B only      **D.** Neither A nor B

5. What is the state of the refrigerant as it leaves the
   evaporator, line 5?
   *Technician A* says that it is low pressure.
   *Technician B* says that it is a vapor.
   Who is correct?
   **A.** A only      **C.** Both A and B
   **B.** B only      **D.** Neither A nor B

6. What is the purpose of the compressor, component E?
   *Technician A* says it is to change the refrigerant
   vapor to a liquid.
   *Technician B* says it is to change the refrigerant
   liquid to a vapor.
   Who is correct?
   **A.** A only      **C.** Both A and B
   **B.** B only      **D.** Neither A nor B

7. What is the state of the refrigerant as it immediately
   enters the evaporator, line 1?
   *Technician A* says it is all liquid with some flash gas.
   *Technician B* says it is all vapor due to flash gas.
   Who is correct?
   **A.** A only      **C.** Both A and B
   **B.** B only      **D.** Neither A nor B

8. What is the purpose of the desiccant?
   *Technician A* says it is to clean the refrigerant.
   *Technician B* says it is to dry the refrigerant.
   Who is correct?
   **A.** A only      **C.** Both A and B
   **B.** B only      **D.** Neither A nor B

9. Which is more serious, a flooded evaporator or a
   starved evaporator? Why?
   *Technician A* says a starved evaporator is most
   serious because of poor cooling and high superheat.
   *Technician B* says a flooded evaporator is most
   serious because of poor cooling and liquid slugging
   of the compressor.
   Who is correct?
   **A.** A only      **C.** Both A and B
   **B.** B only      **D.** Neither A nor B

10. *Technician A* says that the ideal superheat for an
    automotive air conditioning system is 10–20°F.
    *Technician B* says that flash gas is a contributing
    factor of superheat.
    Who is correct?
    **A.** A only      **C.** Both A and B
    **B.** B only      **D.** Neither A nor B

# System Servicing and Testing

Upon completion and review of this chapter you should be able to:

❏ Describe the leak test procedures for an automotive air conditioning system using soap trace solutions, halide leak detectors, halogen leak detectors, and dye solutions.

❏ Discuss the other types of leak detector devices available to the automotive technician.

❏ Explain how moisture collects in an air conditioning system.

❏ Explain the importance of a moisture-free system.

❏ Describe the methods used to remove refrigerant from a system.

❏ Discuss the acceptable methods for charging a system with refrigerant.

## Introduction

Testing and servicing an automotive air conditioning system is a skill that is generally developed with practice and experience. This chapter gives a basic fundamental understanding of these procedures, including leak testing, **moisture** removal, refrigerant recovery, charging the system, and diagnostics.

## Refrigerant Analyzer

Before attempting to recover refrigerant or charge an automotive air conditioning system, one should use a refrigerant analyzer, also called a refrigerant identifier, to test samples taken from the air conditioning system or storage container to determine their purity. Recovered refrigerant should contain less than 2 percent impurities.

It is important to follow instructions that are included with the analyzer to obtain the test sample. The analyzer, such as the one shown in Figure 6-1, will display one of the following:

❏ R-12 or R-134a—If purity is 98 percent or better by weight.

❏ FAIL—If R-12 or R-134a has been identified but is not at least 98 percent pure.

❏ HC (and a horn will sound)— If the gas sample contains hydrocarbon (flammable material).

**Shop Manual**
Chapter 6, page 183

**Moisture** is defined as droplets of water in the air: humidity, dampness, or wetness.

**Figure 6-1** A typical refrigerant analyzer.

**Figure 6-3** A typical fluorescent leak detector.

# Fluorescent Leak Detectors

There are several manufacturers of fluorescent leak detectors. A metered amount of ultraviolet sensitive dye is injected into the system (Figure 6-3). The air conditioner is operated for a few minutes to allow time for the dye to circulate. An ultraviolet lamp is then used to pinpoint the leak. When the ultraviolet light beams come in contact with the dye that has leaked out of the system, the dye will give off a fluorescent glow. It is advisable to first wash the engine compartment before installing dye into the system. In addition, it is easier to detect the dye if ship light levels are low. Though it is not inexpensive, the ultraviolet method of leak detection is most effective for locating small, difficult-to-find leaks.

One-half oz. (0.015 mL) per year is equal to 1 lb. (0.472 mL) in 32 years.

Some automobile manufacturers add fluorescent dye, called scanner solution, to factory-installed air conditioners. The refrigerant identification label under the hood will identify the presence of a leak-detecting agent installed in the system. Ford Motor Company started this practice in 1996. Many technicians add scanner solution to systems being serviced for future troubleshooting. As with any additive, it is important to use the proper scanner solution to ensure system compatibility. More critical than type of refrigerant is the type of lubricant in the system. The scanner solution has either mineral, alkyl benzine, PAG, or polyol ester base stock to match the system lubricant.

Using the improper scanner solution can contaminate an otherwise healthy system. Just 0.3 oz. (0.89 mL) is sufficient to treat a system with a refrigerant capacity up to 2.9 lb. (1.21 L). The average system, however, requires 0.5 oz. (14.79 mL) of scanner solution. This is sufficient for a system with a capacity up to 4.9 lb. (2.33 L) of refrigerant.

Since the scanner solution is soluble in the lubricant, the refrigerant is recyclable and is accepted by most manufacturers and reclaimers. If retrofitting a system, be sure that all trace of the scanner solution is removed with the lubricant before introducing a new refrigerant.

# Electronic (Halogen) Leak Detectors

The electronic (halogen) leak detector is the most sensitive of all leak detection devices. The initial purchase price of a halogen leak detector, however, exceeds the cost of most fluorescent leak detectors. In addition, this more sophisticated device requires routine maintenance in order to maintain accuracy.

Electronic leak detectors must be capable of detecting a refrigerant loss rate of 1/2 oz. (14.79 mL) per year. This value corresponds to one part of refrigerant in ten thousand parts of air or 100 parts per million (ppm).

Electronic leak detectors are either corded or cordless (Figure 6-4). The corded leak detector operates on 120 volts (V), 60 hertz (Hz). The cordless leak detector is portable and operates from a rechargeable battery. Both units are simple to operate and easy to maintain. When the halogen leak detector comes in contact with refrigerant vapor, the audible click noise emitted from the device will become more rapid. If the unit is also equipped with an LED light bar, additional lights will illuminate. The halogen leak detector also allows the technician to diagnose the leak the same day the vehicle is in for the repair. This saves the customer both time and money and avoids the aggravation involved to both you and the customer of having to make a return visit.

A popular portable halogen leak detector is the model 5650 manufactured by TIF Industries (Figure 6-5). This instrument, which is powered by two "C" cell alkaline batteries, requires no

**Shop Manual**
Chapter 6, page 189

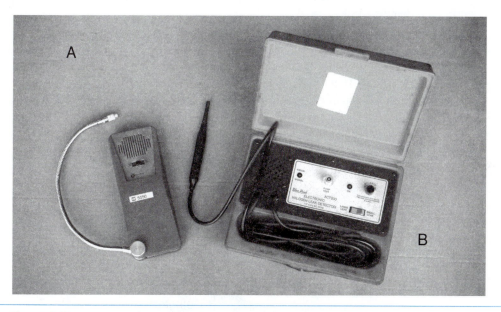

**Figure 6-4** Two types of electronic leak detector: (A) cordless and (B) corded.

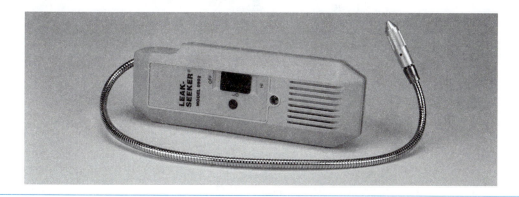

**Figure 6-5** A portable electronic leak detector that may be used for R-12 or R-134a.

warmup period and may be used to detect CFCs, HCFCs, or HFCs (R-12, R-22, or R-134a). In addition, this instrument calibrates itself automatically while in use to ignore ambient concentrations of gas and pinpoint leaks much more easily.

The important consideration in the selection of a halogen (electronic) leak detector that complies with EPA regulations is that it meet SAE standard J1627: it must be capable of detecting a leak at the rate of 0.05 oz. (14.787 mL) or less per year.

## A BIT OF HISTORY

The halide leak detector was once one of the most popular tools for locating R-12 refrigerant leaks. Today, though, the halide leak detector is considered obsolete and a potentially unsafe tool for refrigerant detection by the air conditioning industry.

**Halide** is any compound of halogen with another element such as refrigerant.

The gas (halide) leak detector (Figure 6-6) can detect a leak as slight as 1 lb. (0.472 mL) of R-12 in ten years. However, a lot of practice and experience is required for the technician to be able to recognize and identify a leak so slight.

The **halide** leak detector consists of two major parts: the detector unit—including the valve, burner and search hose—and the gas cylinder.

The gas cylinder is a nonrefillable pressure tank containing a flammable gas such as propane ($C_3H_3$) or butane ($C_4H_{10}$). The detector unit consists of a valve to control the flow of gas to the burner, the burner (a chamber where the gas and air are mixed), and the search hose (a rubber tube through which air passes to the chamber). It does not react to the presence of R-134a as reliably as to R-12 refrigerant and is therefore no longer an effective method of leak testing an automotive air conditioning system. Also, the halide leak detector is not recommended because of dangers associated with open flames, as well as the toxic vapors that are often formed by burning refrigerants.

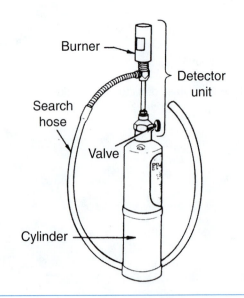

**Figure 6-6** A typical halide leak detector for CFC-12 (R-12).

# Other Types

Several other types of leak detectors, such as ultrasonic units, are available. Space does not permit the description of each type in this text. The technician should contact local refrigeration suppliers for additional information. This will allow a comparison of the different makes and models before purchase. When making a selection, do not overlook the commercial refrigeration parts supply houses. They often have a greater variety to choose from than the automotive parts supply houses.

Regardless of what type of leak detection device you are using, you need to take a systematic approach to detecting leaks. This means you should test the system when it is cold, having sat for several hours or overnight, and again when it is at operating temperature. You need to begin by looking at the most likely areas for a leak to occur. These areas include connection points of lines and components, as well as areas that contain gaskets and seals (Figure 6-7).

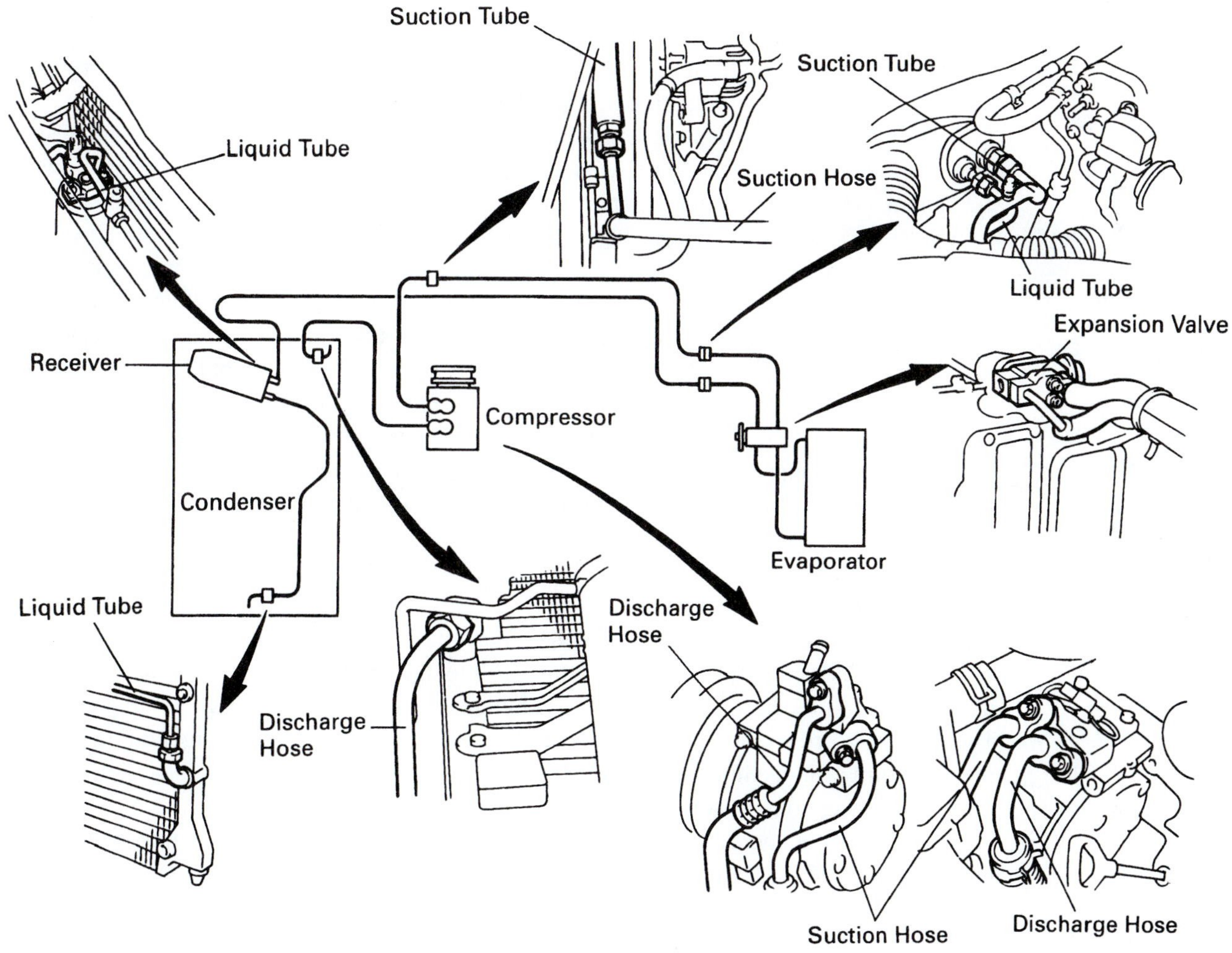

Any leak, regardless of how slight, emits an inaudible noise.

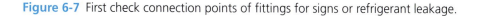

**Figure 6-7** First check connection points of fittings for signs or refrigerant leakage.

# Moisture and Moisture Removal

*Moisture* is a small quantity of diffused or condensed liquid. Actually, any substance that is not "dry" may be considered "moist." Moisture in an air conditioning system is one of its greatest perils. Even a slight amount of free moisture, a water ($H_2O$) vapor, in an air conditioning system can play havoc. When it is heated and mixed with refrigerant and oil, it can cause sludge and can form harmful acids that erode system components.

An air conditioning system should be free of moisture. Any time the system is opened for service, extreme care must be taken to keep the atmosphere within the system as air- and moisture-free as possible. (Air contains moisture in the form of humidity.) This is best accomplished by forming and practicing sound repair procedures.

New refrigerant is generally considered to be moisture-free. The moisture content of new refrigerant should not exceed 10 ppm. This information is given on the label of the container. If the percentage is missing or if there is no label, do not use the refrigerant. This is particularly true for R-12, since it is suspected that impure and/or contaminated refrigerant will become available as "virgin" R-12 vanishes from the marketplace due to the EPA phaseout mandates.

If new refrigerant and refrigeration oil are used in a system, any moisture found inside the system must have come from outside sources, such as a break in a line, or from improperly fastened hoses or fittings during a repair procedure.

Every time a component is removed from the system for repair or replacement, air is inadvertently introduced into the system. As a result, there is always the danger of moisture entering the system. Refrigerant and refrigeration oil, particularly R-134a and its oil, **absorb** moisture readily when exposed to air. To keep the system as moisture-free as possible, all automotive air conditioning systems have an accumulator or a receiver-drier that contains desiccant, a drying agent (Figure 6-8). Desiccants are chemicals that are capable of absorbing and holding moisture.

Any moisture introduced into the system in excess of the amount that the desiccant can handle is free in the system. Even one drop of free moisture ($H_2O$) cannot be controlled and may cause irreparable damage to the internal parts of the air conditioner.

Moisture in concentrations greater than 20 ppm may cause serious damage. For an idea of how small an amount 20 ppm is, consider one small drop of water in a system having a capacity of 6 lb. (0.94 mL) of refrigerant. That one small drop amounts to 20 ppm, or twice the amount that is desired.

Refrigerants react chemically with water ($H_2O$) to form **hydrochloric acid** (HCl). Heat, which is generated in the system, is an aid in the acid-forming process. The greater the concentration of moisture in the system, the more concentrated are the corrosive acids that are formed.

Hydrochloric acid (HCl) corrodes all the metallic parts of the system, particularly those made of steel. Iron (Fe), copper (Cu), and aluminum (Al) parts are damaged by the acid as well. The corrosive process also creates oxides that are released into the refrigerant as particles of metal to form a sludge. Further damage is caused when oxides plug the fine-mesh screens in the metering device, compressor inlet, and the drier or accumulator.

There are commercially available "remedies" that claim to prevent moisture freeze-up problems. There is also a notion that system freeze-up can be avoided by adding 0.07 oz. (0.002 mL) of alcohol per pound (0.03 mL) of refrigerant. However, the addition of alcohol to the system may cause even greater damage. The drier seeks out alcohol even more than moisture and, in doing so, releases all of its moisture to the system. This can cause severe damage to the system components. Once a system is saturated with moisture, irreparable damage is done to the inside of the system. If the moisture condition is neglected long enough, pinholes caused by corrosion appear in the evaporator and condenser coils and in any metal tubing used in the system. Any affected parts must be replaced.

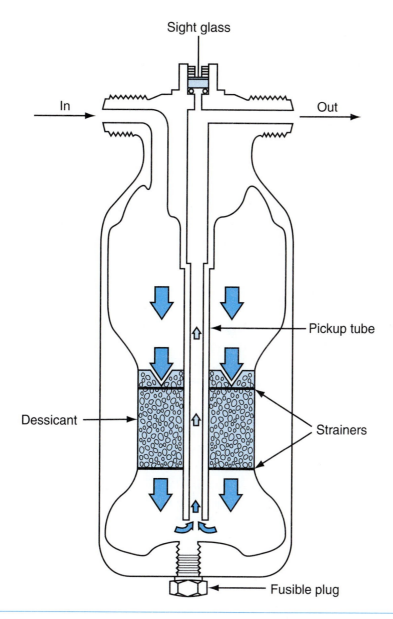

**Figure 6-8** Cutaway of receiver-drier showing construction details.

Additives, which are marketed under various trade names, are available that make the claim of increasing the cooling effect and/or stopping leaks. Most additives have a negative effect on the performance of an air conditioning system, however, and are not recommended.

Whenever there is evidence of moisture in the system, a thorough system clean out is recommended. Such a clean out should be followed by the installation of a new receiver-drier or accumulator and a complete system **pump-down** evacuation using a vacuum pump, charging station, or recovery system.

An additive may cause more problems than it will solve.

**Pump down** is the process of evacuation whereby a liquid is changed to a vapor by lowering pressure exerted on the liquid, thus lowering its boiling point.

**Shop Manual**
Chapter 6, page 191

# Prevention

The automotive air conditioning service technician can prevent unwanted debris and moisture from entering a system by following a few basic rules:

- ❑ Always install the receiver-drier or accumulator last.
- ❑ Always immediately cap the open ends of hoses and fittings.
- ❑ Do not work around water, outside in the rain, or in very humid locations.
- ❑ Do not allow new refrigerant or refrigeration oil to become contaminated.
- ❑ Keep the refrigeration oil container capped when it is not being used.
- ❑ Develop clean habits: do not allow dirt to enter the system; keep all service tools clean; and never charge a unit with refrigerant without first ensuring that all air and moisture have been removed.

Do not remove the protective caps from the accumulator or receiver-drier until it is to be installed.

# Moisture Removal

As discussed earlier, many problems can arise due to moisture in an automotive air conditioning system. After any repairs have been made to the system, it must be "pumped down" (evacuated) to remove any moisture that may have entered during the process.

Moisture removal from a system can cause serious problems for the service technician who is not properly equipped. A vacuum pump is an essential tool for air conditioning service. Other methods may be used, but the vacuum pump is by far the most efficient means of moisture removal. Typical vacuum pumps suitable for automotive service are shown (Figure 6-9).

A pressure below 0 lb. (0 psig) or 0 kiloPascal (0 kPa) gauge pressure is referred to in terms of inches of mercury (in. Hg) on the English scale or kiloPascals absolute (kPa absolute) on the metric scale. Moisture is removed from the air conditioning system by creating a vacuum. In a vacuum, the moisture within the system boils. The action of the vacuum pump then pulls the moisture in the form of a vapor from the system. When the pressure is increased on the discharge side of the pump, the vapor again liquifies. This process usually occurs inside the pump.

A minimum of 30 minutes is required to ensure moisture removal with a compressor speed of about 1,500 revolutions per minute (rpm or r/min). The compressor is lubricated by refrigera-

Pressure below atmospheric is referred to as a vacuum.

Refrigeration oil is hygroscopic and will absorb moisture.

**Figure 6-9** A typical two-stage vacuum pump.

156

| System Vacuum Inches Mercury | Temperature °F Boiling Point | System Vacuum kilopascals absolute | Temperature °C Boiling Point |
|---|---|---|---|
| 24.04 | 140 | 19.66 | 60.0 |
| 25.39 | 130 | 15.61 | 54.4 |
| 26.45 | 120 | 12.02 | 48.8 |
| 27.32 | 110 | 9.07 | 43.3 |
| 27.99 | 100 | 6.80 | 37.7 |
| 28.50 | 90 | 5.08 | 32.2 |
| 28.89 | 80 | 3.75 | 26.6 |
| 29.18 | 70 | 2.77 | 21.1 |
| 29.40 | 60 | 2.03 | 15.5 |
| 29.66 | 50 | 1.15 | 10.0 |
| 29.71 | 40 | 0.98 | 4.4 |
| 29.76 | 30 | 0.81 | −1.1 |
| 29.82 | 20 | 0.60 | −6.7 |
| 29.86 | 10 | 0.47 | −12.2 |
| 29.87 | 5 | 0.44 | −15.0 |
| 29.88 | 0 | 0.40 | −17.8 |
| 29.90 | −10 | 0.33 | −23.0 |
| 29.91 | −20 | 0.30 | −28.8 |
| A | | B | |

**Figure 6-10** Boiling point of water ($H_2O$) under a vacuum: (A) English; (B) Metric. Use the table to determine level of evacuation needed based on ambient air temperature.

tion oil in its sump. Some of the oil is picked up in the refrigerant vapor. If the compressor runs dry of oil when it is operated as a vacuum pump, it may be seriously damaged. Also, vacuum pressure is exposed to atmospheric pressure immediately above the discharge valve plate inside the compressor. Most moisture vapor will liquefy inside the compressor discharge cavity. Little to nothing is gained in this procedure.

A good vacuum pump is capable of pumping a vacuum pressure of 29.76 in. Hg (0.81 kPa absolute) or more. At this pressure, water boils at 40°F (4.44°C). In other words, if the ambient temperature is 40°F (4.44°C) or higher, moisture will boil out of the system.

At 0 in. Hg (101.3 kPa absolute) at sea level, water boils at 212°F (100°C). To find the boiling point of water in a vacuum (absolute pressure), use the tables shown (Figure 6-10). Note that the boiling point is lowered only 112°F (62.2°C) to 100°F (37.7°C) as the pressure is decreased from 0 in. Hg (101.3 kPa absolute) at sea level to 28 in. Hg (0.98 kPa absolute). However, the boiling point drops by 120°F (66.6°C) as the pressure decreases from 28 in. Hg (0.98 kPa absolute) to 29.91 in. Hg (0.30 kPa absolute).

The degree of vacuum and the amount of time the system is under a vacuum determines the amount of moisture removed. The deeper the vacuum and/or the longer the time, the more moisture is removed. The removal of moisture from a system can be compared to the boiling away (vaporization) of water in an open saucepan on a hot burner. It is not sufficient to cause the water to boil; time must be allowed for it to boil away.

The recommended minimum pumping time is 30 minutes below 29 in.Hg. If time allows, however, a four-hour pump down achieves much better results. Vacuum pump manufacturers' specifications and recommendations should be followed for proper maintenance. For example, changing oil on a regular basis is essential to ensure maximum efficiency.

Contaminated vacuum pump oil can reduce the efficiency of the vacuum pump by 10 percent or more.

# Moisture Removal at High Altitudes

The information given for moisture removal by a vacuum pump applies to normal atmospheric pressures at sea level, 14.696 (14.7) psig (101.3 kPa absolute). At higher altitudes, the boiling point must be reduced to a point below the ambient temperature. Moisture ($H_2O$) boils at a lower temperature at higher altitudes. However, it must be pointed out that vacuum pump efficiency is reduced at higher altitudes.

For example, the altitude of Denver, Colorado, is 5,280 ft. (1,609.3 m) above sea level. Water ($H_2O$) will boil at 206.2°F (96.78°C) at this altitude. The maximum efficiency of a vacuum pump, however, is reduced at this altitude. A vacuum pump that can pump 29.92 in. Hg (0.27 kPa absolute) at sea level will pump only 25.44 in. Hg (15.44 kPa absolute) at this altitude. Note in Figure 6-10 that water ($H_2O$) boils at about 130°F (54.4°C) at this pressure.

The English formula for determining vacuum pump efficiency at a given atmospheric pressure is

$$AP_L / AP_S \times PRE = APE$$

where

$AP_L$ = atmospheric pressure in your location

$AP_S$ = atmospheric pressure at sea level

$PRE$ = pump rated efficiency

$APE$ = actual pump efficiency

Assume that a vacuum pump has a rated efficiency of 29.92 in. Hg at sea level (0.27 kPa absolute), and that the atmospheric pressure at Denver is 12.5 psia (86.18 kPa absolute). To determine the actual efficiency at this location, the formula is:

$$\frac{12.5}{14.7} \times 29.92 = 25.44 \text{ in. HG}$$

The metric formula for determining vacuum pump efficiency at a given atmospheric pressure is

$$\text{Atmospheric Pressure at Sea Level} - \text{Atmospheric Pressure in Your Location} + \text{Original Efficiency} = \text{Actual Efficiency}$$

Assuming the same conditions previously mentioned, the formula is applied in the following manner:

$$101.32 - 86.18 + 0.27 = 15.41 \text{ kPa absolute}$$

In this example, the ambient temperature must be raised above 130°F (54.44°C) if the vacuum pump is to be efficient for moisture removal. To increase the ambient temperature under the hood, the automobile engine can be operated with the air conditioner turned off. The compressor, condenser, and some of the hoses may be heated sufficiently; however, some other parts, such as the evaporator and the receiver-drier, will not be greatly affected. Do not overheat components containing refrigerant. Hydrostatic pressure can build up rapidly and rupture the component.

Evacuating an automotive air conditioning system when the ambient temperature is below, say, 60°F (16°C) is generally very inefficient. To remove moisture at this temperature, the vacuum pump must pull a minimum of 29.4 in.hg (2.03 kPa absolute). Unless well maintained, many shop vacuum pumps will not reach the level required for adequate moisture removal at low temperatures.

Another method of moisture removal is the *sweep* or *triple evacuation* method. Although this method cannot remove all the moisture, it should be sufficient to reduce the moisture to a safe level if the system is otherwise sound and a new drier is installed.

# Recovery Systems

There are many manufacturers of refrigerant recovery systems, each of which produces several models. When considering recovery equipment, there are three terms to become familiar with: **recover**, **reclaim**, and **recycle**.

One of the major points of the Clean Air Act was to ensure recovery and recycling of refrigerants, specifically R-12, instead of allowing it to be vented into the atmosphere. A service facility that services mobile air conditioning systems must have the proper recovery/recycling equipment under the EPA Clean Air Act, or it will be charged with "Intent to Vent." The SAE, in conjunction with the EPA, has established guidelines for the recovery and recycling of both R-134a and R-12 refrigerants.

❑ Effective January 1, 1992, no service facility could service mobile air conditioning systems unless it acquired approved recovery/recycling equipment and trained and certified service personnel performing said services.

❑ Recovery of R-134a became mandatory in November 1995.

❑ Recycling of R-134a became mandatory on January 29, 1998.

Beginning in 1992, R-134a was phased into new vehicle production air conditioning systems. With the 1994 model year, all vehicles sold in the United States contained the ozone friendly refrigerant R-134a.

❑ Must have dedicated recovery/recycling equipment for each alternative refrigerant serviced. Refrigerants may not be mixed, and the term *drop-in refrigerant* used by some alternative refrigerants should not imply refrigerants can be mixed. The EPA does not allow the mixing of any refrigerant.

○ Contaminated refrigerant must also be recovered into a dedicated recovery unit for future redemption.

❑ Beginning on June 1, 1998, refrigerant blends may be recycled, provided that recycling equipment meets Underwriter's Laboratories (UL) standard and refrigerant is returned to the vehicle from which it was removed.

## Record Keeping Requirements

The EPA has established that service shops must maintain records of the name and address of any facility to which refrigerant is sent. In addition, if refrigerant is recovered and sent to a reclamation facility, the name and address of that facility must be kept on file. Service shops are also required to maintain records (on-site) showing that all service technicians are properly certified.

Service shops must certify to the EPA that they have purchased or acquired and are properly using approved refrigerant recovery equipment for both R-12 and R-134a. This is accomplished by sending a form to the EPA certifying that the shop owns the equipment. This only has to be done once, and it is not required if additional equipment is purchased. Shops must also certify that each person using the equipment has been properly trained, and that technicians who repair or service R-12 and R-134a have been certified by an EPA-approved organization. Additional information regarding EPA regulations and how they relate to the mobile air conditioning industry may be found at the EPA Web site: www.epa.gov/ozone/title6/609.

To **recover** is to remove refrigerant in any condition from a system and transfer it to an external storage container without necessarily testing or processing it in any way.

To **reclaim** is to process used refrigerant to new product specifications by means that may include distillation. This process requires that a chemical analysis of the refrigerant be performed to determine that appropriate product specifications are met. This term implies the use of equipment for processes and procedures usually available only at a reprocessing facility.

To **recycle** is to clean refrigerant for reuse by oil separation and pass through other devices such as filter-driers to reduce moisture, acidity, and particulate matter. Recycling applies to procedures usually accomplished in the repair shop or at a local service facility.

### Recover

To recover refrigerant is to remove it in any condition and store it in an external container without necessarily processing it further. Under certain conditions, this refrigerant is returned to the system from which it was removed. It may also be sold to a reclamation center where it is processed to new product specifications.

### Reclaim

To reclaim refrigerant is to remove it from a system and reprocess it to new product specifications (ARI 700-88 standards). Analytical testing is required. This is an off-site procedure by a laboratory equipped to make such tests.

### Recycle

To recycle refrigerant is to remove it from a system and reduce contaminants by oil separation and filter drying to remove moisture, acid, and particulate. This is an on-site procedure, and analytical testing is not required.

## The Equipment

The make and model of the equipment selected for recovering and recycling refrigerants should be based on the needs of the service facility. For example, if the air conditioning service is occasional, a simple recovery unit like the one shown in Figure 6-11 should suffice. This inexpensive unit can recover about 0.5 lb. (0.236 mL) per minute. A separate recovery unit, pictured in Figure 6-12, frees up the service technician for other service work while a system is being evacuated. This unit costs about twice as much as the first unit and removes about 0.78 lb. (0.368 mL) per minute. Neither system, however, can be used for recycling.

Many recovery systems are designed to be used for CFC and HCFC recovery only. Some recovery systems may be used for both CFC and HFC refrigerant. These systems have special provisions to prevent mixing the refrigerants. The automotive service technician is primarily concerned with two refrigerants: R-12, a CFC, and R-134a, an HFC. For full service, if a CFC/HFC combination system is not available, the service facility must have two recovery systems: one dedicated for R-12 service (Figure 6-13) and another dedicated for R-134a service (Figure 6-14). This may seem to be an expensive investment, but considering the high cost of refrigerants, an early payback may be realized.

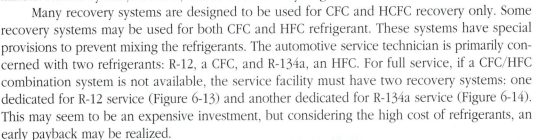
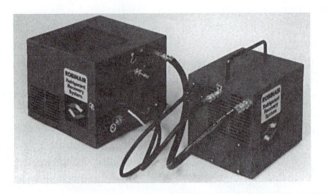

**Figure 6-11** A mechanical refrigerant pump used to recover refrigerant.

Recovered refrigerant should not be used in another application unless it is first reclaimed.

Most service centers impose a recovery fee in addition to their regular charges.

**Shop Manual**
Chapter 6, page 195

Figure 6-12 A typical recovery unit.

Figure 6-13 An R-12 recovery unit suitable for automotive service.

Figure 6-14 An R-134a recovery unit suitable for automotive service.

Many systems manufactured for automotive air conditioning system service are used for recovering, evacuating, recycling, and recharging. Some recover–recycle–recharge systems use a microprocessor to automatically control the functions of the equipment. This eliminates the need for personal attention and the requirement for a separate vacuum pump and charging station. Some recycling machines have automatic air purge capabilities to detect and vent air from the storage cylinder.

A single-pass recycling machine cleans and filters refrigerant as it is being recovered. A multipass recycling machine recovers the refrigerant in one operation and recycles it through multiple filters, driers, and separators in another operation.

It is important that the manufacturer's maintenance and operational instructions be followed for optimum equipment performance and service. Improper start-up procedures, for example, may induce unwanted air into the system.

## PDA Diagnostics

A personal digital assistant (PDA) has become as common as the cell phone, and today PDAs are now part of the automotive diagnostic industry. There are programs and interfaces that allow you to use them as onboard diagnostic scan tools, digital storage oscilloscopes, and air conditioning system diagnostic and testing tools.

The PDA tool is not intended to replace the other air conditioning service equipment that you have but is just one more tool to aid you in quickly and accurately diagnosing and repairing air conditioning problems. One advantage of these tools is that they take a systematic approach to testing and analyzing an air conditioning system. A systematic approach generally only comes with years of experience, and even then no two technicians approach a problem in the same way.

One of these systems is produced by Neutronics and is called the Master A/C System Technician. This is an all-in-one tool for identifying refrigerant and checking the system pressures. It also provides a PDA interface with updatable cartridges for step-by-step diagnostic procedures.

**AUTHOR'S NOTE:** Being a service technician today involves more than just staying up to date on current service trends and technology. It also involves knowing what changes are occurring at both the state and federal levels and how these changes affect your ability to perform certain services on vehicles. To stay in tune with changes in our industry, you must read trade journals and join trade organizations. Two good organizations to look into are Service Technicians Society (STS), www.sts.sae.org and Mobile Air Conditioning Society (MACS), www.macsw.org.

## Charging the System with Refrigerant

Charging the air conditioning system with the correct type and quantity of refrigerant is, perhaps, the most important service procedure that the technician will perform. Proper operation and durability of the system may be directly linked to this procedure. An improperly charged system not only results in less-than-maximum performance, it also leads to inaccurate diagnosis that may result in unnecessary repairs. Before charging an air conditioning system, determine the type of refrigerant.

An undercharged system will

❏ Result in inadequate cooling under high load conditions.

❏ Cause the compressor to cycle rapidly due to the action of the clutch cycling pressure switch (if equipped).

❏ Aid in early compressor failure.

Higher-than-normal high-side pressure does not necessarily indicate an overcharge of refrigerant.

**Shop Manual**
Chapter 6, page 198

An overcharged system will result in

❑ Higher-than-normal high-side pressures.
❑ Reduced cooling capacity under any load condition.
❑ Improperly operating pressure controls.
❑ Early compressor failure.

There are several generally accepted methods of charging an automotive air conditioning system. Not all methods, however, are recommended for all systems. The manufacturer's specifications and procedures should be followed to avoid problems. The air conditioning system may be charged by weight, chart or graph, low-side and high-side pressure, and superheat. The correct charge is critical for an R-134a system. Many recommend initially undercharging by 5 to 10 percent, testing system performance, then adding refrigerant, if necessary.

# Diagnosis

Air conditioning problems may often be diagnosed quickly simply by checking the function of the components of the system. The following should be on the basic checklist for quick diagnosis:

❑ Belt tension
❑ Clutch operation
❑ Radiator/condenser fan operation
❑ Evaporator blower operation
❑ Proper airflow from registers
❑ Observe sight glass, R-12 systems
❑ Refrigerant charge
❑ Suction line
❑ Liquid line
❑ Service valves/ports
❑ Lines, hoses, and connections

## Belt Tension

Is the belt tight? A loose belt will slip under the heavy heat loads of the air conditioning system. Also, if it is a serpentine belt (Figure 6-15), another defective accessory component, such as the alternator, may cause the belt to slip. This is also a good opportunity to check the belt for wear, cracks, and glazing, a sign of early failure.

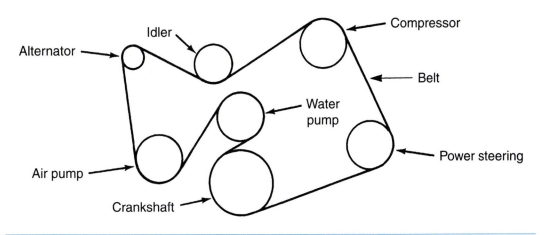

Figure 6-15 Routing of a typical serpentine belt.

## Clutch

Determine if the clutch is engaged but slipping, or if the belt is slipping on the clutch. Both appear nearly the same.

With the engine running and the air conditioning controls set for maximum cooling, make sure that the clutch is fully engaged. If it does not engage or if it slips, check for low voltage at the clutch coil. Other problems that could affect clutch operation are:

❑ Outside ambient air temperature that is too cold

❑ Open high-pressure switch

❑ Open low-pressure switch

❑ Low refrigerant charge

❑ Excessive clutch air gap

❑ Thermostat that is out of adjustment

Also, note the condition of the clutch mating surfaces. If they are covered with grease or oil, a defective compressor shaft seal may be indicated.

## Radiator-Condenser Fan

On car lines equipped with water-pump-mounted direct-drive fans, the fan should turn when the engine is running. If it does not, the belt may be slipping due to a defective (seized) water pump. Whatever the reason, the problem must be corrected.

On some car lines equipped with an electric fan (Figure 6-16), the fan will operate any time the compressor clutch is engaged. On others, the fan only operates during high-temperature conditions. If the fan does not operate as required, check for:

❑ A blown fuse or open circuit breaker

❑ A defective high-pressure switch

❑ An inoperative relay (some models)

❑ A defective wiring or connector

An inoperative fan may result in serious problems associated with high head pressure at slow and idle engine speeds, such as compressor lockup (seizure) or hose rupture.

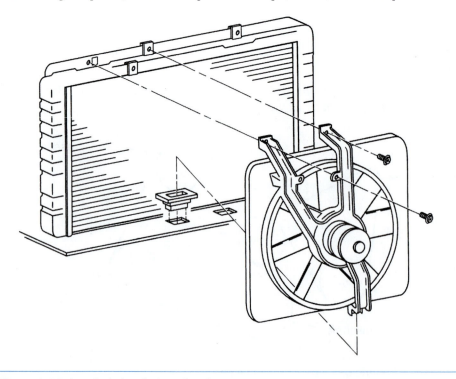

**Figure 6-16** A typical electrical cooling fan.

## Blower Operation

The blower motor should operate any time the air conditioning system controls are in the ON position. If it does not, the cause of the problem must be located and corrected. If it operates, make sure that it operates in all speeds. Most have at least a HI-MED-LO speed, while some have two or more MED speeds. A typical blower and motor assembly is shown (Figure 6-17).

## Airflow

Check to be sure that the air is flowing from the proper registers (Figure 6-18) in all modes. Refer to Chapter 9 of this manual for a description of the proper airflow for the different modes of operation.

## Sight Glass

A sight glass is a window into the high-side liquid line of the refrigerant system. It is generally located on top of the receiver-drier or in the high-side liquid line. The sight glass should be clear when the compressor clutch is engaged and the system is operating properly. This check may be

The sight glass, if present, may be a part of the receiver-drier or it may be found in the liquid line.

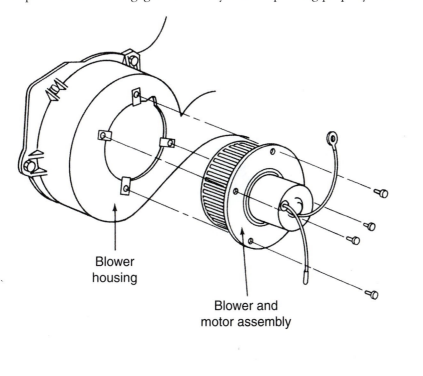

Blower housing

Blower and motor assembly

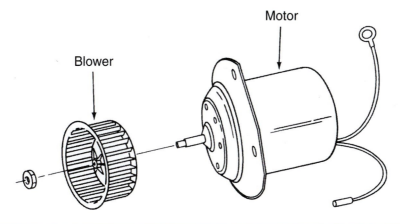

Motor

Blower

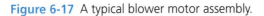

**Figure 6-17** A typical blower motor assembly.

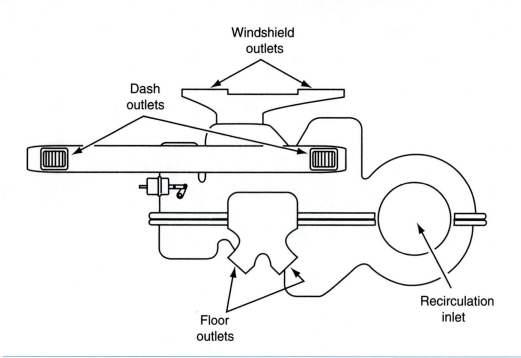

Figure 6-18 Details of the case/duct system.

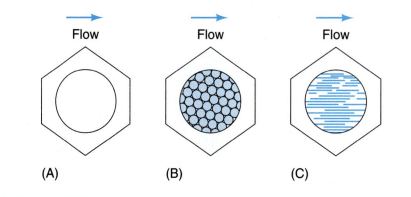

Figure 6-19 Conditions found in a sight glass: (A) clear; (B) foamy or bubbly; (C) cloudy.

made on many, but not all, R-12 systems. Seldom is a sight glass (Figure 6-19) included in an R-134a system because the properties of the oil will erroneously indicate a low charge. Continuous bubbles in the sight glass generally indicate air trapped in the system. Continuous foam indicates that the charge is low, and oil streaks indicate no liquid refrigerant in the system. When the compressor clutch cycles off and on, it is normal to observe bubbles for a short period of time, particularly when the compressor clutch cycles off.

## System Leaks

Visually inspect all hoses, tubing, components, fittings, and service ports for refrigerant leaks. Generally, but not always, a leak will be marked by a trace of refrigeration oil.

## Suction Line

The suction line is the hose or line that connects the evaporator outlet to the compressor inlet. It should feel cool to the touch when the air conditioning system is in operation. If it does not feel cool, install the manifold and gauge set to perform a performance test.

A second suction line may be found between the evaporator outlet and the accumulator inlet.

## Liquid Line

The liquid line connects the condenser or receiver-drier outlet to the evaporator or metering device inlet. It should be warm or even hot to the touch. If it is not warm, install a manifold and gauge set and perform a performance test. It must be noted, however, that on some car line models, such as Jeep's Grand Cherokee and certain General Motors car lines, the metering device is at the outlet of the condenser. The orifice tube is located at the condenser outlet to reduce or eliminate a hissing noise problem caused by refrigerant passing through it. The line between the metering device outlet and the evaporator inlet, in this case, will be cool.

A second liquid line may be found between the metering device outlet and the evaporator inlet.

## Service Ports

Service valve ports (Figure 6-20) are often a problem area for leaking. They are often neglected when leak testing because hoses are generally connected to them. The hose(s) should be disconnected to ensure that no refrigerant is leaking past a defective valve seat. The Schrader-type valve may be replaced if it is found to be leaking. Note that there is a distinct difference in the service port used for R-12 as compared with R-134a. In an R-12 system, the low- and high-side ports will be the same size or the high-side port will be smaller. The opposite is true for an R-134a system which has a larger high-side service port.

Learn to recognize the difference in the two types of fittings.

**Figure 6-20** A typical R-134a service valve port cap.

**Figure 6-21** A leak at a line fitting detected with the use of a soap solution.

## Hoses and Fittings

Throughout the years of automotive air conditioning system service, refrigerant hoses have been the greatest cause of refrigerant leakage problems. Since the introduction and requirement of barrier-type refrigerant hoses, however, the problem has been greatly reduced.

The problem of leaks still exists at the fittings (Figure 6-21). This is particularly true for hoses equipped with spring lock couplers. When replacing fittings, gaskets, or O-rings, be sure to use the proper component. For example, an O-ring may have a round, oval, or square profile. Also, there may be one or two O-rings used on a particular fitting. It must also be noted that some O-rings are refrigerant specific: an R-12 O-ring may not be used on an R-134a system and vice versa. There are O-rings available, however, that are compatible with both refrigerants.

## Summary

- ❑ The least expensive method of leak testing is using a commercially available soap solution.
- ❑ Moisture collects in an air conditioning system during service procedures and improper or careless service.
- ❑ Moisture mixed with refrigerant and oil forms corrosive acids and sludge in the system.
- ❑ Refrigerant must be recovered, not vented, as prescribed by the EPA.
- ❑ Manufacturers' procedures and specifications should be followed when charging an air conditioning system with oil or refrigerant.
- ❑ Many system malfunctions can be diagnosed by visual inspection.

**Terms to Know**

Absorb

Cross-contaminated

Halide

Halogen

Hydrochloric acid

Inject

Moisture

Pump down

Reclaim

Recover

Recycle

Significant New
   Alternative Policy
   (SNAP)

# Review Questions

## Short Answer Essays

1. Explain how moisture enters the system.
2. Describe one type of commonly used leak detector.
3. Is it important to maintain a moisture-free system? Why?
4. How is a system charged with refrigerant?
5. How is the temperature/pressure chart used for system diagnosis?
6. What is the acceptable method of adding dye to the system?
7. Briefly describe how a halide leak detector will react when it comes in contact with raw refrigerant.
8. Define the term *moisture*.
9. What are two rules of developing clean work habits?
10. Describe the process of removing moisture by vacuum.

## Fill-in-the-Blanks

1. A _____ type of leak warrants the use of a dye trace solution.
2. The _____ method of leak detection is for an R-12 system only.
3. The maximum moisture content allowable in new refrigerant is _____ .
4. The _____ part of the system attracts the most moisture.
5. A _____ acid is formed by the chemical combination of refrigerant and moisture.
6. The symbol _____ (English) is used to denote a vacuum pressure.
7. The sensitivity of the electronic leak detector is _____ per year.
8. The pressure 0 in. Hg or 0 psig is equal to _____ on the metric scale gauge.
9. In Denver, Colorado, water ($H_2O$) boils at a temperature of _____ .
10. A compressor clutch may be controlled with the use of a _____ or _____ switch.

## Multiple Choice

1. O-rings are being discussed:
   *Technician A* says that O-rings designated for CFC service may be used for HFC service.
   *Technician B* says that O-rings designated for HFC service may be used for CFC service.
   Who is correct?
   A. A only    C. Both A and B
   B. B only    D. Neither A nor B

2. Moisture removal is being discussed:
   *Technician A* says that a system should be evacuated for a minimum of one-half hour.
   *Technician B* says that a vacuum pump should be allowed to run for as long as four hours.
   Who is correct?
   A. A only    C. Both A and B
   B. B only    D. Neither A nor B

3. Vacuum pump efficiency is being discussed:
   *Technician A* says that vacuum pump efficiency is greatest at sea level.
   *Technician B* says that altitude has little or no effect on vacuum pump efficiency.
   Who is correct?
   A. A only    C. Both A and B
   B. B only    D. Neither A nor B

4. Air conditioning system contamination is being discussed:
   *Technician A* says that air and moisture in an R-12 (CFC-12) air conditioning system is considered contamination that must be removed.
   *Technician B* says that refrigerant R-134a (HFC-134a) must be more than 96 percent pure to not be considered contaminated.
   Who is correct?
   A. A only    C. Both A and B
   B. B only    D. Neither A nor B

5. Fluorescent leak detector scanner solution is being discussed:
   *Technician A* says once introduced into the system, it cannot be removed.
   *Technician B* says a fluorescent light is required for detecting a leak.
   Who is correct?
   A. A only    C. Both A and B
   B. B only    D. Neither A nor B

6. *Technician A* says that a low charge of refrigerant will cause rapid clutch cycling in a cycling clutch system.
   *Technician B* says that a thermostat out of adjustment will cause the same problem.
   Who is correct?
   A. A only    C. Both A and B
   B. B only    D. Neither A nor B

7. *Technician A* says that a sight glass is often found in an R-12 system.
   *Technician B* says that a sight glass is seldom found in an R-134a system.
   Who is correct?
   A. A only    C. Both A and B
   B. B only    D. Neither A nor B

8. *Technician A* says that service ports may be a source of leaks.
   *Technician B* says that hoses are sometimes a source of leaks.
   Who is correct?
   A. A only    C. Both A and B
   B. B only    D. Neither A nor B

9. *Technician A* says that adequate moisture may be removed from the system by purging with clean refrigerant.
   *Technician B* says that the system compressor may be used to successfully remove moisture from the system.
   Who is correct?
   A. A only    C. Both A and B
   B. B only    D. Neither A nor B

10. *Technician A* says that an overcharged system will result in lower-than-normal low-side pressures.
    *Technician B* says that an overcharged system will result in a slight increase in cooling capacity, but only under low load conditions.
    Who is correct?
    A. A only    C. Both A and B
    B. B only    D. Neither A nor B

# The Refrigeration System

Upon completion and review of this chapter, you should be able to:

❑ Diagnose six system malfunctions by gauge readings.

❑ Identify the low and high side of the air conditioning system.

❑ Read and understand temperature-pressure charts.

❑ Discuss temperature-pressure relationships.

❑ Identify differences between R-12 (CFC-12) and R-134a (HFC-134a) systems.

❑ Identify differences between thermostatic expansion valve (TXV) and fixed orifice tube (FOT) systems.

❑ Understand the proper handling of refrigerants.

❑ Understand the proper handling of refrigeration oil.

## Introduction

Study the air conditioning system diagram (Figure 7-1), and note the dividing line between the high side and low side of the system and the manifold and gauge set connected into the system.

As illustrated, any condition (translated to pressure) that occurs in the low side of the system will be indicated on the low-side (compound) gauge. At the same time, any condition in the high side of the system will be indicated on the high-side (pressure) gauge.

There is a direct relationship between the pressure and temperature of refrigerant. For any given pressure, there is a corresponding temperature. For example, if the pressure of the low side of the system is 35 psig (241 kPa), the temperature of the evaporating refrigerant will be 38°F (3.3°C) for Refrigerant-12 and 40°F (4.4°C) for Refrigerant-134a. This is the temperature of the refrigerant, not the temperature of the air passing through the evaporator. Actual air temperature will be several degrees warmer. For convenience of illustration, a typical temperature-pressure chart is given in Figure 7-2.

## System Diagnosis

Knowing the temperature of the ambient air entering the condenser, the normal high-side pressure can be determined from the temperature-pressure chart. This assumes that the system is operating properly and the low-side pressure is correct. For example, if the ambient temperature is 85°F (29.4°C), the proper high-side pressure for an R-12 system should be 172 psig (1,186 kPa); 181 psig (1,248 kPa) for an R-134a system. Allowances must be made in all readings to provide for slight errors in thermometers and gauges.

There are seven basic conditions for the automotive air conditioning system: one condition indicates normal operation, and six conditions indicate a system **malfunction**. Following is a brief description of system function or malfunction for each of the seven conditions. We will assume that the outside ambient air temperature is 90°F (32°C).

**Malfunction** refers to a component's failing to work as designed.

There are no valid temperature-pressure relationships for a malfunctioning system, such as an undercharge of refrigerant.

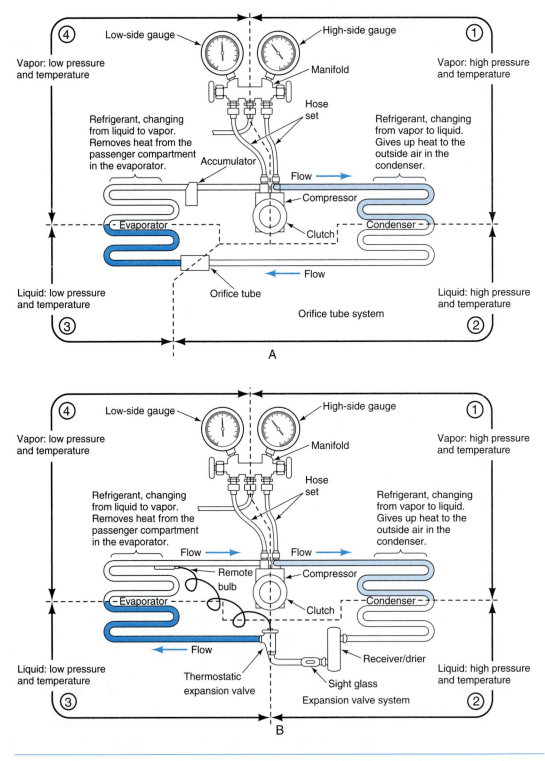

**Figure 7-1** Typical automotive air conditioning system: (A) orifice tube; (B) expansion valve.

## TEMPERATURE-PRESSURE CHART

| TEMPERATURE | | CFC-12 PRESSURE | | HFC-134A PRESSURE | | TEMPERATURE | | CFC-12 PRESSURE | | HFC-134A PRESSURE | |
|---|---|---|---|---|---|---|---|---|---|---|---|
| °F | °C | PSIG | KPA | PSIG | KPA | °F | °C | PSIG | KPA | PSIG | KPA |
| –30 | –23.3 | *5.5 | 37.9 | *9.7 | 66.9 | 55 | 12.8 | 52.1 | 359.2 | 51.3 | 353.7 |
| –25 | –31.7 | *2.3 | 15.9 | *6.8 | 46.9 | 60 | 15.6 | 57.7 | 397.8 | 57.3 | 395.1 |
| –20 | –28.9 | 0.6 | 4.1 | *3.6 | 24.8 | 65 | 18.3 | 63.8 | 439.9 | 64.1 | 442.0 |
| –15 | –26.1 | 2.4 | 16.5 | *0.2 | 1.4 | 70 | 21.1 | 70.2 | 484.0 | 71.2 | 490.9 |
| –10 | –23.3 | 4.5 | 31.0 | 2.0 | 13.8 | 75 | 23.9 | 77.0 | 530.9 | 78.7 | 542.6 |
| –5 | –20.6 | 6.7 | 46.2 | 4.2 | 29.0 | 80 | 26.7 | 84.2 | 580.6 | 86.8 | 598.5 |
| 0 | –17.8 | 9.2 | 63.4 | 6.5 | 44.8 | 85 | 29.4 | 91.8 | 633.0 | 95.3 | 657.1 |
| 5 | –15.0 | 11.8 | 81.4 | 9.1 | 62.7 | 90 | 32.2 | 99.8 | 688.1 | 104.4 | 719.8 |
| 10 | –12.2 | 14.6 | 100.7 | 11.9 | 82.1 | 95 | 35.0 | 108.3 | 746.7 | 114.0 | 186.0 |
| 15 | –9.4 | 17.7 | 122.0 | 15.3 | 105.5 | 100 | 37.8 | 117.2 | 808.1 | 124.2 | 856.4 |
| 20 | –6.7 | 21.0 | 144.8 | 18.4 | 126.9 | 105 | 40.6 | 126.6 | 872.9 | 135.0 | 930.8 |
| 25 | –3.9 | 24.6 | 169.6 | 22.0 | 151.7 | 110 | 43.3 | 136.4 | 940.5 | 146.4 | 1009.4 |
| 30 | –1.1 | 28.5 | 196.5 | 26.1 | 180.0 | 115 | 46.1 | 146.8 | 1012.2 | 157.5 | 1086.0 |
| 35 | 1.7 | 32.6 | 224.8 | 30.4 | 209.6 | 120 | 48.9 | 157.7 | 1087.3 | 171.2 | 1180.4 |
| 40 | 4.4 | 37.0 | 255.1 | 35.1 | 242.0 | 125 | 51.7 | 169.1 | 1166.0 | 184.6 | 1272.8 |
| 45 | 7.2 | 41.7 | 287.5 | 40.1 | 276.5 | 130 | 54.4 | 180.0 | 1241.1 | 198.7 | 1370.0 |
| 50 | 10.0 | 46.7 | 322.0 | 45.5 | 313.7 | | | | | | |

**Figure 7-2** A typical temperature-pressure chart for R-12 and R-134a in English and metric values.

## Condition One: Normal Operation (Figure 7-3)

❑ Low-side gauge: Normal pressure
    ❑ R-12 (CFC-12): 32–33 psig (221–228 kPa)
    ❑ R-134a (HFC-134a): 30–31 psig (207–214 kPa)

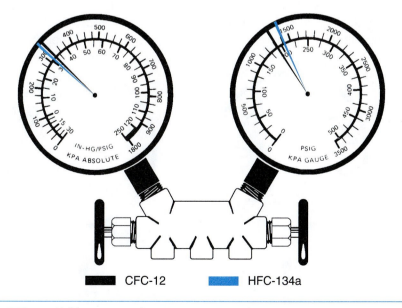

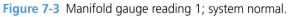

**Figure 7-3** Manifold gauge reading 1; system normal.

❏ High-side gauge: Normal pressure
   ❏ R-12 (CFC-12): 185–190 psig (1,276–1,310 kPa)
   ❏ R-134a (HFC-134a): 204–210 psig (1,407–1,448 kPa)

Assuming a cycling-clutch system, the desired "average" temperature of the evaporator should be about 35°F (1.7°C). To achieve a "theoretical average" temperature, the thermostat should cycle the compressor clutch OFF at about 27°F (–2.8°C) and back ON at about 39°F (3.9°C). According to the R-12 temperature-pressure chart, the gauge reading should be a low of 26 psig (179 kPa) and a high of 36 psig (248 kPa). For R-134a systems, the off cycle should be at 24 psig (165 kPa) and the on cycle at 37 psig (255 kPa).

It should be noted that the theoretical average is seldom accomplished in actual operation. Therefore, it is suggested that manufacturers' specifications be consulted for the operating range of any particular vehicle.

Actually, the concern is with air temperature, not with refrigerant temperature. A low of 14–15 psig (96.5–103.4 kPa) and a high of 40–50 psig (275.8–344.7 kPa), then, is a more realistic indication for the low-side gauge.

The high-side gauge should indicate pressure shown in the temperature-pressure chart for any given ambient temperature, plus or minus a few psig (kPa).

## Condition Two: Insufficient Cooling (Figure 7-4)

❏ Low-side gauge: Low pressure
   ❏ R-12 (CFC-12): 15 psig (103 kPa)
   ❏ R-134a (HFC-134a): 12 psig (83 kPa)
❏ High-side gauge: Normal to slightly low pressure
   ❏ R-12 (CFC-12): 190 psig (1,310 kPa)
   ❏ R-134a (HFC-134a): 208 psig (1,434 kPa)

There are three major possible causes for this condition. They are as follows:

1. A thermostat that is improperly adjusted (temperature), out of adjustment (mechanical), or defective
2. A **restriction** in the low side of the system
3. Moisture in the system

The **control thermostat** may be defective or improperly adjusted. It must be adjusted so its electrical contacts will open at the desired low temperature to allow the clutch to cycle off. The differential must be adjusted so the clutch will cycle back on after a predetermined temperature rise.

Average: A single value that represents the median.

Moisture in the system causes harmful acids.

A restriction is a blockage in the air conditioning system caused by a pinched line, foreign matter, or moisture freeze-up.

A control thermostat is a temperature-actuated electrical switch used to cycle the compressor clutch on and off, thereby controlling the air conditioning system temperature.

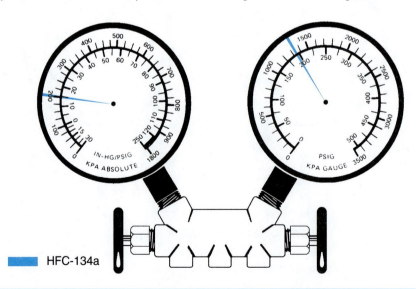

HFC-134a

**Figure 7-4** Manifold gauge reading indicating insufficient cooling due to improperly adjusted temperature control, restriction in the low side, or moisture in the system.

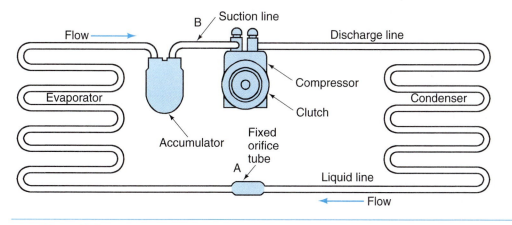

**Figure 7-5** Look for a restriction in the low side of the system between the metering device outlet (A) and the compressor inlet (B).

Another indication of a defective thermostat is that the evaporator coil may be icing over. Ice on the coil blocks the flow of air passing through it. If the system works fine for awhile and then becomes warmer, there may be moisture in the system. If reduced airflow is also noted, the evaporator freeze-up is indicated. If evaporator freeze-up is suspected, check for a frozen evaporator line and/or the compressor clutch not cycling. Causes for this condition are:

1. A defective cycling clutch switch that is stuck in the ON position.
2. An improperly positioned evaporator core sensor (fin sensor) that is not touching the evaporator core or not inserted into the fins.

There may be a restriction in the low side of the system (Figure 7-5) between the **metering device** outlet and the compressor inlet. The screen at the inlet of the metering device may be clogged. If there is excess moisture in the system, it will collect and freeze in the screen at the inlet of the metering device. Refer to Figure 7-1a; restriction will be located in quadrant 3 or quadrant 4.

This condition may be checked by carefully feeling the receiver-drier or condenser outlet, along the liquid line, and finally the metering device inlet. All should be warm. If any part is cool, a restriction is indicated at that point. Only the inlet of the metering device should be warm; the outlet should be cool. In fact, the outlet of the metering device is perhaps the coolest part of the system under normal operating conditions.

If the inlet screen of the expansion valve (Figure 7-6) or the orifice tube (Figure 7-7) is found to be the problem, either may be cleaned. After cleaning the screen, the receiver-drier or

A **metering device** is a component that regulates the proper amount of refrigerant in the evaporator. The two common types for automotive applications are the thermostatic expansion valve (TXV) and the fixed orifice tube (FOT).

A restriction in the system is generally "marked" by a temperature difference.

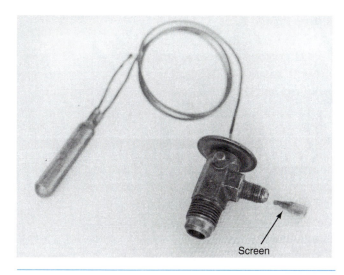

**Figure 7-6** Inlet screen of thermostatic expansion valve.

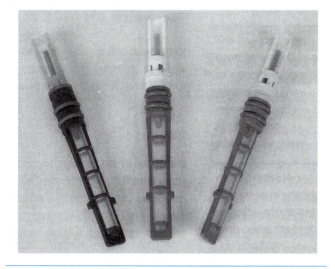

**Figure 7-7** Orifice tube showing inlet screen.

**Shop Manual**
Chapter 6,
page 191

**Shop Manual**
Chapter 6,
page 198

accumulator must be replaced. Also, the receiver-drier must be replaced if the restriction proves to be at its outlet. This is true even though the liquid line and expansion valve inlet screen may be clean. A temperature change at the outlet of the accumulator is expected and does not indicate a problem.

Another problem that can cause the symptoms of Condition Two is moisture in the system. If there is moisture in the system that is not absorbed by the desiccant in the receiver-drier or accumulator, it may freeze at the metering device inlet. The inlet may then become very cold, the same symptom as a clogged inlet screen. To determine if moisture is the problem, turn the air conditioner off for 10 to 15 minutes, then turn it back on. If the gauge reading immediately goes to an abnormal condition, the screen is probably clogged. If the gauge reading is normal for a few minutes, then goes to abnormal, there is probably excess moisture in the system. This condition is corrected by replacing the receiver-drier or accumulator.

Before condemning a component, though, make sure the system is fully charged with refrigerant. A slightly low system charge will cause rapid cycling of the air conditioning compressor clutch when the engine speed is raised. On noncycling-clutch systems (variable displacement compressors), the low side will be low (15–30 psig for R-134a) and the high-side will also be low (110–150 psig for R-134a). You may also notice foamy bubbles in the sight glass if equipped (R-12), and the evaporator outlet line will be warm.

## Condition Three: Insufficient Cooling or No Cooling (Figure 7-8)

❏ Low-side gauge: Very low pressure to low pressure
   ❏ R-12 (CFC-12): 18 psig (124 kPa)
   ❏ R-134a (HFC-134a): 15 psig (103 kPa)
❏ High-side gauge: Low pressure
   ❏ R-12 (CFC-12): 130–135 psig (896 kPa)
   ❏ R-134a (HFC-134a): 139–144 psig (958–993 kPa)

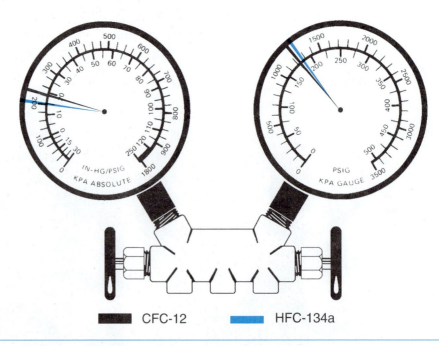

**Figure 7-8** Manifold gauge reading indicating insufficient or no cooling due to undercharge of refrigerant, clogged metering device inlet screen, defective metering device, or excessive moisture in the system.

If the low-side gauge pressure is moderately low, the most probable cause is an undercharge of refrigerant. If the low-side gauge pressure is very low, possibly in a vacuum, there are four other possible causes, all relating to the metering device:

1. Clogged inlet screen
2. Defective valve or tube
3. Moisture in the system
4. High-side restriction

Loss of refrigerant resulting in an undercharge is usually caused by a leak. This condition may also be noted by bubbles in the sight glass, if so equipped. To correct this condition, the cause of the leak must be located and repaired. The system must then be properly evacuated and charged with refrigerant.

The screen in the metering device may be clogged or there may be moisture in the system, as outlined in Condition Two.

An expansion valve may be defective and completely closed. The most probable cause for this condition is that the remote sensing bulb may have lost its charge of volatile gas. If this is the cause, the valve will not regulate (open), and it must be replaced.

If the problem still cannot be found, look for a restriction in the high side before the metering device. Refer to Figure 7-1. The restriction will be located in quadrant 2 or quadrant 3. It should be noted that the gauge reading may be high if the restriction is found shortly after the low-side service fitting.

If there is a loss of refrigerant, there is a leak in the system.

**Shop Manual**
Chapter 7,
page 237

**Shop Manual**
Chapter 7,
page 238

## Condition Four: Insufficient Cooling or No Cooling (Figure 7-9)

❏ Low-side gauge: Low pressure
    ❏ R-12 (CFC-12): 22 psig (152 kPa)
    ❏ R-134a (HFC-134a): 20 psig (138 kPa)
❏ High-side gauge: High to extremely high pressure
    ❏ R-12 (CFC-12): 250 psig (1,724 kPa)
    ❏ R-134a (HFC-134a): 281 psig (1,937 kPa)

The most probable cause of this condition is a restriction in the high side of the system. The restriction may be anywhere from the compressor outlet to the receiver-drier or fixed orifice tube

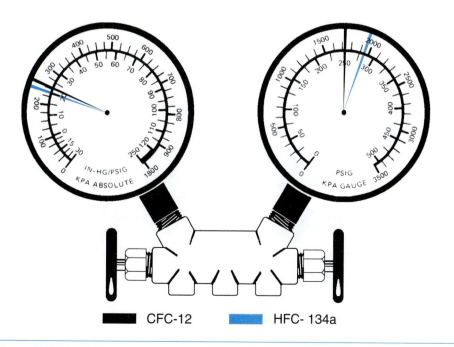

CFC-12      HFC-134a

**Figure 7-9** Manifold gauge reading indicating insufficient or no cooling due to a restriction in the high side of the system, such as a bent or kinked tube.

**Figure 7-10** A damaged return bend at the condensor inlet will result in very high high-side pressure.

inlet. The closer to the compressor, the higher the high-side gauge pressure will be. Refer to figure 7-1. The restriction will be located in quadrant 1 or quadrant 2.

A moderately high high-side pressure may indicate a clogged receiver-drier or liquid line. An extremely high pressure may indicate a restriction, such as a bent tube in the condenser closer to the compressor. The probable location of high-side restrictions is shown in Figure 7-10.

In any event, the restriction must be located and corrected. Often, a marked temperature change will be noted at the point of restriction. The upstream side of the restriction will be very hot while the downstream side will be cooler. High-side restrictions can cause extremely high temperatures. Be careful to avoid personal injury.

## Condition Five: Insufficient Cooling or No Cooling (Figure 7-11)

❑ Low-side gauge: High pressure
    ❑ R-12 (CFC-12): 44 psig (303 kPa)
    ❑ R-134a (HFC-134a): 43 psig (296 kPa)

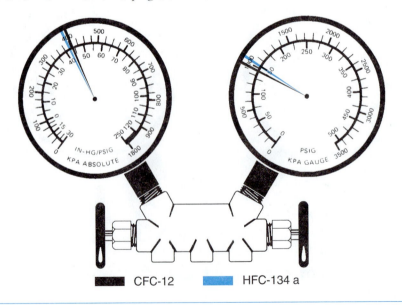

CFC-12        HFC-134 a

**Figure 7-11** Manifold gauge reading indicating insufficient or no cooling due to a defective clutch coil or temperature control. The condition may also be caused by a defective clutch or compressor.

❑ High-side gauge: Low pressure
  ❑ R-12 (CFC-12): 140 psig (965 kPa)
  ❑ R-134a (HFC-134a): 150 psig (1,034 kPa)

This problem may be caused by either an electrical or a mechanical condition. It may be caused electrically by a defective clutch coil or a defective thermostat. Also, inspect for defective:

**1.** Cycling switch
**2.** Pressure switch(es)
**3.** Ambient air temperature switch
**4.** Evaporator temperature sensor (fin sensor)

Mechanically, this condition may be caused by either of the following two problems:

**1.** A defective clutch
**2.** A defective compressor
  **a.** Valve plate(s)
  **b.** Head gasket(s)
  **c.** Broken piston ring

To determine if the problem is due to electrical or mechanical defects, if the air conditioner is operational, visually inspect the clutch center bolt to determine if the compressor crankshaft is turning properly. If it is turning properly, the problem is probably a defective compressor or valve plate assembly. If the compressor is turning erratically, disconnect the clutch wire and connect it to a digital multimeter (Figure 7-12). If there are at least 10.8 volts present required for proper clutch operation, the problem may be a defective clutch coil or clutch assembly. First, however, check to ensure that the clutch coil is properly grounded.

If the multimeter does not indicate at least 10.8 volts, the probable cause is a defective relay, electrical control device, or loose wire.

Also, listen for compressor noise, which is an indication of a defective compressor. If the problem is determined to be the compressor, the valve plate and/or gaskets may be defective. In either case, it will be necessary to remove the compressor head and valve plate assembly to determine and repair the cause or to replace the compressor.

A mechanical malfunction can cause an electrical malfunction.

**Shop Manual**
Chapter 7, page 235

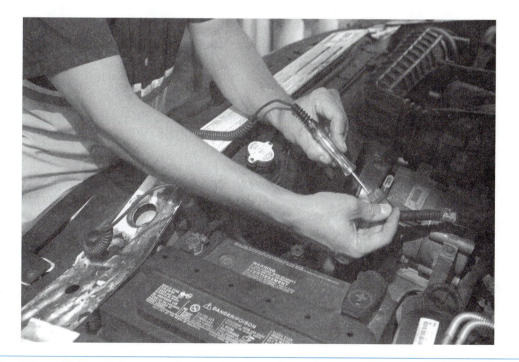

**Figure 7-12** Checking for voltage at the clutch coil connector.

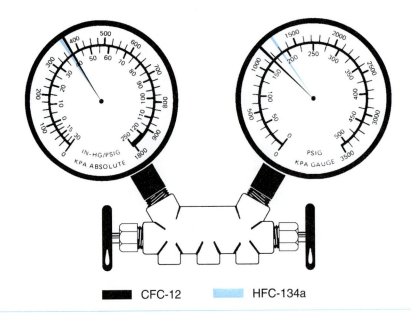

CFC-12    HFC-134a

**Figure 7-13** Manifold gauge reading indicating insufficient cooling due to a defective thermostatic valve or mispositioned remote bulb.

## Condition Six: Insufficient Cooling (Figure 7-13)

❑ Low-side gauge: High pressure
  ❑ R-12 (CFC-12): 40 psig (276 kPa)
  ❑ R-134a (HFC-134a): 38 psig (262 kPa)
❑ High-side gauge: Normal pressure
  ❑ R-12 (CFC-12): 170 psig (1,172 kPa)
  ❑ R-134a (HFC-134a): 184 psig (1,269 kPa)

This condition is found only in systems equipped with a thermostatic expansion valve (TXV). The condition, then, is caused by a defective expansion valve. Unlike expansion valve problems of Conditions Two and Three, however, this indication is that the expansion valve is stuck in the open position or is not closing because the **remote bulb** is not making proper contact with the evaporator outlet tube.

First, make sure that the remote bulb and the evaporator outlet tube are clean and that the two mating surfaces make good mechanical contact with each other. A small piece of cork (no-drip) tape wrapped around the remote bulb and the outlet tube helps to ensure good "sensing" conditions. This tape also acts as an insulator for the remote bulb, preventing it from sensing and being influenced by ambient air.

If the remote bulb is securely fastened to the outlet tube and the condition is not corrected, the expansion valve is probably defective and must be replaced.

One method for determining if the internally regulated thermostatic expansion valve is functioning correctly is to cool it externally with low pressure $CO_2$. With the use of a low pressure $CO_2$ regulator, allow the gas from a discharge line to be bled directly over the expansion valve. This will chill the valve, causing both a pressure and an evaporator temperature change.

If the TXV proves to be functioning properly and the problem still exists, check the heater control valve and the blend air door. A defective heater control valve may let heated coolant flow through the heater core, thereby creating an environment that promotes a higher-than-normal low-side pressure. Though not as likely, the blend air door, if mispositioned, may create a similar environment.

Determine if the system is TXV or FOT equipped before diagnostics.

A **remote bulb** is a sensing device connected to the expansion valve by a capillary tube. This device senses the evaporator outlet temperature and transmits pressure to the expansion valve control diaphragm for proper operation.

**Shop Manual**
Chapter 7,
pages 253–255

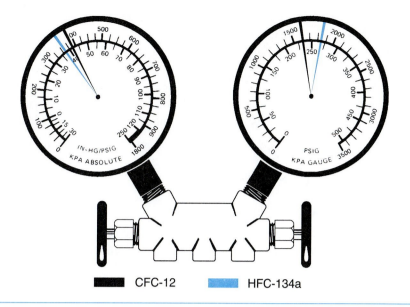

CFC-12    HFC-134a

**Figure 7-14** Manifold gauge reading indicating insufficient or no cooling due to air in the system, overcharge of lubricant or refrigerant, clogged condenser, defective cooling fan(s), or an overheating engine.

## Condition Seven: Insufficient or No Cooling (Figure 7-14)

❑ Low-side gauge: High pressure
    ❑ R-12 (CFC-12): 42 psig (290 kPa)
    ❑ R-134a (HFC-134a): 37 psig (255 kPa)
❑ High-side gauge: High to extremely high pressure
    ❑ R-12 (CFC-12): 235 psig (1,620 kPa)
    ❑ R-134a (HFC-134a): 263 psig (1,813 kPa)

There are several possible causes for this condition:

**1.** Air in the system
**2.** An overcharge (excess) of refrigerant
**3.** An overcharge (excess) of oil
**4.** Condenser air passages clogged
**5.** Defective cooling fan(s)
**6.** An overheating engine
**7.** Incorrect refrigerant
**8.** Contaminated refrigerant

A visual inspection of under-the-hood conditions should give a determination if the problem of Condition Seven is due to clogged condenser air passages or an overheating engine. If the problem is determined to be an excess of refrigerant, oil, or air in the system, it is most difficult to determine which of these is the cause.

If the condenser air passages are clogged, heat cannot be carried away. This will result in moderately high pressures and insufficient cooling. Condenser clogging is generally caused by dirt, leaves, bugs, or other foreign material lodged in the fins.

The condenser may be cleaned with a strong stream of detergent and water ($H_2O$) such as may be found at a do-it-yourself car wash. Whenever possible, if space between the radiator and condenser permits, clean the condenser in the opposite direction of the airflow. Take care not to damage the delicate tubes and fins of the radiator. Use *warm, not hot,* water.

If air or excessive refrigerant is in the system, recover, evacuate, and recharge the system.

When cleaning air conditioning components in a charged system, use cool or warm water only.

A defective or inoperative coolant fan can give the same symptoms as a blocked condenser in shop conditions. At road speeds, however, ram air may suffice for heat removal.

High **head pressure** may also be caused by a kinked hose or a restriction. The high-side restriction may be anywhere between the compressor outlet and receiver-drier or metering device inlet. See also Condition Four.

An overheating engine causes an additional heat load (ambient conditions) which, in turn, will cause high head pressure conditions. Overheating engines may be caused by:

❏ Loss of coolant
❏ Slipping belts
❏ Improper engine timing
❏ A defective water pump
❏ A defective thermostat and/or radiator cap

Engines and engine service are covered in the Delmar Learning's *Today's Technician* series *Automotive Engine Performance,* 3rd edition, and *Automotive Engine Repair and Rebuilding,* 2nd edition (Figure 7-15).

This condition may be caused by air in the system, which can result, for example, through a low-side leak. If the low side goes into a vacuum while running, ambient air will be drawn into the system. Many systems have a low-pressure switch to prevent the system operation in a vacuum. Improper evacuation or failure to evacuate the system before charging with refrigerant can also result in air contamination, as can using improperly recycled refrigerant.

This condition may also be caused by an overcharge of refrigerant. Excess refrigerant may be bled off using the standard practice procedures for recovering refrigerant. Since it is almost impossible to determine if the cause is air or excess refrigerant, it is advisable to recover, evacuate, and recharge the system.

Another cause for this condition is excessive oil in the compressor. If no oil has been added, however, this is not likely to be the problem.

**Shop Manual**
Chapter 6,
page 195

**Figure 7-15** Engine service and engine performance are covered in the *Today's Technician* series.

**Figure 7-16** Two types of refrigerant are used in the automotive air conditioning system: (A) R-12 and (B) R-134a.

# Refrigerant

**Shop Manual**
Chapter 2,
page 46

*Refrigerant* is the term used when referring to the fluid that is used in an automotive air conditioning system. By definition, refrigerant is "a gas used in mechanical refrigeration systems." Actually, there are many types of refrigerant in use today, depending on application (Figure 7-16). Refrigerant is any fluid or vapor that is used to transfer heat from one area or space to another. One may not think of water ($H_2O$) as a refrigerant, but, when used to remove engine heat from a vehicle, it is a refrigerant. As a matter of fact, water is assigned a refrigerant number: R-718. This refrigerant evaporates (boils) and condenses at 212°F (100°C) at sea level atmospheric pressure (14.696 psia or 101.3 kPa absolute). Refrigerant-12, which has been used in automotive air conditioning systems for many years, was also used on other applications, such as domestic refrigeration. Refrigerant-12, more commonly known as R-12 or CFC-12, has the highest human safety factor of any refrigerant available that is capable of withstanding high pressures and temperatures without deteriorating or decomposing. The boiling point of R-12 at sea level atmospheric pressure is −21.67°F (−29.8°C). Therefore, it must be kept contained to prevent it from immediately boiling away.

The basic chemical, a fluorinated hydrocarbon known as carbon tetrachloride ($CCl_4$) was selected. It met the requirements most closely with only a few minor changes. Carbon tetrachloride ($CCl_4$) consists of one atom of carbon (C) and four atoms of chlorine (Cl). To change carbon tetrachloride ($CCl_4$) into a suitable refrigerant, two of the chlorine (Cl) atoms were removed, and two atoms of fluorine (F) were introduced in their place. The new compound, known as dichlorodifluoromethane, is R-12. R-12 has many applications in various types of domestic and commercial refrigeration and air conditioning systems as well as automotive air conditioners. The chemical symbol for R-12 is $CCl_2F_2$. This means that one molecule of this refrigerant contains one atom of carbon, two atoms of chlorine, and two atoms of fluorine (Figure 7-17).

Until the late 1980s, R-12 was considered ideal for automotive use because of its relatively low operating pressures. Its stability at high and low operating temperatures is also desirable. It does not react with most metals such as iron (Fe), aluminum (Al), or copper (Cu). Liquid R-12, however, may cause discoloration of chrome (Cr) and stainless steel (SS) if large quantities are allowed to strike these surfaces.

Air is also a refrigerant: R-729.

Carbon tetrachloride ($CCl_4$), a cleaning agent, is not considered safe for personal use.

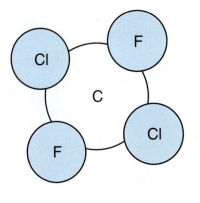

**Figure 7-17** The chemical structure of R-12 (CFC-12).

Hoses with liners are called "barrier" hoses.

R-12 is soluble in mineral oil and does not react with rubber. Some synthetic rubber compositions, however, may deteriorate if used as refrigerant hose. Synthetic rubber hose, such as Buna 'N', designated for refrigeration service is to be used. In applications since the late 1980s, refrigeration hoses have been lined with nylon, nytril, or polyamide veneer to provide a better barrier against leaks.

R-12 is odorless in concentrations of 20 percent or less. In greater concentrations, it can be detected by the faint odor of its original compound, carbon tetrachloride ($CCl_4$).

R-12 does not affect the taste, odor, or color of water or food. It was believed that it was not harmful to animal or plant life. Recent discoveries, however, dispel this belief.

Protocol: The plan of a scientific experiment or treatment.

Unfortunately, it has been determined that R-12 is, by far, the leading single cause of ozone depletion. The United States and 22 other countries signed an agreement in 1987 known as the Montreal Protocol. At that meeting, it was agreed that the production of chlorofluorocarbon (CFC) refrigerants would be phased out in a timely manner. The automotive air conditioning industry was the first to be regulated since it was found that the automotive industry is the greatest offender. It was determined that 30 percent of all R-12 released to the atmosphere is from mobile air conditioning systems.

The production of R-12 ended in the United States on December 31, 1995. Importing virgin R-12 into the United States from other countries is illegal, with the exception of limited quantities that are used for such medical purposes as metered-dose inhalers. It is, however, legal to import used and recovered R-12 under close scrutiny of the federal government. Those who wish to export R-12 to the United States must first petition the EPA with specific and verifiable information about its source. The industry, then, must now rely on surplus and recycled R-12 or equipment conversion to another type refrigerant, such as R-134a.

**Shop Manual**
Chapter 6, page 184

An alternate refrigerant has been developed to take the place of R-12. This new refrigerant, tetrafluoroethane, referred to as R-134a, has many of the same characteristics of R-12 but poses no threat to the ozone. It does not contain ozone-depleting chlorine. Its chemical formula is $CF_3CFH_2$ (Figure 7-18). Though chemically it is referred to as HFC-134a, it is generally called R-134a in the industry.

The automotive industry chose R-134a to replace R-12 because it is a single composition refrigerant. This means that it changes states at a specific temperature and pressure, giving it specific predictability. Blended refrigerants, on the other hand, contain multiple composition refrigerants that react differently at the various operating pressures within the air conditioning system, making them less stable. One downside to R-134a as a refrigerant is that it is classified as a contributor to global warming, although it is *not* an ozone-depleting refrigerant.

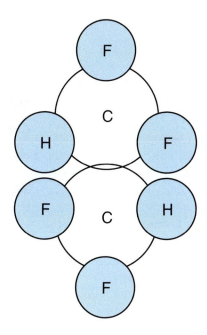

**Figure 7-18** The chemical structure of R-134a (HFC-134a).

**BIT OF HISTORY**

The first R-134a system went into vehicle production for the 1992 model year. By 1994, the entire automotive industry had converted to the new R-134a refrigerant for new vehicle production.

It is important to note that R-134a, a hydrofluorocarbon (HFC) refrigerant, cannot be used in an R-12 air conditioning system without modifications, and in some systems it cannot be used at all. Specific guidelines must be followed in order to convert an R-12 system to an R-134a system. The two refrigerants are not to be mixed: R-12 must not be used in an R-134a system and R-134a must not be used in a R-12 system. Also, the refrigeration lubricant used with the two refrigerants should not be interchanged.

There are many refrigerant retrofit kits available for converting an automotive air conditioning system from R-12 to R-134a. Unfortunately, not all of them contain adequate information and components for a successful conversion. Also, the desiccant in some early systems is not compatible with the new refrigerant. Finally, the lubricant must be changed. The mineral oil used in R-12 systems will not provide adequate lubrication for an R-134a system. Before retrofitting an automotive air conditioning system, always refer to the manufacturer's recommendations and instructions for parts requirements and procedures.

The SAE has developed guidelines for new types of service hoses and service ports for an R-134a system. These guidelines, known as Standards J-2196 and J-639, help to ensure that the accidental mixing of the two refrigerants does not occur. The service ports of the two systems may only be attached to the couplings on respective recovery/recycle/recharge equipment.

# Temperature and Pressure Relationships of R-12 (CFC-12)

R-12 (CFC-12) was a desirable refrigerant for automotive use because the temperature on the Fahrenheit scale and English system pressure values in the 20–70 psig range are very close to the corresponding temperatures of 20–70°F.

There is only a slight variation between the temperature and pressure values of the refrigerant in the 20–70 psig range (Figure 7-19). In this range, the assumption for R-12 is made that for each pound of pressure recorded, the temperature is the same. For example, for a pressure of 23.8 psig, the corresponding temperature is 24°F (Figure 7-20). This value, however, is the temperature of the evaporating refrigerant, not the temperature of the outside surface of the evaporator coil or the air passing over it. Unfortunately, this close correlation does not exist in the metric system (Figure 7-21).

The objective in automotive air conditioning is to allow the evaporator to reach its coldest point without icing. Since ice forms at 32°F (0°C), the fins and cooling coils of the evaporator must not be allowed to reach a colder temperature. Because of the temperature rise through the walls of the cooling fins and coils, the temperature of the refrigerant may be several degrees cooler than that of the air passing through the evaporator.

Evaporator coil temperature must be maintained above 32°F (0°C).

For example, a pressure gauge reading of 28 psig (193.06 kPa) in an R-12 system means that the evaporating temperature of the refrigerant is about 30°F (–1.1°C). Because of the temperature rise through the fins and coils, the air passing over the coil is more on the order of about 34°F or 35°F (1.1°C or 1.7°C).

| Temp. °F | Press. psig | Temp. °F | Press. psig | Temp. °F | Press. psig | Temp. °F | Press. psig | Temp. °F | Press. psig |
|---|---|---|---|---|---|---|---|---|---|
| 0 | 9.1 | 35 | 32.5 | 60 | 57.7 | 85 | 91.7 | 110 | 136.0 |
| 2 | 10.1 | 36 | 33.4 | 61 | 58.9 | 86 | 93.2 | 111 | 138.0 |
| 4 | 11.2 | 37 | 34.3 | 62 | 60.0 | 87 | 94.8 | 112 | 140.1 |
| 6 | 12.3 | 38 | 35.1 | 63 | 61.3 | 88 | 96.4 | 113 | 142.1 |
| 8 | 13.4 | 39 | 36.0 | 64 | 62.5 | 89 | 98.0 | 114 | 144.2 |
| 10 | 14.6 | 40 | 36.9 | 65 | 63.7 | 90 | 99.6 | 115 | 146.3 |
| 12 | 15.8 | 41 | 37.9 | 66 | 64.9 | 91 | 101.3 | 116 | 148.4 |
| 14 | 17.1 | 42 | 38.8 | 67 | 66.2 | 92 | 103.0 | 117 | 151.2 |
| 16 | 18.3 | 43 | 39.7 | 68 | 67.5 | 93 | 104.6 | 118 | 152.7 |
| 18 | 19.7 | 44 | 40.7 | 69 | 68.8 | 94 | 106.3 | 119 | 154.9 |
| 20 | 21.0 | 45 | 41.7 | 70 | 70.1 | 95 | 108.1 | 120 | 157.1 |
| 21 | 21.7 | 46 | 42.6 | 71 | 71.4 | 96 | 109.8 | 121 | 159.3 |
| 22 | 22.4 | 47 | 43.6 | 72 | 72.8 | 97 | 111.5 | 122 | 161.5 |
| 23 | 23.1 | 48 | 44.6 | 73 | 74.2 | 98 | 113.3 | 123 | 163.8 |
| 24 | 23.8 | 49 | 45.6 | 74 | 75.5 | 99 | 115.1 | 124 | 166.1 |
| 25 | 24.6 | 50 | 46.6 | 75 | 76.9 | 100 | 116.9 | 125 | 168.4 |
| 26 | 25.3 | 51 | 47.8 | 76 | 78.3 | 101 | 118.8 | 126 | 170.7 |
| 27 | 26.1 | 52 | 48.7 | 77 | 79.2 | 102 | 120.6 | 127 | 173.1 |
| 28 | 26.8 | 53 | 49.8 | 78 | 81.1 | 103 | 122.4 | 128 | 175.4 |
| 29 | 27.6 | 54 | 50.9 | 79 | 82.5 | 104 | 124.3 | 129 | 177.8 |
| 30 | 28.4 | 55 | 52.0 | 80 | 84.0 | 105 | 126.2 | 130 | 182.2 |
| 31 | 29.2 | 56 | 53.1 | 81 | 85.5 | 106 | 128.1 | 131 | 182.6 |
| 32 | 30.0 | 57 | 55.4 | 82 | 87.0 | 107 | 130.0 | 132 | 185.1 |
| 33 | 30.9 | 58 | 56.6 | 83 | 88.5 | 108 | 132.1 | 133 | 187.6 |
| 34 | 31.7 | 59 | 57.1 | 84 | 90.1 | 109 | 135.1 | 134 | 190.1 |

**Figure 7-19** English temperature-pressure chart for R-12 (CFC-12).

## ENGLISH TEMPERATURE-PRESSURE CHART

| Low-Side Pressure psi | | Temperature °F | High-Side Pressure psi | | Temperature °F |
|---|---|---|---|---|---|
| Absolute | Gauge | | Absolute | Gauge | |
| 25.9 | 11.2 | 4 | 120 | 105 | 60 |
| 27 | 12.3 | 6 | 124 | 109 | 62 |
| 28.1 | 13.4 | 8 | 128 | 113 | 64 |
| 29.3 | 14.6 | 10 | 132 | 117 | 66 |
| 30.5 | 15.8 | 12 | 137 | 122 | 68 |
| 31.8 | 17.1 | 14 | 141 | 126 | 70 |
| 33 | 18.3 | 16 | 147 | 132 | 72 |
| 34.4 | 19.7 | 18 | 152 | 137 | 74 |
| 35.7 | 21 | 20 | 159 | 144 | 76 |
| 37.1 | 22.4 | 22 | 167 | 152 | 78 |
| 38.5 | 23.8 | 24 | 175 | 160 | 80 |
| 40 | 25.3 | 26 | 180 | 165 | 82 |
| 41.5 | 26.8 | 28 | 185 | 170 | 84 |
| 43.1 | 28.4 | 30 | 190 | 175 | 86 |
| 44.7 | 30 | 32 | 195 | 180 | 88 |
| 46.4 | 31.7 | 34 | 200 | 185 | 90 |
| 47.8 | 33.1 | 36 | 204 | 189 | 92 |
| 49.8 | 35.1 | 38 | 208 | 193 | 94 |
| 51.6 | 36.9 | 40 | 215 | 200 | 96 |
| 53.5 | 38.8 | 42 | 225 | 210 | 98 |
| 55.4 | 40.7 | 44 | 235 | 220 | 100 |
| 57.3 | 42.6 | 46 | 243 | 228 | 102 |
| 59.3 | 44.6 | 48 | 251 | 236 | 104 |

**Figure 7-20** A pressure of 23.8 psig corresponds to a temperature of 24°F.

| EVAPORATOR TEMPERATURE °C | EVAPORATOR PRESSURE GAUGE READING KILOPASCAL | | AMBIENT TEMPERATURE °C | HIGH PRESSURE GAUGE READING KILOPASCAL (GAUGE) |
|---|---|---|---|---|
| | (GAUGE) | (ABSOLUTE) | | |
| -16 | 73.4 | 174.7 | 16 | 737.7 |
| -15 | 81.0 | 182.3 | 17 | 759.8 |
| -14 | 87.8 | 189.1 | 18 | 784.6 |
| -13 | 94.8 | 196.1 | 19 | 810.2 |
| -12 | 100.6 | 201.9 | 20 | 841.2 |
| -11 | 108.9 | 210.2 | 21 | 868.7 |
| -10 | 117.9 | 219.2 | 22 | 901.8 |
| - 9 | 124.5 | 225.8 | 23 | 932.2 |
| - 8 | 133.9 | 235.2 | 24 | 970.8 |
| - 7 | 140.3 | 241.6 | 25 | 1 020.5 |
| - 6 | 149.6 | 250.9 | 26 | 1 075.6 |
| - 5 | 159.2 | 260.5 | 27 | 1 111.5 |
| - 4 | 167.4 | 268.7 | 28 | 1 143.2 |
| - 3 | 183.2 | 268.7 | 29 | 1 174.9 |
| - 2 | 186.9 | 288.2 | 30 | 1 206.6 |
| - 1 | 195.8 | 288.2 | 31 | 1 241.1 |
| 0 | 206.8 | 308.1 | 32 | 1 267.3 |
| 1 | 218.5 | 319.8 | 33 | 1 294.8 |
| 2 | 227.8 | 329.1 | 34 | 1 319.7 |
| 3 | 238.7 | 340.0 | 35 | 1 344.5 |
| 4 | 249.4 | 350.7 | 36 | 1 413.5 |
| 5 | 261.3 | 362.6 | 37 | 1 468.6 |
| 6 | 273.7 | 375.0 | 38 | 1 527.9 |
| 7 | 287.5 | 388.8 | 39 | 1 577.5 |
| 8 | 296.6 | 397.9 | 40 | 1 627.2 |
| 9 | 303.3 | 404.6 | 42 | 1 737.5 |
| 10 | 321.5 | 422.8 | 45 | 1 854.7 |

**Figure 7-21** Metric temperature-pressure chart for R-12 (CFC-12).

| Temperature °F | Pressure psig | Temperature °F | Pressure psig |
|---|---|---|---|
| -5 | 4.1 | 39.0 | 34.1 |
| 0 | 6.5 | 40.0 | 35.0 |
| 5.0 | 9.1 | 45.0 | 40.0 |
| 10.0 | 12.0 | 50.0 | 45.4 |
| 15.0 | 15.1 | 55.0 | 51.2 |
| 20.0 | 18.4 | 60.0 | 57.4 |
| 21.0 | 19.1 | 65.0 | 64.0 |
| 22.0 | 19.9 | 70.0 | 71.1 |
| 23.0 | 20.6 | 75.0 | 78.6 |
| 24.0 | 21.4 | 80.0 | 86.7 |
| 25.0 | 22.1 | 85.0 | 95.2 |
| 26.0 | 22.9 | 90.0 | 104.3 |
| 27.0 | 23.7 | 95.0 | 113.9 |
| 28.0 | 24.5 | 100.0 | 124.1 |
| 29.0 | 25.3 | 105.0 | 134.9 |
| 30.0 | 25.3 | 110.0 | 146.3 |
| 31.0 | 27.0 | 115.0 | 158.4 |
| 32.0 | 27.8 | 120.0 | 171.1 |
| 33.0 | 28.7 | 125.0 | 184.5 |
| 34.0 | 29.5 | 130.0 | 198.7 |
| 35.0 | 30.4 | 135.0 | 213.5 |
| 36.0 | 31.3 | 140.0 | 229.2 |
| 37.0 | 32.2 | 145.0 | 245.6 |
| 38.0 | 33.2 | 150.0 | 262.8 |

Figure 7-22 English temperature-pressure chart for R-134a (HFC-134a).

| Temperature °C | Pressure kPa | Temperature °C | Pressure kPa |
|---|---|---|---|
| -15.0 | 63 | 5.0 | 247 |
| -12.5 | 83 | 7.5 | 280 |
| -10.0 | 103 | 10.0 | 313 |
| -7.5 | 122 | 12.5 | 345 |
| -5.0 | 142 | 15.0 | 381 |
| -4.5 | 147 | 17.5 | 422 |
| -4.0 | 152 | 20.0 | 465 |
| -3.5 | 157 | 22.5 | 510 |
| -3.0 | 162 | 25.0 | 560 |
| -2.5 | 167 | 27.5 | 616 |
| -2.0 | 172 | 30.0 | 670 |
| -1.5 | 177 | 32.5 | 726 |
| -1.0 | 182 | 35.0 | 785 |
| -0.5 | 187 | 37.5 | 849 |
| 0.0 | 192 | 40.0 | 916 |
| 0.5 | 198 | 42.5 | 990 |
| 1.0 | 203 | 45.0 | 1066 |
| 1.5 | 209 | 47.5 | 1146 |
| 2.0 | 214 | 50.0 | 1230 |
| 2.5 | 220 | 52.5 | 1315 |
| 3.0 | 225 | 55.0 | 1385 |
| 3.5 | 231 | 57.5 | 1480 |
| 4.0 | 236 | 60.0 | 1580 |
| 4.5 | 242 | 65.0 | 1795 |

Figure 7-23 Metric temperature-pressure chart for R-134a.

# Temperature and Pressure Relationships of R-134a (HFC-134a)

Current research has shown that R-134a and R-12 refrigerants have similar performance characteristics to one another. By comparison, R-134a refrigerant has a lower normal low-side pressure than R-12 and a higher normal high-side pressure than R-12 refrigerant. The power consumption of R-134a is slightly higher, but the refrigerant capacity is 3 to 5 percent less than an R-12 system. The vapor pressure of both systems is essentially equal under normal operating temperatures.

Like R-12, R-134a has its own unique temperature and pressure relationship, as shown in Figure 7-22. The metric equivalent is given in Figure 7-23. Note that the evaporating temperature and pressure of R-134a is reasonably close in the 10–40°F (–12.2–+4.4°C) range. In fact, the temperature and pressure is nearly the same at 15°F (–9.4°C).

A pressure gauge reading of 26 psig (179 kPa) means that the evaporating temperature of the refrigerant in the evaporator is about 30°F (–1.1°C). This may be favorably compared with the temperature and pressure relationship of R-12.

# Refrigerant-22 for Leak Testing

Most leaks in an automotive air conditioning system can be located with a system pressure of 50 psig (434.75 kPa). This pressure is easily obtainable using only refrigerant as a source. For a leak that is difficult to locate, however, it is often desirable to increase the system pressure to about 100 psig (689.5 kPa). This is easily accomplished using a pressure-regulated dry nitrogen charge with the CFC-22.

Though not generally recommended, some technicians prefer to use Refrigerant-22 (HCFC-22) to pressurize the system without the use of nitrogen. There is no law that requires dedicated equipment be used for HCFC-22. The same equipment and fittings that are used to service and leak test CFC-22 can be used to service and leak test HCFC-22. It should be noted, however, that several of the EPA's SNAP-approved blend refrigerants contain HCFC-22 and do require dedicated fittings and equipment for service.

If HCFC-22 is used for leak testing, all refrigerant must first be removed from the system. Also, after leak testing is completed, it is important that all HCFC-22 be removed from the system before introducing any other refrigerant. Do not mix refrigerants.

Refrigerant-22 is a class II hydrochlorofluorocarbon refrigerant that is somewhat less harmful to the ozone than R-12. The container identification color is green, and the chemical formula is $CHClF_2$. The chemical name for this refrigerant is monochlorodifluoromethane. At the present time, HCFC-22 is scheduled to be phased out early this century.

It must be emphasized that HCFC-22 is used for leak testing only. This refrigerant is *not* intended to be used as an automotive refrigerant. HCFC-22 is *not* a suitable replacement for CFC-22. As mentioned above, after leak testing, all traces of HCFC-22 must be removed from the system before it is charged with R-12 or any other refrigerant. HCFC-22 is sold in automotive parts houses and in the automotive section of many chain stores in 15-oz. (425-g) disposable cans (Figure 7-24).

Never use air in combination with refrigerants. Both HCFC-22 and R-134a fall into a category of refrigerants known as combustible. If exposed to oxygen, they will both burn when under pressure or when exposed to high temperatures, but they will not ignite in air at atmospheric pressure and temperature.

## De Minimis Release

The practice of purging small amounts of refrigerant in the course of repair and service is known as a *de minimis* release. The word *minimis* is not to be confused with the Latin word *minimus*, which means smallest. De minimis is taken from the Latin phrase "De minimis non curat lex," which means "The law does not concern itself with trifles."

Figure 7-24  A typical "pound" can of HCFC-22 contains 15 oz. (425 g).

# Handling Refrigerant

All refrigerants must be properly stored, handled, and used.

Liquid refrigerant can cause blindness if sprayed into the eyes. Also, if liquid refrigerant comes into contact with the skin, frostbite may result.

A refrigerant container should never be exposed to heat above 125°F (51.7°C). This means that it should not be allowed to come into contact with an open flame or any type of heating device, and it should not be stored in direct sunlight. The increase in refrigerant pressure inside the container, known as *hydrostatic pressure*, as a result of excessive heat can become great enough to cause the container to explode.

If refrigerant is allowed to come into contact with an open flame or heated metal, a poisonous gas is created. Anyone breathing this gas may become ill. Remember—refrigerant is not a toy. Refrigerant should be handled only by a properly trained and experienced automotive service technician.

The term *Freon* is frequently used when referring to refrigerant. Freon and Freon-12 are registered trademarks of E. I. DuPont de Nemours and Company. These terms, then, should be used only when referring to refrigerant manufactured by this company. A new term, *SUVA*, is used by DuPont to identify a new ozone-friendly group of refrigerants that includes R-134a (HFC-134a). Both refrigerants, as well as others, are also produced by several other manufacturers and are packaged under various trade names.

Either refrigerant is available in sizes from "pound" cans to 1-ton (907-kg) cylinders. Actually, the "pound" can of R-12 contains 12 oz. (340 g). The R-134a can also contains 12 oz. (340 g) (Figure 7-25).

After November 15, 1992, it became unlawful to sell or distribute to the general public R-12 in containers of less than 20 lb. (9 kg). Proper certification is now required for the purchase of refrigerant, in any quantity, to ensure that those dispensing refrigerants are knowledgeable in their profession and may be held accountable for their actions. Some states also require special licensing of the service facility in addition to the federal certification requirements. Also, to legally service automotive air conditioning systems, the service facility must have proper, adequate, and EPA-approved refrigerant service equipment for each type refrigerant they wish to service.

The industry has adopted a standard color code to identify refrigerant containers. An R-12 container is white, and an HCFC-22 container is green. Light blue identifies an R-134a container, which must not be confused with R-114, which is packaged in a dark blue container. This color code, however, does not apply to "pound" cans.

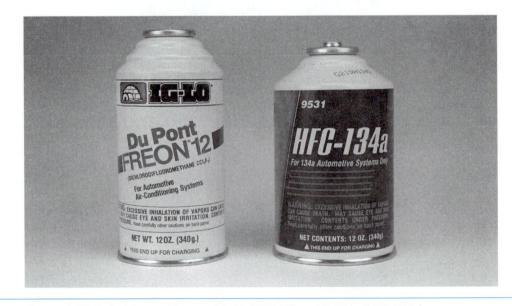

**Figure 7-25** Typical "pound" cans of R-12 (CFC-12) and R-134a (HFC-134a).

It cannot be overemphasized that R-12, a chlorofluorocarbon refrigerant, HCFC-22, a hydrochlorofluorocarbon, and R-134a, a hydrofluorocarbon refrigerant, are not compatible with each other. They must not be mixed under any circumstances or in any other manner substituted one for the other. Mixing refrigerants, even in small quantities, will result in exceptionally high pressures that may cause serious damage to system components, such as the evaporator and hoses. An improper refrigerant may also cause damage to the system due to the incompatibility of the lubricant and desiccant. The appropriate equipment—such as manifold and gauge set, recovery system, and charging station—must be used for each refrigerant.

# Refrigeration Oil

The moving parts of a compressor must be lubricated to prevent damage during operation. Oil is used on these moving parts and on the seals and gaskets throughout the system as well. In addition, oil is picked up by the refrigerant, which circulates through the system. This refrigerant and oil combination also helps to maintain the thermostatic expansion valve in a proper operating condition.

The oil that must be used in an automobile air conditioning system is a nonfoaming sulfur-free grade specifically formulated for use in certain types of air conditioning systems. This special oil is known as refrigeration oil, and it is available in several grades and types (Figure 7-26). The grade and type to be used are determined by the compressor manufacturer and the type of refrigerant in the system. To replace oil that may be lost due to a refrigerant leak, pressurized oil is available in disposable cans. Generally, this container contains 2 fluid oz. (59 mL) of oil and a like measure of refrigerant. The refrigerant provides the necessary pressure required to force the oil into the system.

Mineral oil, used in R-12 air conditioning systems, is clear to light yellow in color. Some synthetic oils used in R-134a air conditioning systems may be blue or some other color. An impurity in refrigeration oil can cause a color change ranging from brown to black. Mineral oil is practically odorless, and a strong odor indicates that the oil is impure. Some synthetic oils, on the other hand, have a pungent odor though not impure. In either case, to ensure optimum system protection and performance, impure oil must be removed and replaced with clean, fresh oil. The receiver-drier or suction accumulator should also be replaced and a good pump down (system evacuation) performed before the air conditioning system is recharged.

**Shop Manual**
Chapter 5,
page 142

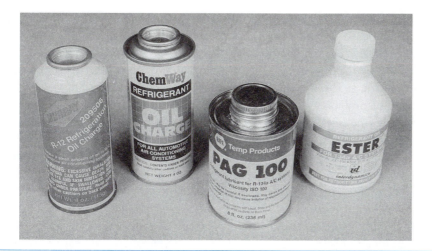

**Figure 7-26** Several types and grades of oil are used in automotive air conditioning systems.

# Lubricants for HFC Refrigerants

Some of the substitute automotive refrigerants are compatible with conventional mineral oil or alkyl benzene lubricants. However, R-134a refrigerant is not **miscible** with conventional mineral oil or alkyl benzene lubricants. Lack of miscibility can lead to system operational problems due to insufficient lubrication. When the two fluids are miscible, the lubricant is carried back to the compressor. When not miscible, however, the lubricant can accumulate in the various components of the air conditioning system.

Lubricant that accumulates in the condenser can reduce heat transfer and restrict the flow of liquid refrigerant. This condition can cause vapor pockets to form in the liquid stream as it flows through the metering device into the evaporator. Lubricant that accumulates in the evaporator will reduce heat transfer and restrict refrigerant vapor flow. Poor lubrication return to the compressor often leads to excessive wear of the compressor due to lubricant starvation.

**Synthetic Lubricants.** Two different types of synthetic lubricant—polyalkylene glycols (PAG) and neopentyl polyol esters (POE)—are available for use with HFC refrigerants. Though first used in automotive air conditioning in 1992, PAG is not a new lubricant. It has been used for years in compressors for natural gas production and for compressors handling other "difficult" gases.

**Polyalkylene Glycol (PAG).** PAGs are extremely hygroscopic and can absorb several thousand parts per million (ppm) of water when exposed to moist air—100 times more than mineral oil, which generally contains less than 100 ppm of water. High water content causes corrosion and copper plating problems in some refrigeration systems when PAG lubricants are used. PAG is also sensitive to chlorine-containing contaminants such as residual R-12 remaining in a system that has been converted.

PAG, however, was selected in 1992 as the lubricant of choice for automotive air conditioning systems in which R-134a is used as the refrigerant. This selection was based on previous success and due to deadline time constraints to phase out R-12. PAG lubricant is available in low- and high-viscosity grades. Always follow the manufacturers specifications when adding or changing compressor lubricant.

**Polyol Ester (POE).** Neopentyl POEs are a group of organic esters that have an application in systems having a wide operating temperature range where good lubricating characteristics are desired. These lubricants also possess good miscibility with HFCs.

Various POE compositions enhance miscibility with HFCs and their resistance to copper plating in refrigeration systems. They also have excellent thermal stability, low volatility, low deposit-forming tendencies, high flash points, and high auto-ignition temperatures.

On the downside, POEs are also hygroscopic, susceptible to **hydrolysis**, and incompatible with certain elastomers. These esters can absorb several thousand ppm of water; however, they are less absorbent than most PAGs. Therefore, like PAGs, POEs must be handled so excess moisture does not enter the refrigeration system. POE should only be used in automotive air conditioning systems that specifically require this type lubricant. A few vehicle manufacturers, for example, recommend POE lubricant be used in specific R-12 air conditioning systems that are being retrofitted to R-134a.

Over time, an air conditioning system may be exposed to moisture contamination during service. While PAG oil is more hygroscopic (absorbs water) than ester oil, moisture remains suspended in PAG oil. This further emphasizes the need to evacuate the air conditioning system beyond the minimum of 30 minutes. One disadvantage of ester oil is that under certain conditions (excess moisture contamination), moisture can drop out of ester oil to form small droplets of water that can cause corrosion and possible freeze-up in the expansion device. Remember, less than one drop exceeds the allowable moisture content in most refrigerant systems.

## Safety

Personal protection equipment—such as rubber- or PVC-coated gloves or barrier creams and safety goggles—should be worn when handling lubricants. Prolonged skin contact or any eye contact can cause irritations and discomfort, such as stinging and burning. One should avoid breathing the vapors produced by these lubricants, and they should only be used in a well-ventilated area. Keep them in tightly sealed containers to prevent moisture contamination by humidity and to ensure that their vapors do not escape.

## The Classification of Refrigeration Oil

The classification of refrigeration oil is based on three factors:
- ❏ Viscosity
- ❏ Compatibility with refrigerants
- ❏ Pour point

**Viscosity.** The viscosity rating for a fluid is based on the time, in seconds, required for a measured quantity of the fluid to pass through a calibrated orifice when the temperature of the fluid is 100°F (37.8°C). The resistance to flow of any fluid is judged by its viscosity rating. The higher the viscosity number, the thicker the fluid.

**Compatibility.** Refrigeration oil must be compatible with the refrigerant with which it is to be used. It should be noted that refrigeration oil now used in an R-12 system is a mineral oil designated "YN-9." This oil cannot be used in an R-134a system. Conversely, a polyalkylene glycol oil, designated "YN-12," for an R-134a system with a reciprocating compressor may not be used in an R-12 system. A second polyalkylene glycol oil is used in systems with a rotary compressor. There may be as many as three polyalkylene oils, each formulated for a particular application. Incompatible oil mixtures may cause serious damage to the air conditioning system.

Do not mix oils.

The Saybolt Universal Viscosity (SUV) is defined as the time, in seconds, required for 60 cubic centimeters (cm) of oil at 100°F (37.8°C) to flow through a standard Saybolt orifice.

Refrigeration oil, to be compatible with the refrigerant used in the system, must be capable of existing (remaining an oil) when mixed with the refrigerant. In other words, the oil is not changed or separated by chemical interaction with the refrigerant.

The compatibility of a refrigeration oil with a refrigerant is determined by a test called a floc test F. This test is performed by placing a mixture containing 90 percent oil and 10 percent refrigerant in a sealed glass tube. The mixture is then slowly cooled until a waxy substance appears. The temperature at which the substance forms is recorded as the floc point.

Compatible: Capable of forming a mixture that does not separate and is not altered by chemical interaction.

**Pour Point.** The temperature at which an oil will just flow is its pour point. This temperature is recorded in degrees Fahrenheit. The pour point is a standard of the American Society for Testing Materials (ASTM).

The pour point temperature for oil and lubricant used in high-temperature refrigeration systems, such as automotive air conditioning, is between –40°F (–40°C) and –10°F (–23.3°C), depending on grade and type.

## Servicing Tips

The oil level of the compressor should be checked each time the air conditioner is "opened" for service. Always check the manufacturer's recommendations before adding oil to the air conditioning system.

When the oil is not being used, the container must remain capped. Always be sure that the cap is in place and tightly secured. Refrigeration oil is very hygroscopic; it absorbs moisture. Moisture is very damaging to the air conditioning system. It should be noted that polyalkylene glycol oil is 100 times more hygroscopic than mineral oil. It is also ten times more expensive. For these

Hygroscopic: Readily taking up and retaining moisture.

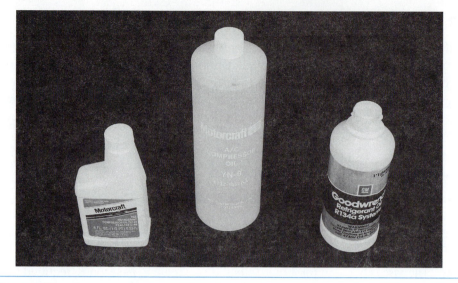

**Figure 7-27** Refrigeration oil is packaged in several container sizes.

Do not refill disposable cylinders.

reasons, it is suggested that refrigeration oil be purchased in small containers (Figure 7-27). Refrigeration oil is packaged in 1 qt. (0.946 L), 1 gal. (3.785 L), 5 gal. (18.925 L), and larger containers.

In conclusion, the properties of a good refrigeration oil are low wax content, good thermal and chemical stability, low viscosity, and a low pour point. A few simple rules are listed as follows for handling refrigeration oil:

**DO**

❏ use only approved refrigeration oil.
❏ be sure that the cap is tight on the container when not in use.
❏ replace oil if there is any doubt of its condition.
❏ avoid contaminating the oil.
❏ dispose of used oil in a proper manner.
❏ always use safety goggles and gloves when handling lubricants.
❏ avoid breathing the fumes of lubricants.

**DO NOT**

❏ transfer oil from one container to another.
❏ return used oil to the container.
❏ leave the oil container uncapped.
❏ use a grade or type of oil other than that recommended for the air conditioner being serviced.
❏ dispose of used oil in an improper manner.
❏ overfill an air conditioning system with oil.

**AUTHOR'S NOTE:** Compressor input shaft seals are a source of refrigerant leakage causing a low system charge level. It is a common practice for technicians to slip a note card in the air gap between the compressor clutch hub and pulley to see if oil is detected. Oil on the card indicates that the shaft seal is leaking.

# Preventive Maintenance

Preventive maintenance (PM) pays off in the long run. Whenever servicing an automotive air conditioning system, potential problems can sometimes be discovered before they occur. A thorough visual check of the mechanical and electrical system is well worth the time invested.

## Mechanical

Check the air conditioning system for damaged hoses (Figure 7-28) and connections that may be caused by rubbing or chafing. Slight oil staining may indicate a refrigerant leak. With the engine off, inspect the belt(s) for glazing and cracking. Heavy glazing may indicate a slipping belt. Some glazing, however, is acceptable. Inspect the hoses and hose connectors. Soft or brittle hoses are an indication that they are deteriorating and should be replaced. Do not neglect the heater hoses. A slight leak in a heater hose is often overlooked.

## Electrical

Check for loose connections and frayed (Figure 7-29) or broken wires. If the problem is a "blown" fuse or circuit breaker, it is possible that a bare wire is intermittently "shorting" to ground due to vibration.

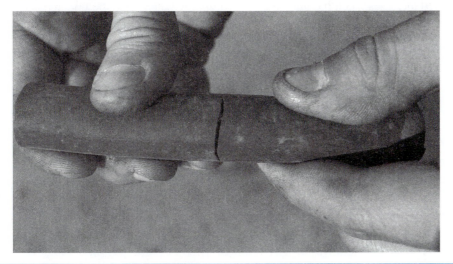

**Figure 7-28** Check for defective hoses.

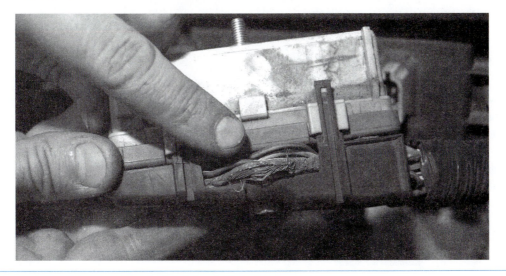

**Figure 7-29** Check for frayed or broken wires.

Figure 7-30 Always disconnect the battery ground (–) cable.

The blower motor can sometimes give an indication of other problems. If, for example, the blower speed increases when the engine is revved up, the battery may be undercharged, a defective voltage regulator may cause overcharging, or the battery ground cable may be corroded or poorly connected. A slipping compressor clutch may be an indication of improper adjustment or low voltage supplied to the coil.

The fuse, circuit breaker, and fusible links are provided for protection against an electrical fire. Never bypass a circuit protection device simply because it "blows" frequently. If it blows, there is a reason. To prevent further damage, locate the problem and correct it.

Never take chances—if in doubt, disconnect the battery cable. Always disconnect the battery ground (–) cable, not the hot (+) cable (Figure 7-30). If the wrench grounds out while disconnecting the ground cable, no harm is done. If, however, the wrench grounds out while disconnecting the hot cable (with the ground cable attached), the electrical system is "shorted" and may be damaged.

A fully charged 12V automotive battery is capable of delivering very high current. In a matter of seconds, a shorted electrical system can cause extensive damage to the automobile's wiring harness.

From the information given related to system conditions, it should now be obvious that the manifold and gauge set is a very important tool in air conditioning service. It is not only used to service the system, but also as a diagnostic tool.

## Advanced Diagnostic Tools

As was noted in Chapter 6, software-based system diagnostics have become integrated into the automotive air conditioning service industry. One of these tools, the Neutronics Inc. Master A/C System Technician (Figure 7-31), attaches to the high-side and low-side pressure service fittings and uses a temperature sensor to check ambient air temperature and component temperature. The technician follows the diagnostic steps listed and inputs requested information, such as component temperatures. Using the FlexTemp's™ temperature probe to check component temperature differences, the PDA uses the Delta T method, low- and high-side pressures, as well as look-up tables to calcu-

A fully charged automotive battery has a surface charge of 12.8–13.2 volts.

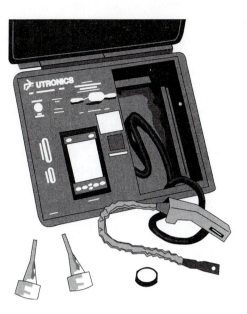

**Figure 7-31** Air conditioning system electronic analyzer used to diagnose system performance.

late charge levels on FOT systems. On thermostatic expansion valve systems, it bases its calculations on the temperature of refrigerant leaving the condenser and high-side line pressure to determine system charge levels.

Temperature and pressure comparisons are a standard practice to determine superheat, subcooling, and system change levels and performance. On an FOT system, the outlet line from the evaporator should be 3–10°F (2–6°C) colder than the evaporator inlet line temperature on a properly charged system. If the evaporator outlet line is warmer than the inlet line, the system is low on refrigerant. If the evaporator outlet line is colder than 10°F (2–6°C), the system may be overcharged. If you do not own a sophisticated diagnostic tool, you can use two contact thermometers and a manifold gauge set to perform a Delta T system charge level test. Run the engine at 1000 rpm and, if equipped with a cycling-clutch switch, jump the connector so the compressor will run continuously. Check both the evaporator inlet and outlet line temperatures simultaneously. Compare your results to a Delta T chart for the manufacturer and type of vehicle you are working on.

By checking both superheat and subcooling, you can gain information above and beyond what your pressure gauges are telling you. When you adjust the system charge based on superheat, you are charging the system based on the amount of air passing over the evaporator. You should not, however, base your refrigerant charge levels on superheat results for thermal expansion valve systems. Thermal expansion valve (TXV) systems control superheat by automatically adjusting to evaporator refrigerant temperature. Superheat will help you to determine if the TXV is working, though.

A method for determining the superheat capacity of the refrigerant is to:

1. Check the low-side pressure reading of the system and convert it to a temperature based on the type of refrigerant in the system. An example of a pressure-to-temperature comparison chart was given in Figure 7-2.

2. Place the blower fan on high speed setting.

3. Next, check the temperature of the low-side (suction) line about 6 in. before the compressor.

4. Now calculate the difference between the low-side line temperature and the saturation temperature based on the chart (low-side line temperature minus saturation temperature).

5. If the ambient air temperature is 75–85°F (23.89–29.44°C), the superheat should be 12–15°F (–11.11 to –9.44°C). If the ambient air temperature is above 85°F (29.44°C), the superheat should be 8–12°F (–13.33 to –11.11°C).

   Example for an R-134a system:

   Low-side line temperature is 45°F (7.22°C)
   Low-side line pressure is 30.4 psig, saturation temperature will be 35°F (1.67°C)
   45°F (7.22°C) – 35°F (1.67°C) = 10°F (12.22°C) superheat

6. If superheat is low, then the evaporator may be flooded, and if the superheat is high, then the evaporator may be starved for refrigerant. Do not adjust charge levels until subcooling has been tested.

Subcooling

7. To determine subcooling, check the high-side pressure reading of the system and convert it to a temperature based on the type of refrigerant in the system (saturation temperature).

8. Next, check the high-side liquid line temperature as close to the evaporator as possible but before the metering device (i.e., FOT or TXV).

9. Now calculate the difference between the high-side liquid line temperature and the saturation temperature based on the chart (saturation temperature minus high-side temperature). The subcooling temperature should be 12–15°F (–11.11 to –9.44°C). It should be noted that the temperature of the liquid line at the condenser outlet and the temperature of the liquid line at the metering device inlet should be within 2°F (–16.67°C) of each other. If not, there could be a restriction in the liquid line.

   Example for an R-134a system:

   High-side liquid line temperature is 195°F (90.55°C)
   High-side liquid line pressure is 198.7 psig, saturation temperature will be 180°F (82.22°C)
   180°F (82.22°C) – 195°F (90.55°C) = 15°F (9.44°C) subcooling

Using the information gained from both the superheat and the subcooling test, we will have some idea of how the system is operating.

1. If both the superheat and subcooling are low, the TXV is stuck open or the wrong orifice tube is installed (too large).

2. If both the superheat and subcooling are high, look for a restriction at the metering device, evaporator, or refrigerant line.

3. If the superheat is low and subcooling is high, the system may be overcharged.

4. If the superheat is high and subcooling is low, the system may be undercharged.

Another method for determining system performance and charge levels is to compare the on and off times of the compressor clutch. The charts in Figure 7-32 represent typical on and off times of the compressor clutch on a cycling-clutch system compared to ambient air temperature. The charts in Figure 7-33 depict the typical duct discharge temperature and the expected high- and low-side system pressure for a typical R-134a system at various ambient temperatures. The system should operate within the shaded areas. More detailed information is given in Chapter 7 of the Shop Manual.

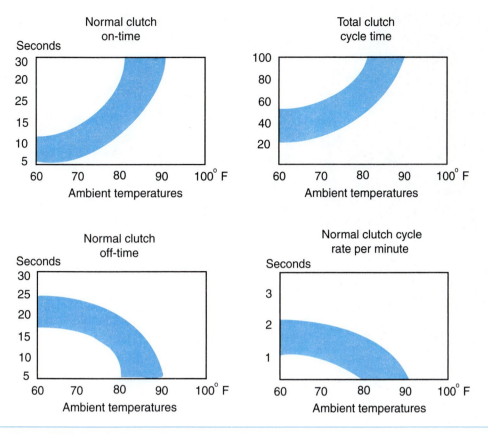

Figure 7-32 Typical diagnostic and testing chart for cycling clutch systems.

## CONDITIONAL REQUIREMENTS FOR CYCLING CLUTCH SYSTEM

- Stabilzed pressure
- Stabilized in-car temperatures 70 to 80°F (21 to 27°C)
- Maximum blower speed
- Maximum A/C (Recirculation)
- Compressor clutch engaged
- 1500 Engine RPM

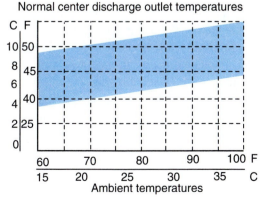

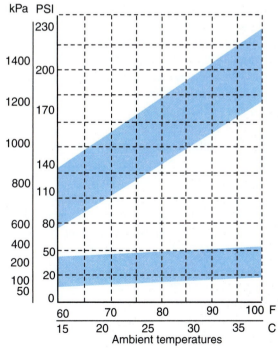

Figure 7-33 Typical duct discharge temperature and expected high-and-low side system pressures of a typical R-134a system.

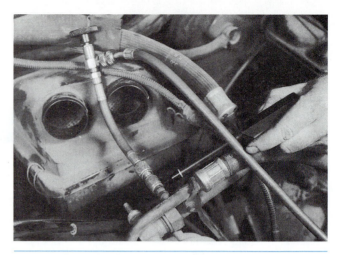

**Figure 7-34** Service valve with protective cap removed.

**Figure 7-35** Service valves with hoses connected are often neglected when leak testing.

## Leaks

Service valves and protective caps (Figure 7-34) are among the most common causes of refrigerant leaks. The primary purpose of the cap and O-ring is to serve as a dirt seal. As much as a pound (0.45 kg) of refrigerant per year can escape from the service valve if the cap is missing or the O-ring is defective. Leak testing the service valve is often neglected because the service hoses are generally connected to them (Figure 7-35). Service valves should be leak tested with the caps and the service hoses removed. System integrity should not depend on the sealing power of a protective cap. The primary purpose of the cap is to keep debris out of the service valve. If found to be leaking, the service valve should be repaired or replaced as applicable. Often, a new Schrader assembly is sufficient to stop most leaks.

An insufficient refrigerant charge, for any reason, will cause oil to become trapped in the evaporator. Oil also leaks out with refrigerant at the point of a leak. Any oil loss due to any reason can result in compressor seizure.

The compressor circulates a small amount of oil through the system with the refrigerant. Oil pumped out of the compressor in small quantities is mixed with the refrigerant in the condenser. This oil enters the evaporator with the refrigerant, and if the evaporator is properly flooded with refrigerant, passes to the compressor through the low-pressure line. Some of the oil passes to the compressor in small droplets. Most of the oil, however, is swept along the walls of the refrigerant lines by the velocity of the refrigerant vapor. This oil is returned to the compressor as a mist. If the evaporator is starved of refrigerant, oil will not return to the compressor in sufficient quantity to keep it properly lubricated. The major cause of premature compressor failure is a lack of lubricant. The tendency of a customer to have refrigerant added to the system "every few months or so" is a sure sign that the compressor is doomed. If the system is leaking refrigerant, it is a good bet that it is also leaking lubricant, and compressor failure is sure to follow.

# High Pressure

As refrigerant pressure increases in an air conditioning system, its temperature also increases. The resulting high temperature quickly accelerates the failure of a contaminated system. An increase in temperature of only 15°F (8°C) doubles the chemical reaction rate in the system. High temperature starts a chain of harmful reactions even in a clean system. Contamination, resulting from high temperature, may cause seizure of the compressor bearings.

High heat may also cause the refrigerant in the system to decompose or break down. High heat can cause synthetic rubber parts to become brittle and susceptible to cracking and breaking.

As temperature and pressure in an air conditioning system increase, stress and strain on compressor discharge valves increase. If this condition is not corrected, the discharge reeds in the valve plates may fail.

High pressure and the accompanying high temperature can be caused by air in the air conditioning system. Air can enter the system through careless or incomplete service procedures. Systems that have been opened to the atmosphere during service procedures must be properly evacuated. If the system is not properly evacuated, the results, most surely, will be an air-contaminated system.

A system with air contamination does not operate at full efficiency. Air in the air conditioning system can cause oil to oxidize. Oxidized oil forms gums and varnishes that coat the inside walls of the tubes, reducing the efficiency of the heat transfer process. Still more damaging, air usually carries moisture into the system in the form of humidity.

When an air conditioning system is operated with a low-side pressure below atmospheric pressure (14.696 psig at sea level), air will be drawn into the system through the leak. This occurs when a noncycling system is low on refrigerant; the low side often operates below atmospheric pressure, in a vacuum. If a system contaminated in this way is recharged without proper evacuation procedures, high temperature and pressure conditions will result. Air, a noncondensable gas, has a tendency to collect in the condenser during the off cycle.

> The top of the condenser is often the highest point of the system; air, lighter than refrigerant, seeks the highest point.

# Connections

If there is a compression fitting, avoid overtightening. Overtightening can cause O-ring damage, resulting in a leak or early failure. Before assembly, inspect the fitting for burrs, which may cut the O-ring. It is important that the proper O-ring be used for the type of refrigerant and the type of fitting. It is also important to follow the manufacturer's recommendations for selecting O-rings.

When a connection is made with a compression fitting, place the gaskets or O-ring over the tube before inserting it into the connection (Figure 7-36). Use a torque and backing wrench to ensure a proper connection. Again, follow the manufacturer's specifications for proper torque requirements.

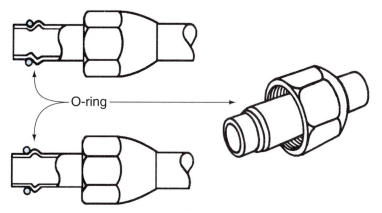

O-ring

**Figure 7-36** Place the O-ring over the fitting before inserting it into the connection.

Figure 7-37 A supplemental liquid line filter/drier.

# Restrictions

Most restrictions are caused by dirt, foreign matter, or corrosion. Corrosion is generally due to excess moisture in the system. Contaminants can lodge in filters and screens and can block the flow of refrigerant through the system. Filters are found in the receiver-drier and suction line accumulator, usually as a means to hold the desiccant in place. Screens are generally found:

❏ At the metering device inlet
❏ In the receiver-drier or accumulator
❏ At the compressor inlet

A restriction in the system can cause a "starved" evaporator. This can result in reduced cooling, poor oil return, and eventually, if not corrected, compressor seizure.

Supplemental aftermarket liquid line filters are available for installating in air conditioning systems that have been contaminated (Figure 7-37). The filter should be installed in the system:

1. After repeated metering device plugging
2. When a seized compressor has been replaced

The liquid line filter contains a screen and a filter pad. It does not contain a desiccant. The fine-mesh screen catches larger particles and holds the filter in place. The filter catches smaller particles and filters the refrigerant oil.

The filter is installed in the liquid line between the condenser outlet and the evaporator inlet. Filters are available with or without an expansion tube orifice. The filter without an orifice is generally preferred. This type can be installed anywhere in the liquid line, preferably close to the metering device. A filter with an orifice is required when the installation is to be made in the low-pressure side of the system beyond the original expansion tube location. This installation, which is usually found on General Motors vehicles, requires that the original expansion tube be removed from the system.

A contaminated system may have both a strainer and a drier.

# Contamination

Contamination by foreign matter has many sources, including:

❏ Failed desiccant
❏ Preservative oils
❏ Lint
❏ Soldering or brazing fluxes
❏ Loose corrosion flakes

Any of these materials in the air conditioning system can cause:

❏ Compressor bearings to seize
❏ Metering device failure
❏ Corrosion of metal parts
❏ Decomposition of refrigerant
❏ Breakdown of the oil

Corrosion and the by-products of corrosion can clog metering device screens, ruin compressor bearings, and accelerate the failure of compressor discharge valves. Moisture is the primary cause of corrosion in the air conditioning system.

In fact, the greatest enemy of an air conditioning system is moisture. When combined with the metals found in the system, moisture causes the formation of iron hydroxide and aluminum hydroxide. When combined with refrigerant, moisture can form three acids:

**1.** Carbonic ($H_2CO_3$)
**2.** Hydrochloric (HCl)
**3.** Hydrofluoric (HF)

Avoid contact with hydrochloric and hydrofluoric acids; both are very poisonous.

Moisture also causes metering devices to freeze up. As the operating temperature of the evaporator is reduced to the freezing point, moisture collects in the metering device orifice and freezes. This, in turn, restricts the flow of refrigerant into the evaporator. The result is an erratic or poor cooling condition of the evaporator.

High temperature and foreign matter are responsible for many refrigerant system difficulties. In most cases, it is the presence of moisture that accelerates these conditions. The acids that result from the combination of high pressure, moisture, and refrigerant cause damaging corrosion.

**Shop Manual**
Chapter 6,
page 184

Carbonic acid is a weak solution generally found in solutions of carbon dioxide in water.

# Summary

❏ There are but six basic abnormal conditions for air conditioning system diagnosis.
❏ The evaporator coil temperature is kept above 32°F (0°C) to prevent freeze-up.
❏ A misadjusted or defective thermostat may cause evaporator freeze-up.
❏ An undercharge of refrigerant is an indication of a leak in the system.
❏ A resistance in the high side of the system will cause high high-side pressure.
❏ A defective thermostatic expansion valve (TXV) can cause the same symptoms as a low-side restriction.
❏ Air in the system can cause the same symptoms as an overcharge of refrigerant or oil.
❏ An overheated engine can cause high high-side pressure.
❏ The proper cure for an undercharged system is to first repair the leak, then recharge the system.
❏ Water ($H_2O$) is the "refrigerant" (R-718) used in the cooling system.
❏ If HCFC-22 is used for leak testing, *do not* exceed 100 psig (690 kPa) to avoid damage to the evaporator.
❏ Observe all safety practices when handling refrigerants.

**Terms to Know**
Control thermostat
Head pressure
Hydrolysis
Malfunction
Metering device
Miscible
Remote bulb
Restriction

# Review Questions

## Short Answer Essays

1. Explain the pressure-temperature relationship of refrigerant.
2. How can moisture in the system cause a problem?
3. How does one determine if a problem is due to electrical or mechanical failure?
4. How does one clean a dirty condenser?
5. Why was R-12 a desirable refrigerant?
6. Why must the temperature of an evaporator be kept above 32°F (0°C)?
7. Why does one have to be licensed and certified to purchase refrigerant?
8. Under what conditions is R-134a combustible?
9. How does one determine that refrigeration oil is not pure?
10. How does one determine if the battery ground (–) cable is poorly connected?

## Fill-in-the-Blanks

1. _____ on the evaporator coil _____ the flow of air through it, resulting in poor or _____ cooling.
2. Very low low-side pressure may be caused by a _____ screen in the metering device _____.
3. A high low-side pressure is an indication that the thermostatic expansion valve (TXV) _____ _____ restricting the flow of _____.
4. High high-side pressure may be caused by excessive _____, oil, or _____ in the system.
5. The alternate refrigerant for R-_____ is R-_____.
6. When leak testing, do not exceed _____ psig (_____ kPa) to avoid damage to the evaporator.
7. Never heat a refrigerant cylinder above _____ °F (_____ °C).
8. Most states have laws that prohibit the use of _____ refrigerants in _____ air conditioning systems.
9. The compressor _____ should be checked each time the system is _____ for service.
10. The _____ and _____ _____ is an important tool for air conditioning service.

## Multiple Choice

1.  *Technician A* says that a gauge reading of 21 psig (145 kPa) corresponds to an R-12 evaporator temperature of about 20°F (–6.7°C).
    *Technician B* says that a gauge reading of 21 psig (145 kPa) corresponds to an R-134a evaporator temperature of about 23.5°F (–4.7°C).
    Who is correct?
    **A.** A only          **C.** Both A and B
    **B.** B only          **D.** Neither A nor B

2.  *Technician A* says that if R-134a evaporating temperature is 30°F (–1.1°C), the gauge pressure should be about 26 psig (179 kPa).
    *Technician B* says that a low-side gauge pressure of 26 psig (179 kPa) indicates a refrigerant evaporating temperature of 27°F (–2.8°C) in an R-12 system.
    Who is correct?
    **A.** A only          **C.** Both A and B
    **B.** B only          **D.** Neither A nor B

3.  *Technician A* says that the R-12 evaporating temperature with an English gauge reading of 37 psig is 40°F (4.4°C).
    *Technician B* says that pressure corresponds to a metric pressure of 255 kPa.
    Who is correct?
    **A.** A only          **C.** Both A and B
    **B.** B only          **D.** Neither A nor B

4.  *Technician A* says that with an evaporating temperature of 35°F (1.7°C), the low-side gauge metric pressure should be 209–210 kPa.
    *Technician B* says this is equal to 33–34 psig.
    Who is correct?
    **A.** A only          **C.** Both A and B
    **B.** B only          **D.** Neither A nor B

5.  *Technician A* says that between 20 and 70 psig, the pressure and temperature of R-12 on the English scale is nearly the same.
    *Technician B* says that between 10 and 40 psig, the pressure and temperature of R-134a on the English scale is nearly the same.
    Who is correct?
    **A.** A only          **C.** Both A and B
    **B.** B only          **D.** Neither A nor B

6.  *Technician A* says to prevent ice formation on the fins and coils of an R-12 evaporator, the coil temperature should never be allowed to fall below 32°F (0°C).
    *Technician B* says to prevent ice formation on the fins and coils of an R-134a evaporator, the coil temperature should never be allowed to fall below 32°F (0°C).
    Who is correct?
    **A.** A only          **C.** Both A and B
    **B.** B only          **D.** Neither A nor B

7.  *Technician A* says liquid refrigerant, if allowed to strike the eye, can cause frostbite.
    *Technician B* says refrigerant in the vapor form is harmless.
    Who is correct?
    **A.** A only          **C.** Both A and B
    **B.** B only          **D.** Neither A nor B

8.  *Technician A* says an explosion will occur if R-12 refrigerant comes into contact with an open flame.
    *Technician B* says that refrigerant R-12, in contact with an open flame, creates a harmful vapor.
    Who is correct?
    **A.** A only          **C.** Both A and B
    **B.** B only          **D.** Neither A nor B

9.  *Technician A* says that mineral oil can be used in CFC or HFC systems.
    *Technician B* says that POE lubricant is used in an R-134a system.
    Who is correct?
    **A.** A only          **C.** Both A and B
    **B.** B only          **D.** Neither A nor B

10. *Technician A* says that a receiver-drier identifies an R-12 system.
    *Technician B* says that an accumulator identifies an R-134a system.
    Who is correct?
    **A.** A only          **C.** Both A and B
    **B.** B only          **D.** Neither A nor B

# Compressors and Clutches

Upon completion and review of this chapter, you should be able to:

❏ Discuss and explain the operating principals of a reciprocating compressor.

❏ Discuss and explain the operating principles of a scroll compressor.

❏ Discuss and explain the operating principles of a rotary compressor.

❏ State the purpose and describe the function and operation of a magnetic clutch in an air conditioning system.

❏ Compare fixed- and variable-displacement compressors.

## Introduction

There are many different types, makes, and models of compressors used for automotive air conditioning applications.

A prime consideration for new compressor design is to help to reduce overall vehicle weight. Overall vehicle weight is reduced by reducing the weight of individual components. A reduction in overall (gross) vehicle weight provides greater economy, or more miles per gallon (kilometers per liter) of fuel.

The compressor, as well as other **auxiliary** components, must also be designed to be efficient and durable to withstand long hours of heavy use.

Chapter 3 of this manual generally covered the refrigeration system, and Chapter 5 considered other basic components of the system. If necessary, refer to these chapters to review the compressor's role in a vehicle air conditioning system.

## Function

The compressor in an automotive air conditioning system serves two important functions. It creates a low-pressure condition within the system, and it compresses refrigerant vapor from a low pressure to a high pressure, thereby increasing its temperature. It is important that these two functions be accomplished at the same time.

### Low-Pressure Condition

One function, creating a **low-pressure** condition at the compressor inlet, aids in the removal of heat-laden refrigerant vapor from the evaporator. This low-pressure condition is essential to allow the refrigerant metering device to admit the proper amount of liquid refrigerant into the evaporator (Figure 8-1).

### Compress Refrigerant

The second function of the compressor is to compress the low-pressure refrigerant vapor into a **high-pressure** refrigerant vapor. This increased pressure raises the heat content of the refrigerant. High pressure with high heat content is essential if the refrigerant is to condense, giving up its heat, in the condenser. It is in the condenser that the refrigerant vapor is changed to a liquid. While it is a slightly lower temperature, it is still at a high pressure until it again reaches the metering device, generally at the inlet of the evaporator.

**Auxiliary** components are those such as the rear evaporator in a dual air conditioning system, which is often referred to as an "auxiliary evaporator."

Kilometer is the metric conversion for the English mile, and liter (litre) is the metric conversion for the English quart or gallon.

**Low pressure** is a relative term used to describe normal pressure in the low side of an air conditioning system.

The low-pressure condition exists in an air conditioning system from the metering device outlet to the compressor inlet.

**High pressure** is a relative term used to describe refrigerant pressure in the high side of an air conditioning system.

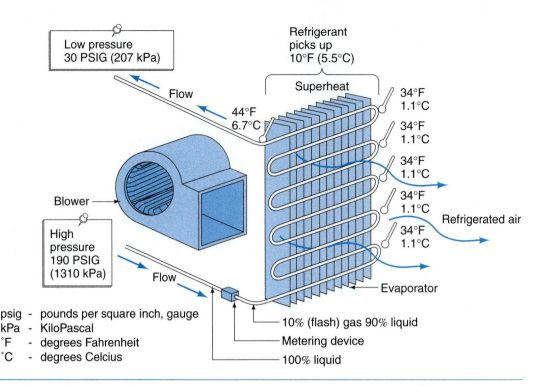

psig - pounds per square inch, gauge
kPa - KiloPascal
°F - degrees Fahrenheit
°C - degrees Celcius

**Figure 8-1** The intake stroke of the compressor creates a low-pressure condition to draw refrigerant into the evaporator.

The high-pressure condition exists from the compressor outlet to the metering device inlet.

A **crankshaft** is the part of a reciprocating compressor on which the wobble plate or connecting rods are attached. It is splined to the clutch plate and receives reciprocating power from the drive pulley assembly when the clutch is engaged.

An **axial plate** is the part of an automotive air conditioning compressor piston assembly that rotates as a part of the drive shaft.

**Swash plate** is another term used for a wobble plate.

A **wobble plate** is a type of offset concentric plate attached at an angle. It is found on some compressor crankshafts and is used to move the pistons up and down as the shaft is turned. Another term used for a wobble plate is a swash plate.

Failure of either function of the compressor will result in a loss or reduction of the circulation of refrigerant within an air conditioning system. Without proper refrigerant circulation in the system, the air conditioner will not function properly or may not function at all.

# Design

Several types of compressors are used in automotive air conditioning systems. Regardless of the type, however, with few exceptions, most compressors are basically of the reciprocating piston design. Reciprocating means that the piston moves up and down, to and fro, or back and forth (Figure 8-2 and Figure 8-3).

Two basic methods of driving the piston of a reciprocating compressor are by **crankshaft** or **axial plate**. The axial plate is often called a **swash plate** or **wobble plate**.

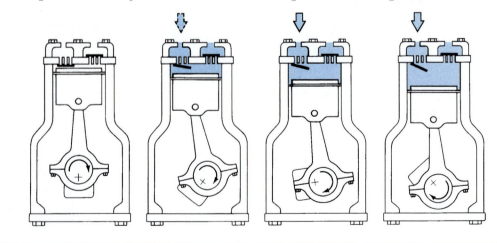

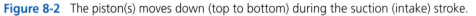

**Figure 8-2** The piston(s) moves down (top to bottom) during the suction (intake) stroke.

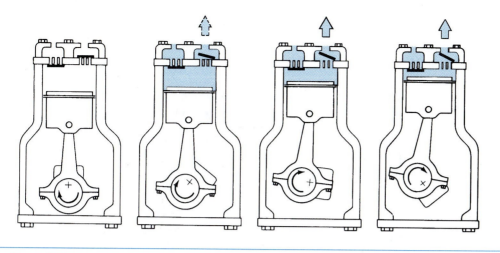

Figure 8-3 The piston(s) moves up (bottom to top) during the compression (discharge) stroke.

The exceptions, **rotary** and **scroll** compressors, found on a limited number of car lines beginning in the early 1990s, are discussed later in this chapter.

## Crankshaft

Driving the piston of a reciprocating compressor by crankshaft (Figure 8-4) is an operation that is very similar to an automobile engine. The main difference is that a compressor crankshaft drives the piston, whereas in an engine, the piston drives the crankshaft. The compressor crankshaft is driven directly or indirectly off the engine crankshaft by means of pulleys and belts (Figure 8-5, Figure 8-6, Figure 8-7, and Figure 8-8).

**Rotary** compressors use vanes attached to a rotor assembly and is driven by the input shaft to compress refrigerant.

A **scroll** compressor is a spiral corkscrew design compressor used on limited applications to produce a more continuous, steady supply of refrigerant pressure.

Turning the crankshaft causes a to-fro, fore-aft, or up-down action of the piston(s).

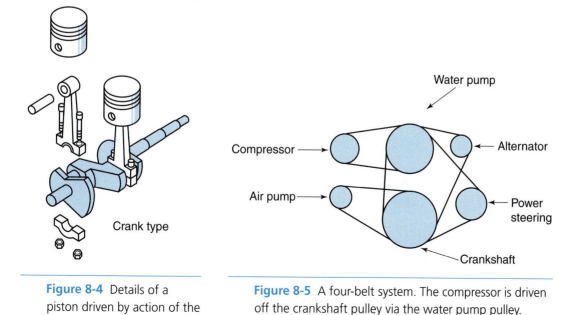

Figure 8-4 Details of a piston driven by action of the crankshaft in a compressor.

Figure 8-5 A four-belt system. The compressor is driven off the crankshaft pulley via the water pump pulley.

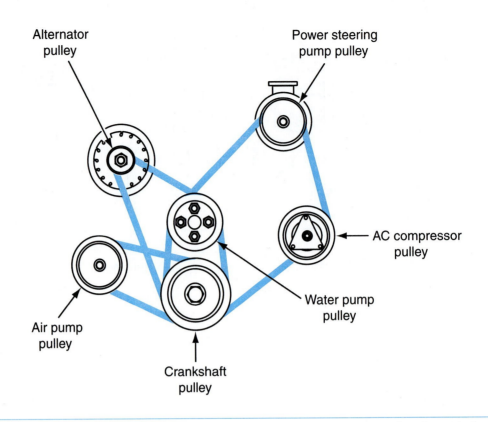

Figure 8-6 A three-belt system. The compressor is driven off the crankshaft pulley with the alternator used for belt tensioning.

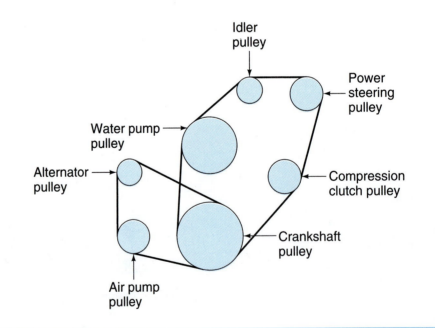

Figure 8-7 A two-belt serpentine drive system. The compressor belt is tensioned by a manually adjusted idler pulley.

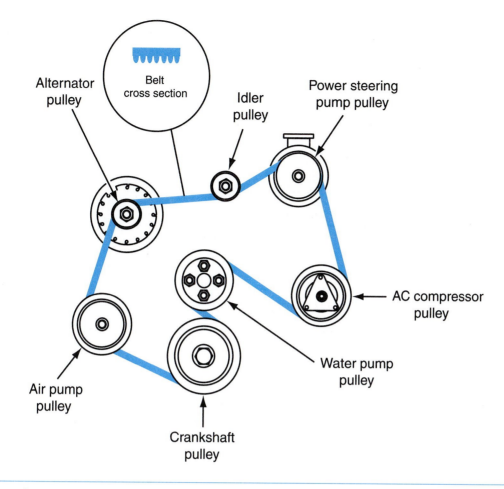

Figure 8-8 A single-belt drive system. The belt is tensioned by a spring-loaded idler pulley.

## Axial Plate

The other method of driving the piston of a reciprocating compressor is by an axial plate pressed on the main shaft, providing a reciprocating motion of the piston (Figure 8-9). The axial plate is driven directly or indirectly by the main shaft off the engine crankshaft by means of pulleys and belts.

# Clutch

All automotive air conditioning compressors have an electromagnetic clutch attached to their crankshaft or main shaft (Figure 8-10). The clutch provides a means of turning the compressor on and off. Some compressors are driven by one or two belts off the engine crankshaft. An idler pulley (Figure 8-11) is provided to adjust belt tension. Most compressors are driven off the crankshaft by a single belt, along with such other accessories as the power steering pump, alternator,

Turning the axial plate will create the same conditions as turning a crankshaft.

**Shop Manual**
Chapter 8,
page 272

Other terms used for V-rib or serpentine belt are polyrib and microgroove.

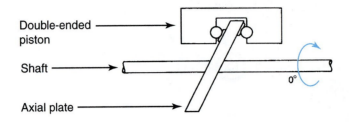

Double-ended piston

Shaft

Axial plate

0°

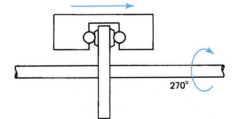

90°

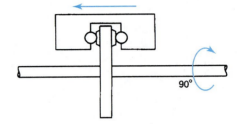

180°

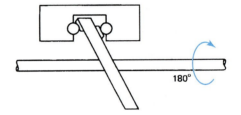

270°

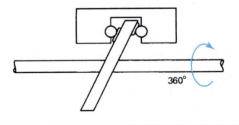

360°

**Figure 8-9** The piston(s) is moved back and forth or to and fro by an axial plate.

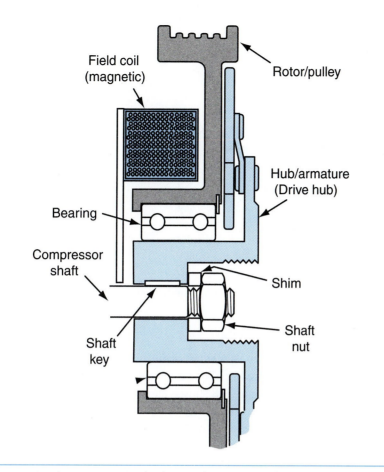

Field coil
(magnetic)

Rotor/pulley

Hub/armature
(Drive hub)

Bearing

Compressor
shaft

Shim

Shaft
nut

Shaft
key

**Figure 8-10** An electromagnetic clutch provides a means of turning the compressor on and off.

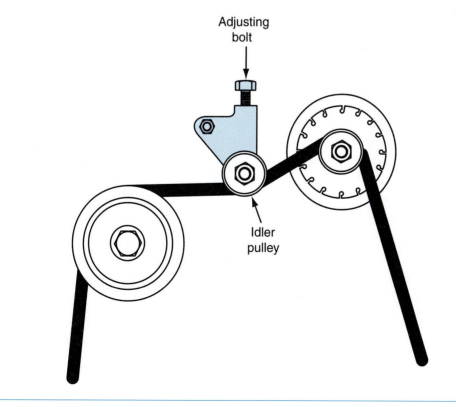

Adjusting
bolt

Idler
pulley

**Figure 8-11** An idler pulley used to adjust belt tension.

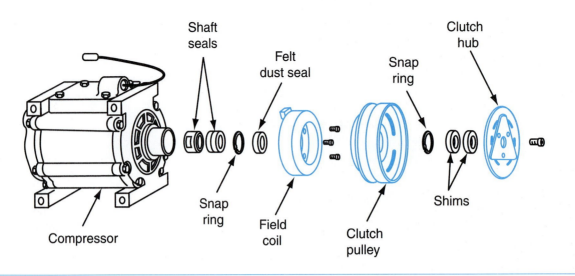

Figure 8-12 The three main parts of the compressor clutch assembly are the field coil, clutch pulley, and the clutch hub.

A **serpentine** belt is a flat or V-grooved multiribbed design that winds through all of the engine accessories to drive them off the engine crankshaft pulley.

and water pump. This system is known as a **serpentine** drive. This serpentine belt is tensioned by a spring-loaded or manually adjustable idler pulley assembly, which generally rides on the back (flat) side of the belt. Refer to Figure 8-8 shown earlier.

The three main parts of the compressor clutch assembly are the coil magnet, the pulley and idler bearing and the clutch plate (shoe) (Figure 8-12). The clutch drive plate is splined to the input shaft of the compressor.

The compressor clutch is a large electromagnet that when energized draws the clutch plate into the clutch pulley. The magnetic field holds the clutch plate tightly against the clutch pulley as long as current is supplied to it. This in turn engages the drive pulley to the compressor input shaft causing the shaft to spin. When the compressor clutch is not engaged, the input shaft of the compressor does not spin and the drive pulley freewheels on a sealed bearing assembly. If a noise is heard when the clutch is not engaged, it is generally an indication of a faulty bearing, which in many cases can be serviced without the replacement of the entire compressor assembly. If, however, the noise is only heard when the compressor clutch is engaged, this may indicate that there is an internal problem with the air conditioning compressor.

The operation of the air conditioning clutch today is controlled by the heater control head and often uses a solid-state control module. The powertrain control module (PCM) is also integrated into the system.

The PCM controls compressor clutch engagement when:

❑ The low-pressure switch senses below 25 psig.
❑ The high-pressure switch senses pressure above 450 psig.
❑ Coolant temperature is above 230°F (110 °C).
❑ Engagement is delayed for 5–10 seconds when the engine is first started.
❑ Engine speed is below 400 rpm.
❑ The throttle is opened above 80 percent.

When the air conditioning switch on the climate control head assembly is first turned to the on position, the PCM runs a logic loop to check the operation of its sensors to make sure they are within operational parameters prior to allowing the compressor clutch to engage. The PCM will also look at the air conditioning system high- and low-pressure transducers to verify that the system contains the proper refrigerant charge before allowing the compressor to engage. The idle speed will also be raised to compensate for the added load on the engine.

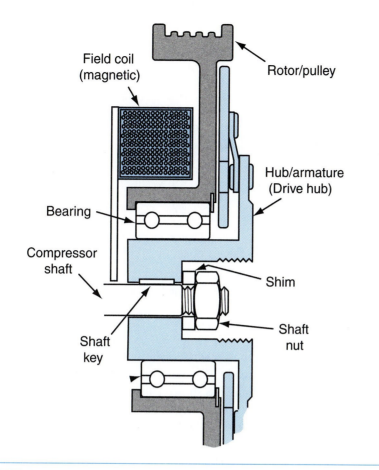

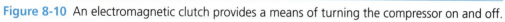

**Figure 8-10** An electromagnetic clutch provides a means of turning the compressor on and off.

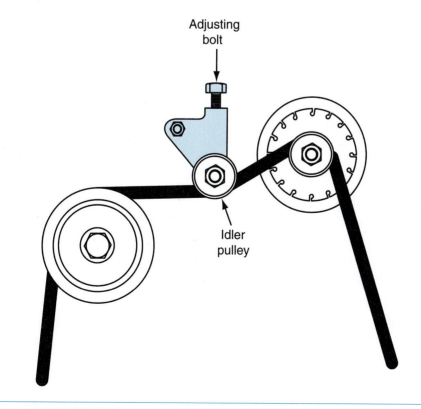

**Figure 8-11** An idler pulley used to adjust belt tension.

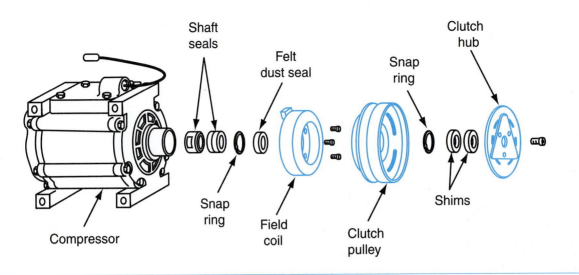

**Figure 8-12** The three main parts of the compressor clutch assembly are the field coil, clutch pulley, and the clutch hub.

A **serpentine** belt is a flat or V-grooved multiribbed design that winds through all of the engine accessories to drive them off the engine crankshaft pulley.

and water pump. This system is known as a **serpentine** drive. This serpentine belt is tensioned by a spring-loaded or manually adjustable idler pulley assembly, which generally rides on the back (flat) side of the belt. Refer to Figure 8-8 shown earlier.

The three main parts of the compressor clutch assembly are the coil magnet, the pulley and idler bearing and the clutch plate (shoe) (Figure 8-12). The clutch drive plate is splined to the input shaft of the compressor.

The compressor clutch is a large electromagnet that when energized draws the clutch plate into the clutch pulley. The magnetic field holds the clutch plate tightly against the clutch pulley as long as current is supplied to it. This in turn engages the drive pulley to the compressor input shaft causing the shaft to spin. When the compressor clutch is not engaged, the input shaft of the compressor does not spin and the drive pulley freewheels on a sealed bearing assembly. If a noise is heard when the clutch is not engaged, it is generally an indication of a faulty bearing, which in many cases can be serviced without the replacement of the entire compressor assembly. If, however, the noise is only heard when the compressor clutch is engaged, this may indicate that there is an internal problem with the air conditioning compressor.

The operation of the air conditioning clutch today is controlled by the heater control head and often uses a solid-state control module. The powertrain control module (PCM) is also integrated into the system.

The PCM controls compressor clutch engagement when:

❏ The low-pressure switch senses below 25 psig.
❏ The high-pressure switch senses pressure above 450 psig.
❏ Coolant temperature is above 230°F (110 °C).
❏ Engagement is delayed for 5–10 seconds when the engine is first started.
❏ Engine speed is below 400 rpm.
❏ The throttle is opened above 80 percent.

When the air conditioning switch on the climate control head assembly is first turned to the on position, the PCM runs a logic loop to check the operation of its sensors to make sure they are within operational parameters prior to allowing the compressor clutch to engage. The PCM will also look at the air conditioning system high- and low-pressure transducers to verify that the system contains the proper refrigerant charge before allowing the compressor to engage. The idle speed will also be raised to compensate for the added load on the engine.

Most air conditioning compressor clutch circuits also use a clamping diode placed across the clutch coil to prevent unwanted electrical spikes as the clutch is disengaged which could damage control modules and relay contacts. The air conditioning clutch can generate a voltage spike of over 200 volts, and the diode provides a path back through the coil assembly for this unwanted voltage. The diode is wired in parallel with the air conditioning compressor clutch and may be part of the field coil assembly or it may be located in the engine wiring harness near the clutch. Other systems use a bidirectional **zener clamping diode** that turns on at voltages above the 60-volt level. Use a digital volt ohmmeter (DVOM) set to diode testing to inspect the integrity of the diode. In addition, clutch coil resistance and amperage draw should be measured and compared to the manufacturer's specifications.

When servicing compressor clutches, be sure to properly set the air gap of the clutch plate to the pulley hub to the manufacturer's specifications (generally 0.020 in. [0.50 mm]) using a non-magnetic feeler gauge. If the air gap is set too great, the clutch may not engage or may slip. If the air gap is set too tight, the clutch may drag, causing noise and leading to overheating of the clutch coil.

Air conditioning compressor clutches can fail for many reasons. They may slip if improperly adjusted or if the proper current is not supplied. Coil assembly may develop a short or an open. The bearing may fail, a noise may develop, the clutch may drag due to weak return springs, to name a few failures.

A **zener clamping diode** is a semiconductor rectifier diode one-way voltage gate that allows current to flow when voltage levels increase above its threshold voltage.

### A BIT OF HISTORY

Early automotive air conditioning systems did not have a convenient driver-operated means of en-gaging and disengaging the compressor. Most compressors were belt and pulley driven off the crankshaft or accessory device. If one wished to disable the compressor for the winter months, the belt was removed. It was then replaced for the warm months. In-car temperature was controlled by means of a hot gas bypass valve. The compressor operated any time the engine was running and the hot gas bypass valve simply routed the unwanted gas from the compressor **discharge** back to the **suction** side of the system. This inefficient method of temperature control has not been used for automotive service since the mid 1960s.

The hot gas is no longer used as a method of temperature control in automotive air conditioning systems.

To **discharge** is to bleed some or all of the refrigerant from the high side to the low side of the system on early models.

## Types of Compressors

According to a leading compressor rebuilder, there are currently over 160 makes and models of remanufactured compressors readily available for use in mobile air conditioning systems. The various types include reciprocating piston (Figure 8-13), scroll (Figure 8-14), rotary vane (Figure 8-15), and scotch yoke (Figure 8-16).

The **suction** side is another term used to describe the low side of the refrigerant system.

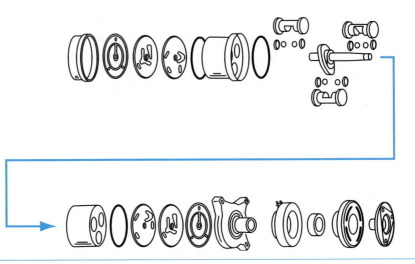

**Figure 8-13** A typical reciprocating piston compressor details.

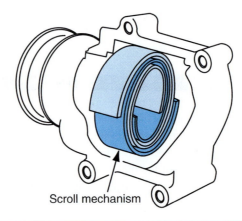

Scroll mechanism

**Figure 8-14** Scroll compressor details.

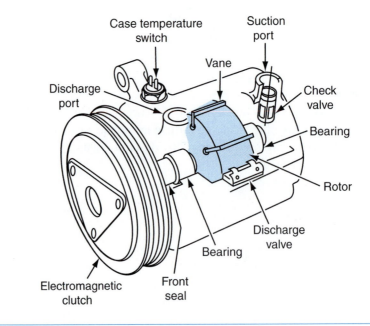

Case temperature switch

Suction port

Vane

Discharge port

Check valve

Bearing

Rotor

Discharge valve

Electromagnetic clutch

Front seal

Bearing

**Figure 8-15** A typical rotary valve compressor details.

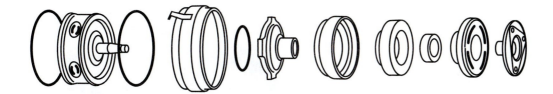

Figure 8-16 A typical scotch yoke compressor details.

# Reciprocating (Piston-Type) Compressors

Reciprocating, piston-type mobile air conditioning compressors, depending on their design, may have one, two, four, five, six, seven, or ten pistons (cylinders). Tecumseh manufactured a single-cylinder compressor for use with aftermarket air conditioning systems in compact imports.

A two-cylinder V-type compressor was manufactured by Chrysler Air-Temp but was discontinued due to its heavy weight. Two-cylinder, in-line reciprocating compressors manufactured by Nippondenso, Tecumseh, and York may be found on some early model vehicles, as well as some heavy duty and off-road equipment.

A four-cylinder, radial-design scotch yoke reciprocal compressor, manufactured by Harrison (Frigidaire) as their model R-4, is available in either standard or lightweight versions. A similar compressor, model HR-980 by Tecumseh, was produced through the late 1980s. A version of the radial scotch yoke reciprocating compressor design was produced by Keihin in Japan for use on some Honda automobiles.

Chrysler Air-Temp manufactured the only V-type compressor for automotive use. It is now discontinued.

**AUTHOR'S NOTE:** In order to understand what can physically go wrong in an air conditioning system, you must know how an air conditioning compressor is built and how it functions. Even if you never intend to overhaul the assembly, diagnosing a system failure will be all but impossible without this level of understanding.

Sanden (Sankyo), Harrison (Frigidaire), and Calsonic manufacture a five-cylinder compressor. The Sanden compressor is a positive displacement compressor; the Harrison V-5 and Calsonic V-5 (Figure 8-17) compressors are of a variable displacement design.

Figure 8-17 The Calsonic V-5 compressor.

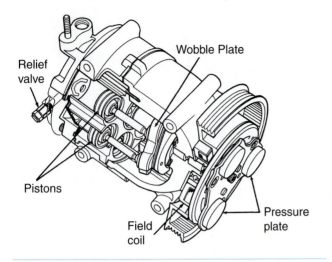

Figure 8-18 Honda Air Device Systems (HADS) compressor details.

Figure 8-19 Harrison's seven-cylinder variable displacement compressor.

**Shop Manual**
Chapter 8,
page 277

Six six-cylinder axial design compressors are currently available. The Harrison model A-6 was manufactured for over 20 years, from 1962 through the mid 1980s. This compressor was superseded by a lighter version, model DA-6, in 1982. Two more changes soon followed: the "Harrison Redesigned" HR-6 and the "High Efficiency" HR6HE version. Ford and Chrysler also have models of a six-cylinder compressor similar to one developed originally by Nippondenso.

A six-cylinder variable displacement compressor by Calsonic, model V-6, is very similar in appearance to Calsonic's model V-5 compressor.

Honda Air Device Systems (HADS) manufactures a seven-cylinder compressor (Figure 8-18) for use with refrigerant R-134a air conditioning systems. Harrison manufactures a seven-cylinder variable displacement compressor (Figure 8-19).

A ten-cylinder compressor was introduced by Nippondenso in 1986. This compressor has the same general appearance as their six-cylinder compressor.

## Applications

Tecumseh's single-cylinder compressor may be found on early aftermarket applications for both domestic and imported cars. Nippondenso's two-cylinder compressor was primarily used on some Japanese import vehicles. The Tecumseh and York two-cylinder compressors may be found on some early intermediate and full-size aftermarket applications, as well as on some Audi, Ford, Nissan, Porsche, Subaru, and Volkswagen factory-installed systems. Current applications include some heavy-duty trucks as well as some off-road equipment. Hitachi compressors are found on some Nissan car lines, and Keihin compressors are found on some Honda car lines.

The four-cylinder compressor by Harrison was standard equipment on some General Motors car lines and may also be found on some Peugeot, Volvo, and Mercedes-Benz car lines. The Sankyo compressor may be found on Dodge, Plymouth, BMW, Nissan, Fiat, Honda, Jeep, Mazda, Porsche, Subaru, Toyota, and Volkswagen car lines.

Harrison six-cylinder compressors may be found on General Motors, Ford, Lincoln, Mercury, Audi, Avanti, Jaguar, Mercedes-Benz, Peugeot, Rolls-Royce, and Volvo car lines.

Sankyo (Sanden) compressors are found on some Dodge, Mazda, Peugeot, Chrysler, Jeep, Renault, Honda, Subaru, and Volkswagen car lines.

The Nippondenso six-cylinder compressor may be found on some Toyota, Ford, Acura, Chevrolet, Honda, Mitsubishi, Mazda, and Mercury car lines. The Nippondenso ten-cylinder compressor may be found on some Acura, Chevrolet, Ford, Honda, Mercury, Mitsubishi, and Toyota car lines. A Chrysler-built compressor, Acustar, is found on some Chrysler car lines. This fixed displacement compressor is based on a Nippondenso design. The Harrison variable displacement compressor, the V-5, may be found on some General Motors car lines.

## Action

Low-pressure refrigerant vapor is compressed to high-pressure refrigerant vapor by action of the pistons and valve plates. For each piston, there is one intake (suction) valve and one outlet (discharge) valve mounted on a valve plate. For simplicity of understanding, a single-cylinder (piston) compressor is discussed.

By action of the crankshaft, the piston travels from the top of its stroke to the bottom of its stroke during the first one-half revolution. On the second one-half revolution, the piston travels from the bottom of its stroke to the top of its stroke. The first action, top to bottom, is called the **intake** or suction stroke; the second action, bottom to top, is called the **compression** or discharge stroke.

The piston is fitted with a piston ring to provide a seal between the piston and the cylinder wall. This seal helps to provide a negative (low) pressure on the down or intake stroke, and a positive (high) pressure on the up or **exhaust** stroke.

**The Intake Stroke.** During the intake stroke, a low-pressure area is created atop the piston and below the intake (suction) and exhaust (discharge) valves. The higher pressure atop the intake valve, from the evaporator, allows this valve to open, admitting low-pressure heat-laden refrigerant vapor into the compressor cylinder chamber. The discharge valve is held closed during this time period. The much higher pressure atop this valve, as opposed to the low pressure below it, prevents it from opening during the intake stroke.

**The Discharge Stroke.** During the compression stroke, a high-pressure area is created atop the piston and below the intake and exhaust valves. This pressure becomes much greater than that above the intake valve and closes that valve. At the same time, the pressure is somewhat greater than that above the exhaust valve. The pressure difference is great enough to cause the exhaust valve to open. This allows the compressed refrigerant vapor to be discharged from the compressor.

**Continuous Action.** This piston action is repeated rapidly—once for each revolution of the crankshaft; perhaps 600 times each minute at curb idle. At over-the-road speeds, the action may be repeated 1,500 or more times each minute for each cylinder of the compressor.

# Rotary Vane Compressors

The rotary vane compressor, by design, provides the greatest cooling capacity per pound of compressor weight. It has no pistons and only one valve: a discharge valve. The discharge valve actually serves as a check valve to prevent high-pressure refrigerant vapor from entering the compressor through the discharge provisions during the off cycle, or when the compressor is not operating. The function of the rotary vane compressor is the same as that of the piston- or reciprocating-type compressor. Its operation, however, is entirely different.

The **intake** stroke of the compressor creates a negative pressure that draws refrigerant in from the low side of the system.

The **compression** stroke of the compressor creates a positive pressure greater than that contained on the high-side hot gas line leaving the compressor, and it thus forces refrigerant under pressure through the system when the exhaust valve is opened.

**Exhaust** is the final stage that occurs as the piston is moving up on the compression stroke and pressures exceed the preset calibration on the exhaust valve forcing refrigerant in the high side of the system.

Compression action is repeated over 6,000 times each minute at road speeds in an R-4 compressor.

**Shop Manual**
Chapter 8, page 312

The concept and use of rotary-type compressors for refrigeration service is not new. Two basic types of rotary vane compressors have been available for nonautomotive refrigeration use for many years: rotating vane and stationary vane. York was first to introduce this compressor to the automotive marketplace in the early 1980s. Only about 50,000 rotary vane compressors were manufactured by York before being discontinued, however. With some exceptions, a rotary vane compressor may be found on some Geo Prism and Toyota Corolla and Tercel car lines as early as 1989. In 1993, Panasonic manufactured a rotary compressor that was introduced on some Ford car lines. The Zexel rotary compressor is also used on Nissan's Altima.

## Operation of Rotary Compressors

Follow the illustration shown (Figure 8-20) for a brief description of the operation of a rotary vane compressor.

- ❏ The compressor shaft turns a rotor assembly that has vanes that extend to the wall of the cylinder block.
- ❏ This forms a compression chamber, or several chambers if there is more than one vane.
- ❏ The rotating vanes then draw in refrigerant vapor through the suction ports.
- ❏ Compression of the refrigerant starts after the vanes have crossed the suction ports, increasing the refrigerant pressure and temperature.
- ❏ The hot vapor is then forced out through the discharge valves to the condenser.

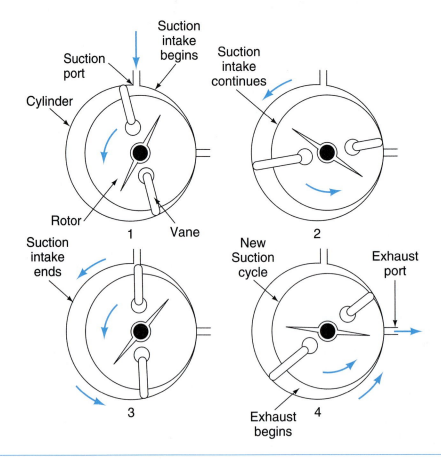

**Figure 8-20** The operational sequence of a rotary vane compressor.

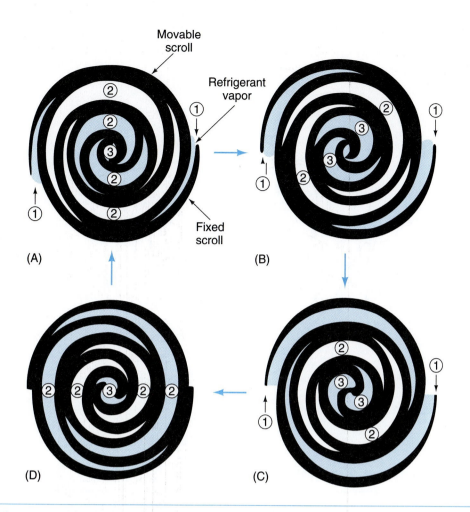

**Figure 8-21** The operational sequence of a scroll compressor.

# Scroll Compressors

Although the scroll compressor was first patented in 1909, it did not meet practical application until it was introduced by Copeland Corporation in 1988 for use in home air conditioners and heat pumps. Sanden introduced the scroll compressor to the automotive marketplace in 1993. Its unique design is considered by many to be a major technological breakthrough in compressor design.

Follow the illustration shown (Figure 8-21) for a brief description of the operation of a scroll compressor.

❑ Compression in the scroll compressor is achieved by the interaction of a rotating scroll and a stationary scroll.

❑ Refrigerant vapor enters the compressor suction port and an outer opening of one of the rotating scrolls.

❑ This open passage allows refrigerant vapor to be drawn into the passage of the scroll, which is then sealed off.

❑ As the scroll continues to rotate, the passage becomes smaller and the refrigerant vapor is compressed.

❑ As the refrigerant vapor is discharged from the compressor discharge port, its temperature and pressure has been increased.

This brief explanation is of just one vapor passage of the scroll. During actual operation, all vapor passages of the scroll are in various stages of compression at the same time. This provides a nearly continuous suction and discharge pressure at all times.

A scroll compressor has only one moving part; the scroll.

The scroll compressor was first introduced by Copeland Corporation for use in residential heat pump systems.

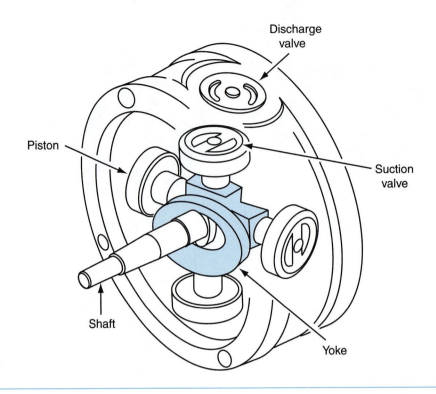

**Figure 8-22** A typical scotch yoke compressor details.

# Scotch Yoke Compressors

In a scotch yoke compressor, (Figure 8-22), opposed pistons are pressed into opposite ends of a yoke riding upon a slider block located on the shaft eccentric. Rotation of the shaft moves the yoke, with attached pistons, in a reciprocating motion. Counterweights are used to balance the rotating assembly. A suction reed valve is located at the top of each piston, and a discharge valve plate is located at the top of each cylinder. Like all reciprocating compressors, low-pressure refrigerant is drawn into the cylinder through the suction valve on the intake stroke and is forced out through the discharge valve on the exhaust stroke at a high pressure.

# Variable Displacement Compressors

**Shop Manual**
Chapter 8,
page 284

Harrison first introduced a variable displacement compressor in 1985. It is used on some models of General Motors car lines. Designated as model V-5, this compressor can match any automotive air conditioning load demand under all conditions. This is accomplished by varying the displacement of the compressor by changing the stroke (displacement) of the pistons.

The five axially oriented pistons are driven by a variable-angle wobble plate. The angle of the wobble plate is changed by a bellows-activated control valve located in the rear head of the compressor. This control valve (Figure 8-23) senses suction pressure and controls the wobble plate angle based on crankcase-suction pressure differential.

When the air conditioning demand is high, suction pressure will be above the control point, and the control valve will maintain a bleed from the compressor crankcase to the suction side. In this case, there is no crankcase-suction pressure differential, and the compressor will have maximum displacement. The wobble plate is at maximum angle, providing greatest piston travel (stroke) (Figure 8-24).

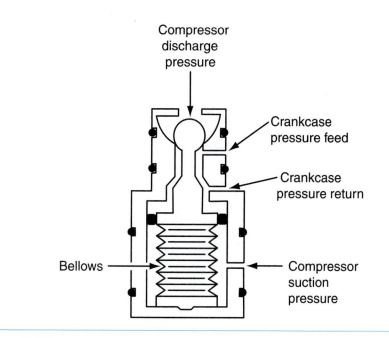

Figure 8-23 Variable displacement compressor control valve assembly.

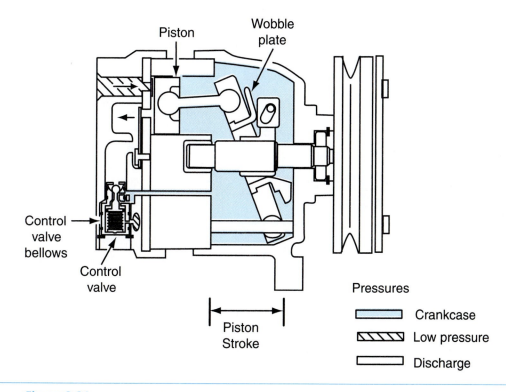

Figure 8-24 Variable displacement compressor at maximum displacement.

Conversely, when the air conditioning demand is low and the suction pressure reaches the control point, the control valve will bleed discharge gas into the crankcase to the suction plenum (Figure 8-25).

The angle of the wobble plate is actually controlled by a force balance on the five pistons. Only a slight increase of the crankcase-suction pressure differential is required to create a force on the pistons sufficient to result in a movement of the wobble plate.

Operation of the control valve is dependent on differential pressure, known as delta p ($\Delta$p).

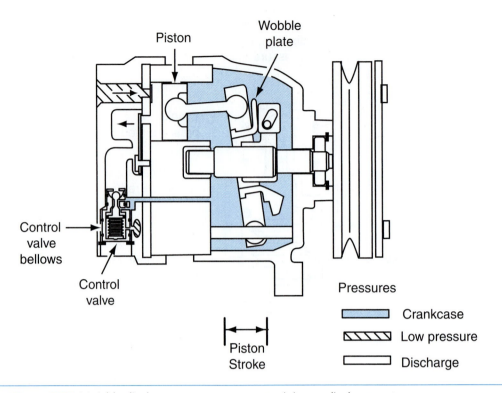

Figure 8-25 Variable displacement compressor at minimum displacement.

Temperature, then, is maintained by varying the capacity of the compressor, not by cycling the clutch on and off. This action provides a more uniform method of temperature control and, at the same time, eliminates some of the noise problems associated with a cycling clutch system.

## Diagnosing Problems and Making Repairs

A broken discharge valve plate will set up a mini-vibration sufficient to "shake" the compressor loose enough to cause belt slippage.

**Shop Manual**
Chapter 8, page 290

Broken discharge valves in compressors (Figure 8-26) are not uncommon. Broken suction valves and piston rings are less often encountered, but lead to the same diagnosis. Broken valves and/or rings are easier to diagnose in one- and two-cylinder reciprocating compressors than in multi-cylinder compressors. The manifold and gauge set is the diagnostic tool most often used to determine valve plate condition. The first indication of failure is a higher-than-normal low-side (suction) pressure accompanied by a lower-than-normal high-side (head) pressure.

Valve and ring failures, however, are not as easily diagnosed in four-, five-, and six-cylinder compressors. The first indication of valve or ring failure in these compressors is that the belt(s) will not remain tightened. One defective discharge valve plate in a six-cylinder compressor, for example, sets up a vibration that, when not otherwise detected, literally shakes the belt(s) loose. This is true regardless of how well the adjustment provisions are tightened.

Many simple compressor repairs are usually a routine service provided by the automotive air conditioning technician. These repairs include checking and adding oil, replacing the crankshaft seal, and, in many units, replacing the valve plate assembly. More complex repairs are often "shopped out" to a specialty shop that has the facilities for semi-mass-rebuilding procedures. Because of the general high cost of labor, one-on-one compressor rebuilding is not usually economically feasible.

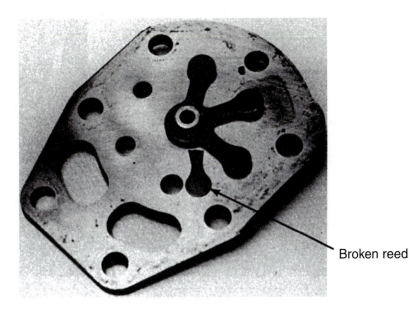

Broken reed

**Figure 8-26** Broken reed in valve plate.

## Compressor Failure

Compressor failure, representing almost 30 percent of all vehicle air conditioning system repairs, is the leading cause of system failure according to a survey conducted in the late 1990s by the Mobile Air Conditioning Society Worldwide (MACSW). The principal cause of compressor failure was found to be leaks, followed by internal mechanical problems. Clutch problems were the least common reasons for compressor failure.

The survey revealed that over half of the reported compressor failures were to R-134a air conditioning systems in vehicles that had been retrofitted to avoid using R-12 refrigerant. This is probably because many older compressors designed for R-12 simply will not withstand the rigors of R-134a's higher operating pressures. The lack of proper lubrication is also implicated as a problem with vehicle air conditioning system compressors and is generally due to not properly changing the lubricant during retrofit procedures or not checking lubricant during repair procedures.

Most compressors are designed to function with a compression ratio between 5:1 and 7:1. One may make a quick check of a compressor's operating compression ratio by dividing high-side psia by low-side psia. Note that these are absolute pressures, so one must add 15 to both low-side and high-side gauge readings. The formula is:

$$\text{COMPRESSION RATIO} = \frac{\text{HIGH-SIDE PRESSURE} + 15}{\text{LOW-SIDE PRESSURE} + 15}$$

For example, assume that the low-side pressure is 30 psig and the high-side pressure is 220 psig. When 15 is added to these values, they become 45 psia and 235 psia, hence:

$$\frac{235}{45} = 5.2$$

Pressure ratios above 7.5:1 can cause early compressor failure because of the added load on bearings, pistons, and seals. Also, higher operating temperatures generated by the higher operating pressures can cause lubrication breakdown, which result in harmful deposits on the compressor's internal assembly.

**Shop Manual**
Chapter 7, page 235

# Summary

❑ Reciprocating compressors have a piston or pistons that draw low-pressure heated refrigerant vapor into a chamber, increases its heat content and pressure, and "pump" it out as a high-pressure high-temperature vapor.

❑ A scroll compressor draws low-pressure heated refrigerant vapor through its suction port into a continuously rotating scroll where the vapor's pressure and temperature are increased, and are then forced out through its discharge port as a high-pressure high-temperature vapor.

❑ In a rotary compressor, a rotating vane draws in low-pressure heated refrigerant vapor through the suction port and increases its temperature and pressure before forcing it out through the discharge port. It is discharged as a high-temperature high-pressure vapor.

❑ An electromagnetic clutch is used to engage and disengage (turn on and off) a compressor, as desired, in present applications of automotive air conditioning systems.

## Terms to Know

Auxiliary

Axial plate

Compression

Crankshaft

Discharge

Exhaust

High pressure

Intake

Low pressure

Rotary

Scroll

Serpentine

Suction

Swash plate

Wobble plate

Zener clamping diode

# Review Questions

## Short Answer Essays

1. Describe the operating principals of a reciprocating compressor.

2. Why is a low pressure important?

3. What are other terms used to describe an axial plate?

4. How is a compressor clutch generally driven off an engine?

5. What are some of the design considerations for an automotive air conditioning compressor?

6. Describe the function of a variable displacement compressor.

7. Describe the operating principals of a rotary compressor.

8. What is the purpose of a magnetic clutch:

   a. in a fixed-displacement compressor system?

   b. in a variable-displacement compressor system?

9. What are the two primary functions of a compressor?

10. Why is the scroll compressor considered to be the most efficient?

## Fill-in-the-Blanks

1. In-car temperature is controlled in a variable displacement compressor system by varying the capacity of the _____ , not by cycling the _____ on and off.

2. Compression in a scroll compressor is achieved by the interaction of a rotating _____ and a stationary _____ .

3. During the compression stroke of a reciprocating compressor, a high-pressure area is created above the _____ and below the _____ .

4. Reciprocating means that the piston(s) moves up and down, to and fro, or _____ and _____ .

5. Compressors may have from _____ to _____ cylinders; there are, at the present time, no _____-cylinder compressors, however.

6. A single belt driving all accessories, is often called a _____-drive system.

7. Two methods of driving a piston are by _____ or _____ .

8. An electromagnetic clutch is used to turn the _____ on and off.

9. As refrigerant condenses, it gives up its _____ in the _____ .

10. Other terms for a metering device include _____ expansion valve and fixed _____ tube.

## Multiple Choice

1. *Technician A* says that a reciprocating compressor pumps refrigerant as a vapor.
   *Technician B* says that a reciprocating compressor pumps refrigerant as a liquid.
   Who is correct?
   **A.** A only          **C.** Both A and B
   **B.** B only          **D.** Neither A nor B

2. The methods used to drive a compressor are being discussed:
   *Technician A* says that all automotive air conditioner compressors have an electromagnetic clutch.
   *Technician B* says that a serpentine belt system is often used to drive a compressor clutch.
   Who is correct?
   **A.** A only          **C.** Both A and B
   **B.** B only          **D.** Neither A nor B

3. *Technician A* says that the rotary compressor has double-ended pistons.
   *Technician B* says that the scotch yoke compressor is a reciprocating type.
   Who is correct?
   **A.** A only          **C.** Both A and B
   **B.** B only          **D.** Neither A nor B

4. *Technician A* says that the angle of the wobble plate is controlled in a variable displacement compressor.
   *Technician B* says that the capacity of the compressor is varied by the angle of the wobble plate.
   Who is correct?
   **A.** A only          **C.** Both A and B
   **B.** B only          **D.** Neither A nor B

5. *Technician A* says that the proper designation for refrigerant pressure is psig.
   *Technician B* says that the proper designation for refrigerant pressure is kPa.
   Who is correct?
   **A.** A only          **C.** Both A and B
   **B.** B only          **D.** Neither A nor B

6. Reciprocating compressors are being discussed:
   *Technician A* says that the suction valve is opened to allow refrigerant vapor to enter due to a differential in pressure above and below the valve.
   *Technician B* says that the discharge valve is opened to allow refrigerant vapor to leave due to a differential in pressure above and below the valve.
   Who is correct?
   **A.** A only          **C.** Both A and B
   **B.** B only          **D.** Neither A nor B

7. The function of a scroll compressor is being discussed:
   *Technician A* says that its function is to create a low-pressure condition in the system.
   *Technician B* says that its function is to increase the temperature and pressure of refrigerant vapor.
   Who is correct?
   **A.** A only          **C.** Both A and B
   **B.** B only          **D.** Neither A nor B

8. Compressor design is being discussed:
   *Technician A* says that all reciprocating compressors have a crankshaft.
   *Technician B* says that all rotary compressors have an axial plate.
   Who is correct?
   **A.** A only          **C.** Both A and B
   **B.** B only          **D.** Neither A nor B

9. The rotary vane compressor is being discussed:
*Technician A* says that this compressor is unique in that it has only one rotating vane.
*Technician B* says that a suction check valve prevents liquid refrigerant from entering the compressor.
Who is correct?
**A.** A only
**B.** B only
**C.** Both A and B
**D.** Neither A nor B

10. The following are automotive air conditioning system compressor types, *except*
**A.** Rotary
**B.** Swashplate
**C.** Centrifugal
**D.** Scroll

# Case and Duct Systems

Upon completion and review of this chapter, you should be able to:

❏ Identify types of case/duct systems.

❏ Discuss air distribution through the case/duct system.

❏ Understand the air flow through the case/duct system for defrost mode, heat mode, and cool mode.

❏ Understand and control unpleasant HVAC odor.

❏ Identify the need for and location of cabin air filters.

❏ Understand Mode Door Actuator operation: cable, vacuum, and electric.

## Introduction

This chapter is intended to provide a basic understanding of the automotive heater/air conditioner case/duct system for factory-installed heater/air conditioning systems. The system discussed in this unit should be considered typical. It is not representative of any particular automotive case/duct system. A typical automotive heater/air conditioner case/duct system (Figure 9-1), at first glance, may seem to be a complicated maze of passages and doors. Actually, it is much simpler than it first appears.

The case/duct system serves two purposes. First, it houses the heater core and the air conditioner evaporator. Second, it directs fresh or recirculated conditioned air into the vehicle. This air is directed through selected components into the passenger compartment via selected outlet provisions, such as panel registers, a floor outlet, and defroster outlets.

The heater coolant flow control valve is generally found outside the case/duct system for ease of service.

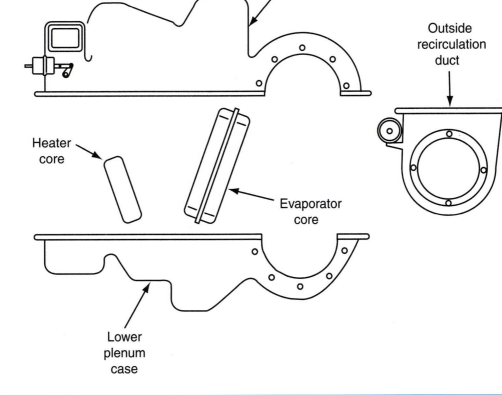

**Figure 9-1** A typical bathtub design heating/air conditioning plenum/duct system.

The supply air may be either fresh (outside) and/or recirculated (in-car) air, depending upon the system **mode** selected. After air is heated and/or cooled (conditioned), it is delivered to either the floor outlet, dash (panel) outlets, and/or the **defrost** (windshield) outlets.

Two basic types of case assemblies are used to house the heater core and air conditioner evaporator: the independent case assembly and the split case assembly.

The independent case, which is used on compact and small cars, may have an upstream blower (Figure 9-2) or a downstream blower (Figure 9-3). Either an upstream integral blower (Figure 9-4) or an independent blower (Figure 9-5) is used on split case systems. The split case system, which is used on larger cars, is located on both sides of the engine firewall. The independent case system is usually located under the dash, on the inside of the firewall.

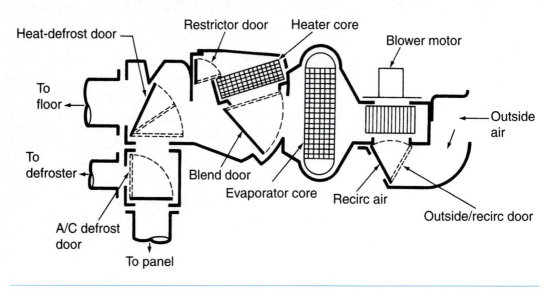

**Figure 9-2** An independent case/duct system with an upstream blower.

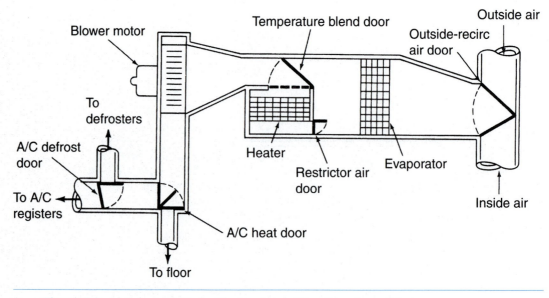

**Figure 9-3** An independent case/duct system with a downstream blower.

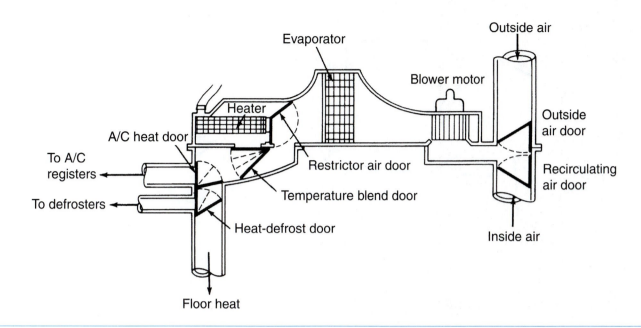

Figure 9-4 A split case system with an upstream blower.

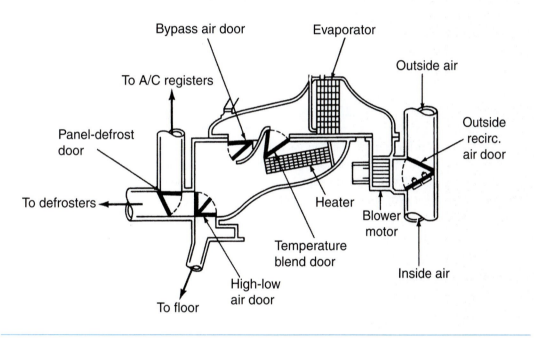

Figure 9-5 A split case system with an independent blower.

For simplicity of understanding, a typical hybrid case/duct system is illustrated in this unit. Also, for the purposes of explanation, this system is theoretically divided into three sections (Figure 9-6): the air intake, heater core and air conditioning evaporator (**plenum**), and air distribution.

Each will be studied, first individually, then as a complete system. Remember, however, that this discussion is of factory-installed or original equipment manufacturer (OEM) installation.

There are many considerations involved in the design of an automotive air conditioning system and the volume of airflow requirements of the case and duct system. The interior passenger compartment soak temperatures of the vehicle are affected by many factors. Temperatures are affected by both exterior and interior surface colors and tint versus nontint windows. Heat load on the air conditioning system varies with the number of passengers in the vehicles, due to

**Shop Manual**
Chapter 9, page 326

The **plenum** is an area filled with air at a pressure that is slightly higher or lower than the surrounding air pressure, such as the chamber just before the blower motor.

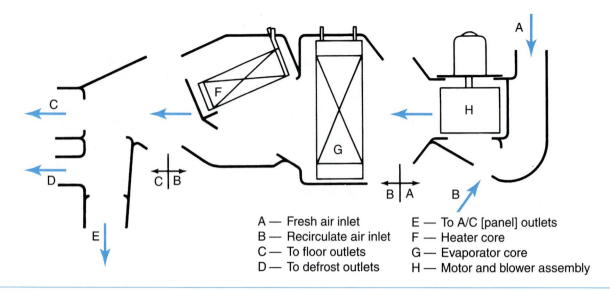

A — Fresh air inlet　　　　E — To A/C [panel] outlets
B — Recirculate air inlet　F — Heater core
C — To floor outlets　　　G — Evaporator core
D — To defrost outlets　　H — Motor and blower assembly

**Figure 9-6** Three sections, right to left: (A) air intake section; (B) plenum section; (C) air distribution section.

both body heat and breath temperatures, which are typically 40°–60°F above ambient air temperatures. The temperature of the interior surfaces due to the radiant heat of the sun can range from 50°–100°F above ambient air temperatures. All of these factors and more affect the overall performance of the heating and air conditioning system. Understanding how the entire system functions is essential to proper diagnosis of the system as a whole.

# OEM or Aftermarket?

There are "custom" **aftermarket** installations that have the appearance of factory-installed systems. This type of system has no provision for outside air and is not connected to the heater duct system. If in doubt, use the following simple test to determine which type of system is being serviced. To perform this test, however, it is assumed that the air conditioning and heating system is in proper working condition.

1. Note the in-car **ambient** temperature.
2. Start the engine.
3. Turn on the air conditioning system.
4. Move the temperature control to HOT.
5. Measure the temperature of the air coming out of the dash registers.

If the delivery air temperature does not increase rapidly and exceed the ambient in-car temperature, the system is obviously a "custom" installation. This simple test has determined that the air conditioning system has no air passage connection with the heater circuit.

**Aftermarket** is a term given to a device or accessory that is added to a vehicle that was not manufactured or installed by the vehicle's manufacturer.

**Ambient** means all around, surrounding, encompassing, such as ambient air temperature.

This test also assumes that the heating system is in proper working order.

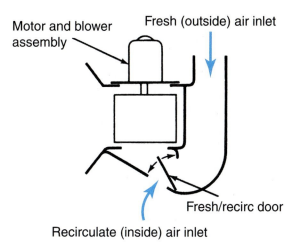

Figure 9-7 Air intake (inlet) section.

**Shop Manual**
Chapter 9, page 325

# Air Intake

The air intake or inlet section (Figure 9-7) consists of a fresh (outside) air inlet, a **recirculate** (inside) air inlet, and a fresh-recirculate blend-air door. The outlet of this section is to the blower inlet. The fresh air inlet provides the system with a fresh outside air; the recirculate air inlet provides a recirculated in-car air.

The position of the fresh-recirculate door depends on the system mode. Generally, in all modes except maximum cooling (MAX A/C), the air supply is from the outside ambient. In MAX A/C, the air supply is from the inside (recirculated). Even in the MAX A/C mode, some systems provide for up to 20 percent fresh air. This is to provide for a slightly positive in-vehicle pressure. A slightly positive pressure must be maintained inside the vehicle to prevent the possibility of the entrance of dangerous exhaust gases that could produce a hazardous, if not lethal, in-vehicle atmosphere when all the windows are tightly closed.

# Core Section

The core section, more appropriately called the plenum section, is the center section of the system. It consists of the heater core, the air conditioning evaporator, and a **blend door**. The blend door may be operated by a **Bowden cable** or, on many systems today, it is operated by an electric or vacuum actuator and provides a full range control of the airflow either through or around the heater core. All air passes through the air conditioning evaporator. It is in this section that full-range temperature and humidity conditions are provided for in-car comfort. A description of how this is accomplished follows.

Fresh air intake is generally through vents provided just in front of the windshield, often hidden by the hood cowl.

To **recirculate** is to reuse, to circulate over and over again.

The **blend door** is a door in the duct system that controls temperature by blending heated air and cool outside air.

A **Bowden cable** is a wire cable inside a metal or rubber housing used to regulate a valve or to control a remote device.

**Shop Manual**
Chapter 10,
page 382

Some may refer to the
core section as the
mixing section; it is in
this section that
heated and cooled air
is mixed.

The coolant flow
control may allow from
partial to full flow of
coolant based on the
temperature selected
by the operator.

A full flow of
refrigerant in the
evaporator core
provides maximum
cooling at all times.

The bi-level control is
sometimes referred to
as the HI/LO door or
control.

Mode doors are
diverters within the
duct system for
directing air to various
locations.

Even on recirculate, up
to 20 percent fresh air
may be brought in to
maintain a positive in-
car pressure.

## Heating

The heater coolant valve is open to allow hot engine coolant to flow through the heater core. Cool outside fresh air is heated as it passes through the heater core. In the heating mode, the air conditioner is not operational; therefore, it has no effect on temperature as the air first passes through the evaporator. The desired temperature level is achieved by the position of the blend door. This allows a percentage of the cooler outside air to bypass the heater core, tempering the heated air. The heated and cool air are blended in the plenum to provide the desired temperature and humidity level before passing to the air distribution section.

## Cooling

If all other conditions are correct, the compressor is turned on in the cooling mode. In maximum cooling (MAX A/C), recirculated air passes through the air conditioner evaporator and is then directed back into the vehicle. In other than MAX A/C, fresh outside air passes through the air conditioning evaporator and is cooled before delivery into the vehicle.

The desired in-vehicle temperature level is achieved by the position of the blend door. The blend door allows a percentage of cooled air to pass through the heater core to be reheated. The cooled air passing through the evaporator and the reheated air passing through the heated core are blended in the plenum to provide the desired temperature level. This tempered air is then directed to the air distribution section.

# Distribution Section

The air distribution section directs conditioned air to be discharged to floor outlets, defrost outlets, or dash panel outlets. Depending on the position of the **mode doors**, conditioned air may be delivered to any combination of these outlets. There are two mode (blend) doors in the air distribution section: the HI/LO door and the DEF/AC door. The HI/LO door provides 0–100 percent full-range conditioned air outlet control to the HI (dash) and LO (floor) outlets. The DEF/AC door provides conditioned air outlet control either to the defrost (windshield) outlets or to the dash panel outlets.

# Combined Case

The combined case/duct system provides full-range control of air circulation through the heater core and air conditioner evaporator. Figure 9-8 shows 100 percent recirculated air through the air conditioner evaporator and out through the panel outlets.

This may typically represent mode and blend door positions when maximum cooling (MAX A/C) is selected during high in-car ambient temperature conditions.

Figure 9-9 shows 100 percent fresh air circulation through the heater core and out through the floor outlets. This may typically represent the mode and blend door positions when heat is selected during low in-car ambient temperature conditions. A variation (Figure 9-10) shows some of the heated air diverted to the defrost outlets. This would be the typical application to clear the windshield of fog or light icing conditions.

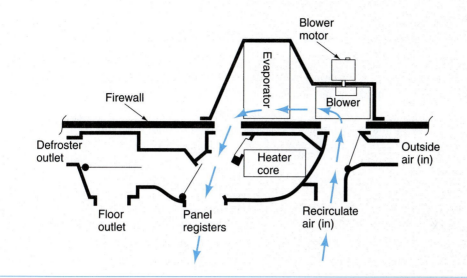

**Figure 9-8** All recirculated air through the evaporator and out the panel registers (outlets).

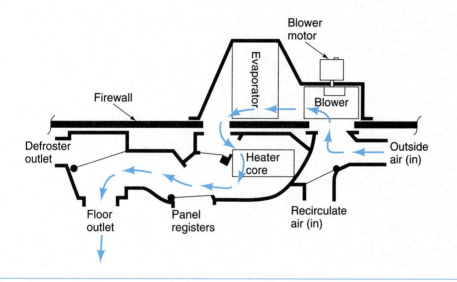

**Figure 9-9** All fresh air through the heater core and out the floor outlets. Though air flows through the evaporator, the compressor is not running and there is no cooling effect.

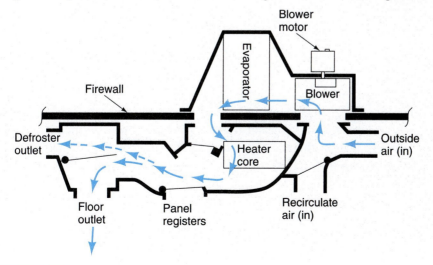

**Figure 9-10** The same condition as illustration 9-9 but with some air diverted to the defroster outlet.

# Air Delivery

In addition to OFF, there are six selections for the condition of the air to be provided to the passenger compartment of the car. Some may require recirculated air, and others may require fresh air. While the select conditions may differ slightly from one car model to another, they typically are MAX, panel, panel/floor (**bi-level**), floor, floor/defrost, and defrost.

Following are some of the typical duct door routing of conditioned air for the various selections available at the driver control panel.

**Bi-level** is a condition whereby air is delivered to two levels in the vehicle, generally the floor and dash outlets.

## MAX

In MAX (maximum) cooling (Figure 9-11), the compressor is running, and the outside/recirculate air door is closed to ambient air. Flow is from in-car air, through the evaporator, and out through the panel registers. Bi-level, which will provide some air to the floor outlet (Figure 9-12), may be selected.

In MAX cooling, the heater coolant control valve is closed if the system is equipped with one.

If MAX heating (Figure 9-13) is selected, the compressor is not running, and the heater coolant valve is open if the system is equipped with one. Airflow is from in-car, through the evaporator and heater core, and out the floor outlet. If bi-level is selected (Figure 9-14), some air is directed to the panel registers. A small amount of air in either condition is directed to the windshield to prevent fogging.

## Panel (Norm)

If normal (panel) cooling is selected, the air conditioner compressor is running. Airflow is from outside ambient, through the evaporator, and out the panel registers (Figure 9-15). For humidity control, some air may be directed through the heater core (Figure 9-16) as well.

The "panel" registers are those visible on the dash assembly.

If normal (panel) heating is selected, the air conditioning compressor is not running, and the coolant control valve is open if the system is equipped with one. Airflow is from the outside ambient, through the heater core, and out the floor outlets (Figure 9-17).

In either condition, cooling or heating, a small amount of conditioned air is directed to the defrost outlets as an aid to prevent windshield fogging (Figure 9-18).

## Panel/Floor (Bi-level)

Bi-level air in the cooling mode can be selected (Figure 9-19) to provide some conditioned air to the floor outlet. Bi-level air may also be selected in the heating mode to provide some air through the panel registers (Figure 9-20).

Floor outlets are not generally visible from the seated position.

ATC is a recognized acronym for automatic temperature control.

The bi-level setting simply means that conditioned air may be provided at two outlets, panel and floor, as desired by some vehicle occupants. In some systems, this is referred to as HI-LO or PNL/FLR. This condition is similar in operation to **MIX**.

**Mix** is a term used to describe the bi-level or HI/LO mode position.

## Vent

The **vent** brings in unconditioned, ambient air when neither heating nor cooling is desired. The compressor is not running, and the heater coolant valve is not open if the system is equipped with one. Air passage is from ambient air through the heater or evaporator core to the selected outlets—floor outlets and/or panel registers. Figure 9-21 shows the vent setting selected with bi-level air delivery.

To **vent** is to introduce fresh outside air into the vehicle.

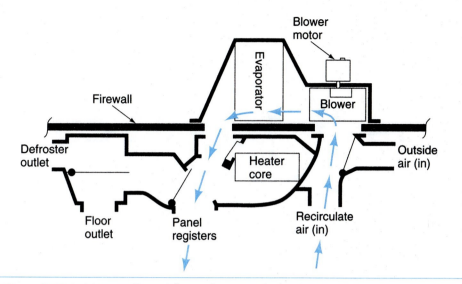

Figure 9-11 In MAX cooling, airflow is from in-vehicle, through the evaporator, and out the panel outlets.

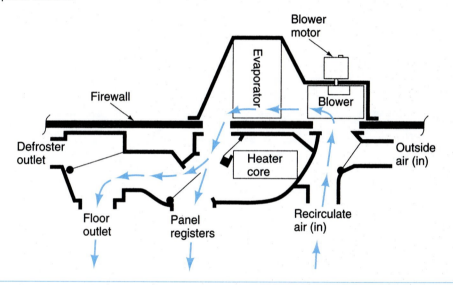

Figure 9-12 MAX cooling with BI-LEVEL selected.

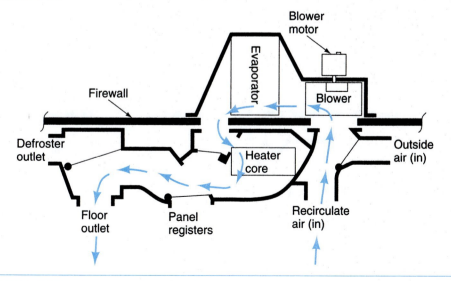

Figure 9-13 Airflow when MAX heating is selected.

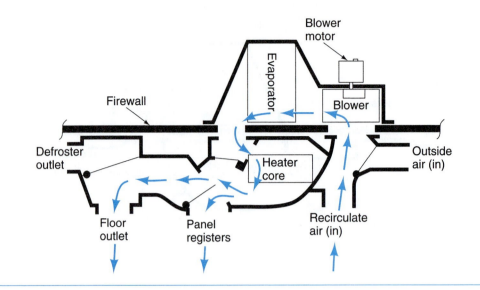

**Figure 9-14** MAX heating with BI-LEVEL selected.

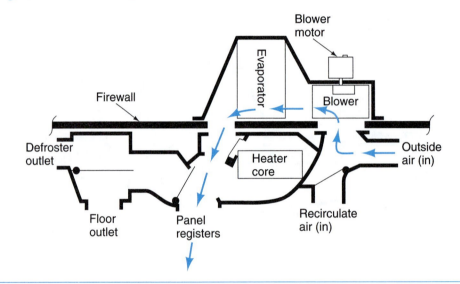

**Figure 9-15** Normal cooling (air conditioning) is selected.

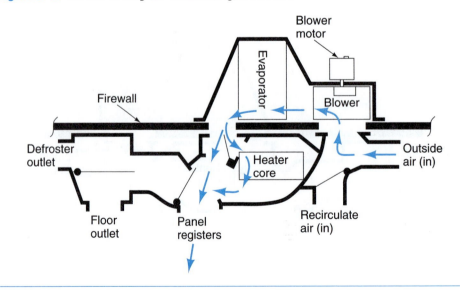

**Figure 9-16** Airflow when humidity control is required with normal cooling.

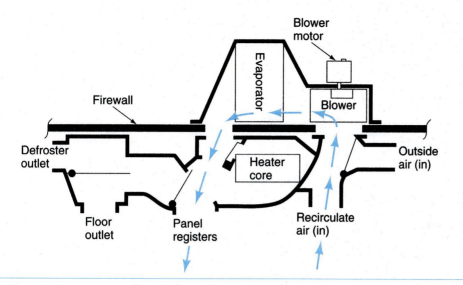

**Figure 9-11** In MAX cooling, airflow is from in-vehicle, through the evaporator, and out the panel outlets.

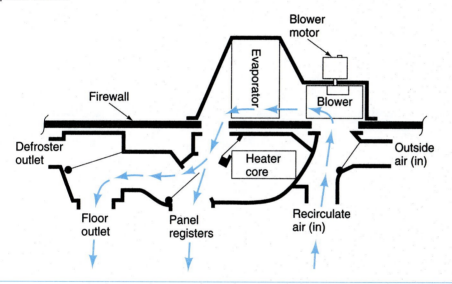

**Figure 9-12** MAX cooling with BI-LEVEL selected.

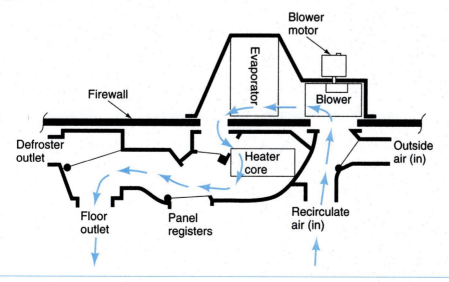

**Figure 9-13** Airflow when MAX heating is selected.

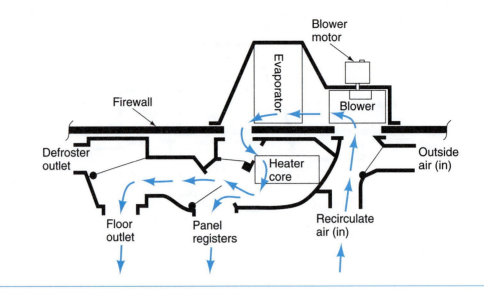

**Figure 9-14** MAX heating with BI-LEVEL selected.

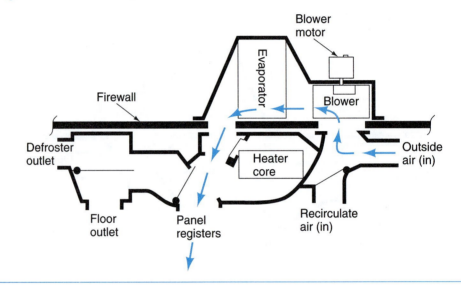

**Figure 9-15** Normal cooling (air conditioning) is selected.

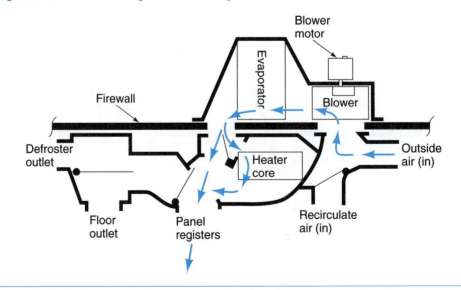

**Figure 9-16** Airflow when humidity control is required with normal cooling.

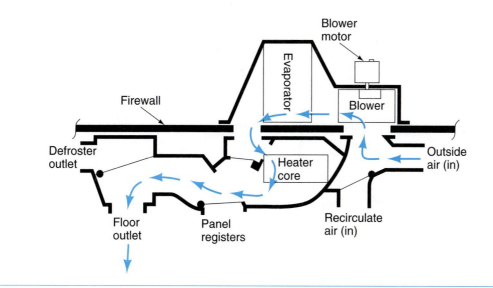

**Figure 9-17** Airflow when normal heating is selected.

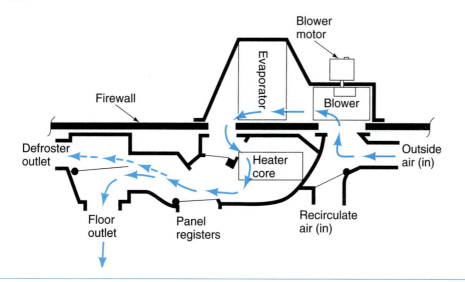

**Figure 9-18** Some conditioned air is directed to the defroster outlets to prevent windshield fogging.

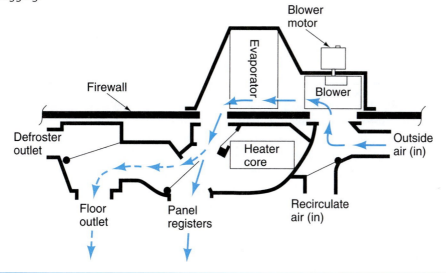

**Figure 9-19** Airflow in the cooling mode when BI-LEVEL is selected.

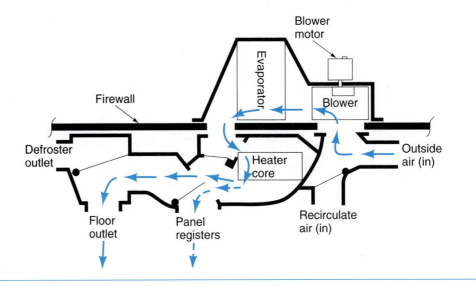

**Figure 9-20** Airflow in the heating mode when BI-LEVEL is selected.

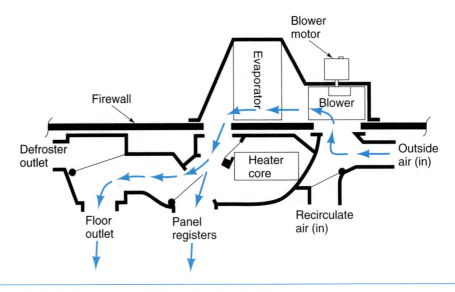

**Figure 9-21** Airflow when VENT is selected in the bi-level condition.

**Shop Manual**
Chapter 10,
page 390

SATC stands for
semiautomatic
temperature control.

ATC stands for
automatic
temperature control.

# Heat/Cool

A temperature control is generally provided to select in-car temperature. There are two methods: manual/semiautomatic and automatic (Figure 9-22). Temperature and mode are manually selected in the manual/semiautomatic temperature control (**SATC**) system. In the automatic temperature control (**ATC**) system, the selected temperature and mode are a fully automatic function of a digital microprocessor. The microprocessor compares data from designated sensors to maintain the desired in-car temperature. These sensors will be discussed in greater detail in Chapter 10, System Controls.

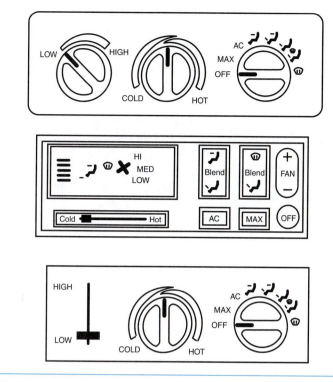

Figure 9-22 Typical air conditioner/heater controls.

## Defrost

In the defrost position (Figure 9-23), outside ambient air passes through the heater core and is directed to the defroster outlets. A slight amount of heated air is directed to the floor outlets (Figure 9-24). If the outside ambient air temperature is above 50°F (10°C), the compressor may operate to temper the heated air for humidity control.

**Shop Manual**
Chapter 9,
page 337

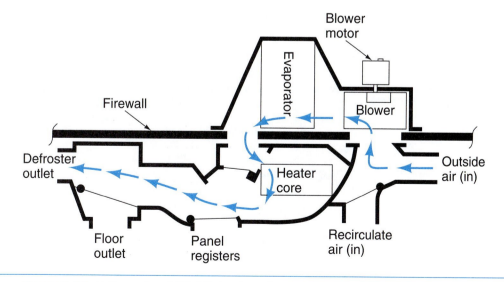

Figure 9-23 Airflow when DEFROST is selected.

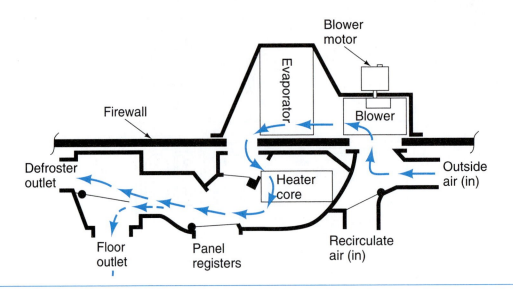

**Figure 9-24** With DEFROST selected, some air will be diverted to the floor outlets.

## Mix

MIX may be selected on some models. Generally, those with a MIX select do not have a bi-level (HI-LO) select provision. When in the MIX position, the floor/defroster door opens halfway (Figure 9-25). In this selection, conditioned air is delivered to the floor and defrost outlets. In-car temperature is controlled by adjusting the temperature control lever. The compressor will operate if in-car temperature conditions warrant. The compressor will also operate if outside ambient air temperature is above 50°F (10°C) as an aid for in-car humidity control.

Other settings for MIX are HI/LO and BI-LEVEL.

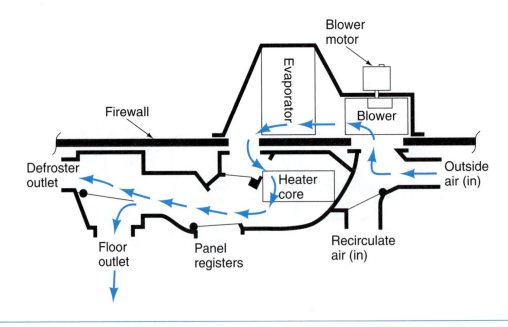

**Figure 9-25** Airflow when MIX or Bi-level is selected.

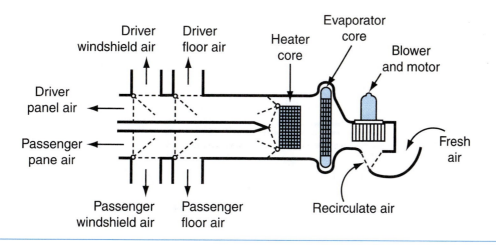

Figure 9-26 A typical dual-duct system.

# Dual-Zone Duct System

The dual-zone duct system found in some cars has a separate driver- and passenger-side duct system (Figure 9-26). Both sides have a defrost/air conditioning outlet door and a heater/floor outlet door that operate together. The passenger has control of the passenger-side temperature door only.

The dual-zone duct air distribution system can be controlled by either a manual or automatic climate control system and has a separate temperature control for the passenger. The passenger may adjust the temperature of the air at the outlet vents on the passenger side in an automatic climate control system only within the limits set by the driver—generally up to 30°F (16.7°C) cooler or warmer than that selected by the driver. Passenger control on a manual climate control system is not usually restricted by the driver's temperature selection.

The passenger manually controls the position of the passenger-side temperature air door, controlling the discharge temperature of the passenger-side air outlets between full hot (Figure 9-27) and full cold (Figure 9-28). The actual passenger-side temperature depends on the general operation of the system. The passenger controls do not engage or disengage the compressor, change blower speed, or reposition the passenger mode door.

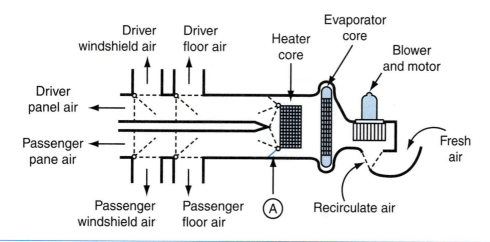

Figure 9-27 A typical dual-zone duct system with passenger-side full hot selected (A).

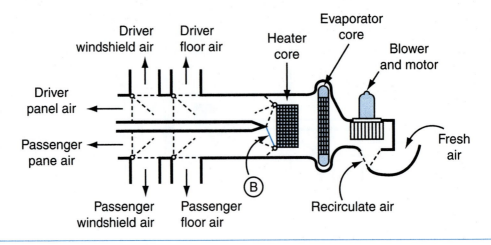

Figure 9-28 A typical dual-zone duct system with passenger-side full cold selected.

# Rear Heat/Cool System

Some trucks and vans may be equipped with a rear air distribution system to provide rear heating, cooling, or a combination of both. The rear air distribution system is often referred to as an auxiliary air conditioning system (Figure 9-29).

Depending on design, it may have the following major components: blower and motor, temperature door, evaporator core with metering device, heater core with flow control, outlet mode door, control panel(s), and controller.

The rear auxiliary system that provides only heating or cooling does not require an outlet or temperature mode door. The heat-only control panel has a blower speed control accessible to the rear-seat passengers. The rear blower master control for the cooling-only system is generally in the front control panel. The switch in the REAR position permits the rear blower switch to select the speed of the rear blower.

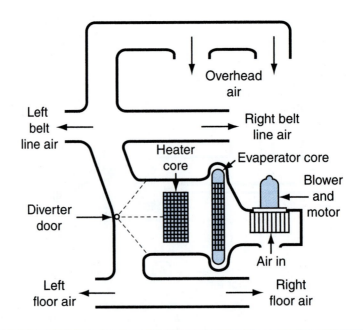

Figure 9-29 A typical rear (auxiliary) heat/cool system duct.

Systems that provide both heating and cooling have an outlet mode door to direct outlet air to the upper or lower vents (Figure 9-30 and Figure 9-31). Some systems may have a temperature door controlling outlet air temperature, while others are controlled by the front master control. The heat/cool system generally has both front and rear control panels for controlling the rear air distribution system. The control panels allow selection of the blower speed, the mode door, and in some systems, the temperature door position.

Since the rear system is connected in parallel to the front system, the rear controls cannot override the master controls, such as to energize or de-energize the compressor or heater control valve. The rear system can only provide cooling or heating when cooling or heating is selected in the front system.

It should be noted that some minivan rear heat/cool temperature control is determined by the driver's temperature control setting and only offers heating or cooling to the rear compart-

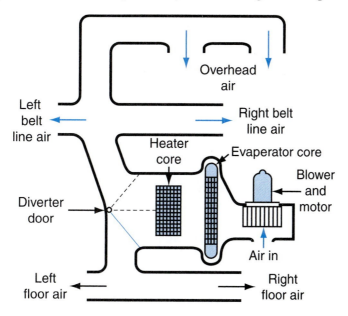

**Figure 9-30** Air diverted to upper vents.

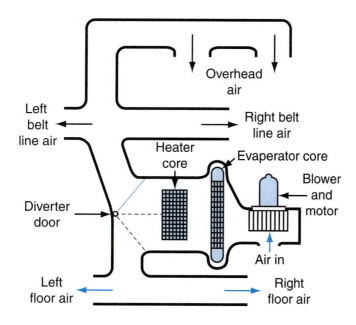

**Figure 9-31** Air diverted to lower (floor) vents.

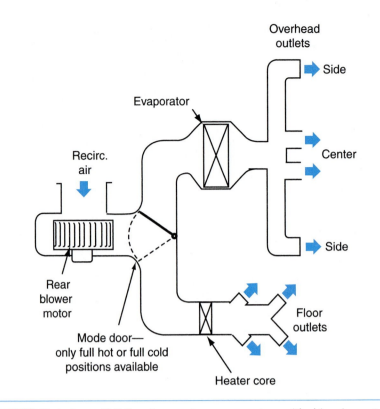

**Figure 9-32** Typical rear HVAC system on two zone system with driver in control of temperature control.

ment. This is considered a two-zone system (front driver/passenger separate zones) with the rear compartment only able to control the fan speed inorder to control the temperature. The driver must slide the temperature control past the 75 percent point toward full hot position in order for the rear compartment to be heated or past the 25 percent full cold position in order for the rear compartment to be cooled (Figure 9-32). If the midpoint on the driver's temperature control is selected, the rear compartment will receive full heating or full cooling depending on the last position selected by the driver, no temperature blending if available to the rear compartment. True three-zone systems have a rear HVAC duct system as depicted in Figure 9-29 Figure 9-30, and Figure 9-31 with full blend features.

# Evaporator Drain

Moisture extracted from the air in the evaporator is readily expelled from the evaporator case through a drain tube that extends through the floorboard of the vehicle. To prevent insects from entering the evaporator through this tube, it has a molded, accordion shape (Figure 9-33). The weight of the moisture, as it collects, overcomes the rigidity of the tube closure and allows the water to pass.

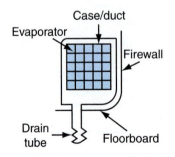

**Figure 9-33** An evaporator drain extends through the floorboard of a vehicle.

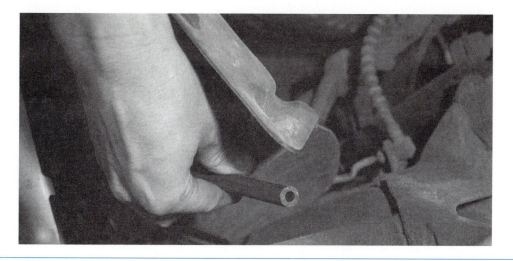

Figure 9-34 An evaporator drain hole hose extending from the bottom of a vehicle.

Over time, however, airborne debris and dust may restrict the tube to the point that causes water to back up inside the case. This is sometimes evidenced by water droplets exiting the dash outlets with the air or dripping onto the floor mats in the passenger compartment. There have even been reports of drivers getting a cold, wet right foot when making a hard right turn.

If this becomes a problem, it is necessary to clean out the drain tube to ensure that it will open to allow water to pass. This is best done from under the vehicle (Figure 9-34). For obvious reasons, do not stand immediately under the tube while cleaning it.

# Odor Control

During the normal operation of the passenger comfort heating/ventilation/air conditioning (**HVAC**) system, moisture can accumulate in the ductwork and collect on the evaporator core surface. Under normal operation, most of this moisture will drain out of the case drain causing no problems. Air that enters the passenger compartment contains microscopic contaminants and bacteria that will stick to the moisture on the evaporator and case. During periods of high humidity or when the recirculation mode is used extensively, this becomes an ideal environment for odor-causing mold, bacteria, and mildew to grow. When these environmental conditions arise, a musty odor develops and becomes very pronounced when the HVAC system is first turned on.

The industry has developed commercially available treatments to combat this problem by chemically coating the evaporator core and duct with an antimicrobial deodorizer and disinfectant product to eradicate these contaminants. These products generally offer protection for three cooling seasons or more under normal air conditioning use. They are applied using a siphon-type sprayer (Figure 9-35).

In addition to chemically treating the HVAC system, the case drain vent must be checked to be sure that it is not plugged and will properly drain the system of excess moisture. Some manufacturers have also integrated a feature into their HVAC systems that leaves the blower motor on for a brief period of time after the air conditioner is turned off to allow the evaporator core and ducts to dry even after the vehicle has been turned off. There are also kits available to add this delay timer feature to other vehicles. Some manufacturers have sent out service bulletins recommending the installation of a blower delay feature on troublesome HVAC systems and have developed specific kits for specific models. General Motors calls their system Electronic Evaporator Dryer (EED), and it is not polarity sensitive, which means it may be installed on any GM vehicle without the need for a special harness. The EED pulses the blower motor in 10-second bursts,

**HVAC** stands for heating/ventilation/air conditioning and is generally used when referring to the system as a whole.

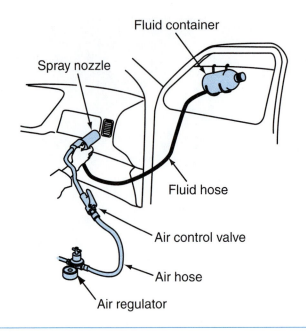

Fluid container

Spray nozzle

Fluid hose

Air control valve

Air hose

Air regulator

**Figure 9-35** A typical siphon-type sprayer for the application of antimicrobial deodorizer to eliminate musty odors.

and it also incorporates an ambient temperature sensor that automatically disables the EED if the ambient temperature drops below 60°F (15.56°C) due to low levels of microbial growth at low temperatures.

In addition, many makes and models of vehicles today offer cabin air filters to trap these microscopic contaminants and bacteria before they enter the HVAC system. The next section will discuss this topic in more detail.

# Cabin Air Filters

The cabin air filter is another feature of many vehicles today. It is a passenger compartment filter medium installed in the duct system to filter out pollen and dust particles, which would otherwise enter the interior of the vehicle. The introduction of the air filters in the automotive air conditioning system of domestic vehicles has been slow. The first occurrence was found in the 1938 Nash; the next occurrence was not until more than 35 years later in Oldsmobile's 1974 Toronado and 88. They were first introduced across major car lines in European vehicles during the mid 1980s but have since become a feature on many vehicles produced both in the United States and abroad. It is expected that the popularity of cabin filters will grow, and some estimates predict that by the year 2006, 85 percent of the cars and light trucks sold in the United States will contain one or more cabin filters.

As a vehicle travels down the road or is sitting in traffic, the air outside the vehicle (which may contains high levels of dust and pollen as well as other impurities) are drawn in through the fresh air intake system even when the blower motor is not on. The cabin filter is placed in the fresh air intake ductwork (Figure 9-36) and is designed to reduce pollens, bacteria, dust, exhaust gases, and mold spores, as well as other tiny airborne allergens that may enter a vehicle's ventilation system. Mold spores are the main contributor to the musty, stale smell that may be emitted from the ventilation system.

Most cabin air filters have the ability to remove up to 95 percent of all particles that are 3 microns or larger. There are two main filter designs used today: the particle filter and the absorption filter. The particle filter is designed to remove solid particles larger than 3 microns (less than

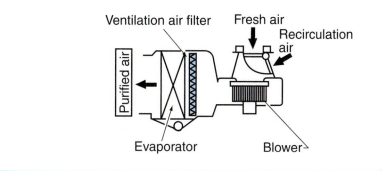

**Figure 9-36** Many vehicles today have a cabin air filter.

one millionth of an inch in diameter) such as dust, pollen, soot, and mold spores. The filter element is made of a special paper or nonwoven microfiber fleece. The filter material may also be electrostatically charged to improve its efficiency. The absorption filter is designed to remove odor-causing particles and gases. It uses activated charcoal to remove these particles. Activated charcoal is a carbon substance that has been treated with oxygen to open up millions of tiny pores, which increases its surface area. As the impurities pass by the activated charcoal's surface, they are attached to the charcoal surface and trapped, much like a magnet attracts and holds metal particles. Since activated charcoal attracts and holds impurities, it will eventually become saturated and require replacement. The combination filter (or two-stage filter) combines both the particle filter and the absorption filter into one assembly.

The cabin air filter is part of routine maintenance and is generally changed every 15,000 miles (24,000 km), but you should refer to specific vehicle service schedules for manufacturer's recommendations. If the filters are not serviced regularly, they will eventually cause an airflow restriction as they become clogged. The cabin air filter is generally located at the fresh air intake under the hood (Figure 9-37) or under the dash (Figure 9-38) on the passenger side of the vehicle. Consult the manufacturer's service information for exact locations and service procedures. A clogged filter can create an air pressure drop, placing a greater demand on the blower motor and, perhaps, leading to an early failure. Because it restricts airflow, a clogged filter will also affect air conditioning, heating, and defroster performance.

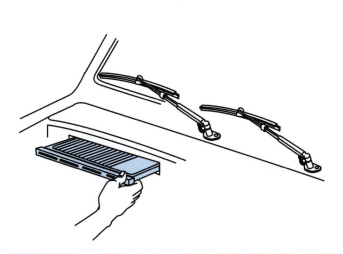

**Figure 9-37** Typical location of an underhood cabin air filter.

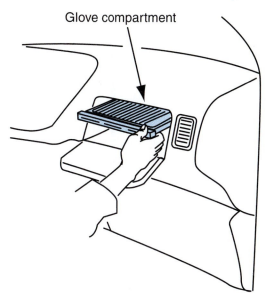

**Figure 9-38** Typical location of an underdash cabin air filter.

# The Air Door Control System

The air door control system uses vacuum-operated or electrically powered motors to position the air doors, also referred to as mode doors, to provide the desired in-vehicle air delivery conditions. These generally include OFF, MAX, VENT, BI-LEVEL, HTR, BLEND, and DEF. The airflow pattern for each of these conditions are given in Chapter 8 of the Classroom Manual.

There are basically three types of control systems: vacuum, rotary vacuum, and vacuum solenoid and electric motor.

## Vacuum Control

In the vacuum control system, vacuum actuators, also called vacuum motors, are used to position the air doors and valves. This system relies on a vacuum signal from either the engine manifold or an onboard vacuum pump. Vacuum is applied to the selected actuator by a rotary vacuum valve (RVV) or a vacuum solenoid in the main control panel.

## Rotary Vacuum Valve

When a rotary vacuum valve system (Figure 9-39) is used to control air doors and valves, the master control head selector rotates a vacuum switch that aligns the vacuum passages in the valve to direct a vacuum signal to the appropriate vacuum actuator(s) for the mode selected.

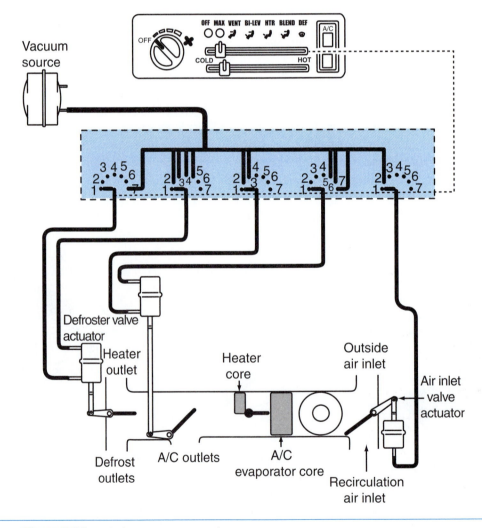

**Figure 9-39** Typical rotary vacuum valve system.

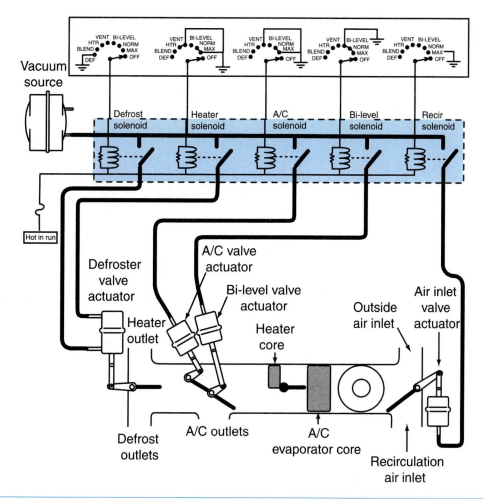

**Figure 9-40** A typical vacuum solenoid control.

## Vacuum Solenoids

When vacuum solenoids (Figure 9-40) are used to control doors and valves, the master control head selector contains electrical circuits that provide a ground path for the selected vacuum solenoid. The selected (energized) solenoid allows vacuum to be applied to the selected actuator.

An automatic air distribution system often uses vacuum solenoids that are located inside the programmer to control the position of the mode doors. The programmer controls the electrical ground side of the solenoids to establish a ground path to the selected vacuum solenoid. When the ground path is removed, the vacuum actuator is allowed to vent.

## Electric Actuator Motors

Many vehicles today use electric actuator motors to control air distribution mode doors and temperature blend doors. Electric actuators may be used solely or in combination with cable or vacuum control, with some doors operated by electric actuators and others controlled by cables. There are several types in use as electric mode door actuators. The two-position type either fully opens or fully closes a mode door; the fresh air/recirculation door is often this type. Another type is the variable-position actuators which can position the mode door at any point from fully open to fully closed; temperature blend doors are typically of this design.

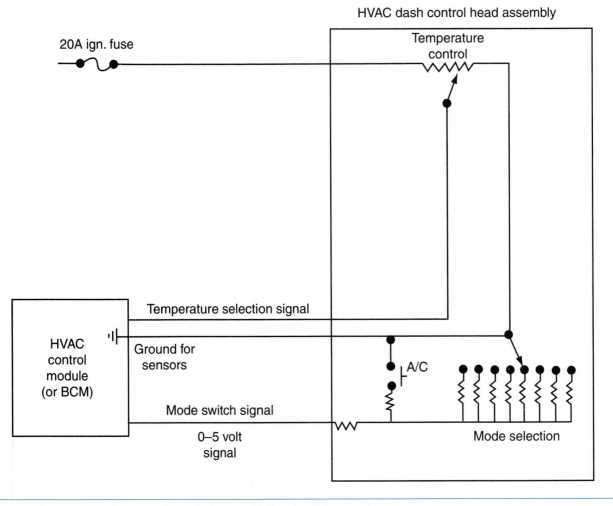

**Figure 9-41** A typical wiring schematic for a multiplexed HVAC control system.

The manual control head (HVAC dash control assembly) on many of these systems does not directly control the actuators. The manual control head is instead wired to the body control module (BCM) or a separate HVAC control module that is connected to the actuators and controls their position in response to inputs from the control head. Many of these systems use a multiplexed switch in the control head to control air distribution mode door position, meaning they only use one wire to communicate to the control module by using a different resistance value in the switch for each function. The control module interprets this information by dropping a voltage through the circuit (Figure 9-41). Most temperature selectors use a potentiometer to command the temperature blend door.

Mode door actuators all perform the same function. They position the mode doors based on driver input to the control head assembly. Electric mode door actuators may be five-wire, three-wire, or two-wire controlled. Both the two-wire and the five-wire actuators (Figure 4-42) generally use a driver circuit in the control module to control their movement. The control module will supply 12 volts to one driver circuit and ground the other driver circuit, thus giving bidirectional control depending on the polarity of the two wires to move the motor in one direction or the other. Which driver is negative and which is positive controls the rotational direction of the motor. When both sides of the actuator motor is power or ground, the motor stops (it is electrically balanced). The control module determines door position through feedback circuits. On the two-wire actuator, the control module counts the actuator commutator pulses to determine door position. On the five-wire actuator, the control module determines

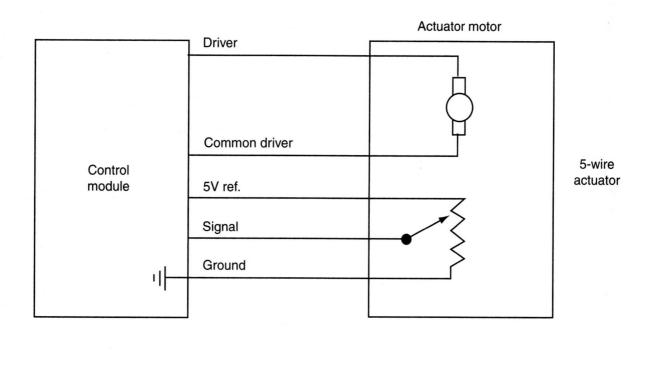

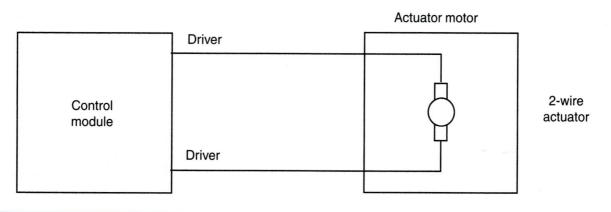

**Figure 9-42** Typical wiring diagrams for both 5-wire and 2-wire bi-directional mode door actuators.

mode door position through the potentiometer feedback voltage signal, which is built into the actuator assemblies. The three-wire actuator (Figure 4-43) generally has an external 12-volt supply and ground. Control of the actuator is through a logic module built-in to the actuator, in essence, a smart motor. The three-wire actuators are self-calibrated. Remember, when checking a three-wire actuator that the 12-volt power and ground circuits are constants, and the input line from the control head is the position control (command) circuit. Electric mode door actuators are not adjustable and must be replaced if faulty. It is also necessary to initialize a calibration procedure in order for the control module to relearn mode door position if the actuator or control module is replaced or otherwise loses its memory. Consult the manufacturer's service information for exact procedures on recalibrating the systems.

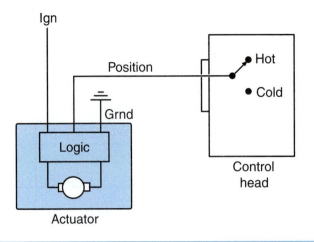

**Figure 9-43** Typical mode door motor schematic for a 3-wire actuator motor.

# Control System Faults

An inoperative vacuum motor could be due to a loss of vacuum signal at the appropriate time. This could be the fault of the vacuum source, vacuum switch, check valve, reserve tank, hose, restrictor, or vacuum motor. To determine the cause, disconnect the suspected vacuum motor (Figure 9-44) and substitute another vacuum source, such as the vacuum pump. If the motor is inoperative, it should be replaced. If it is operative, check further for the source of the problem.

If an inoperative fresh air door or mode door is the problem, a fault in the vacuum control system is again indicated. Most older systems use vacuum motors with a vacuum selector valve at the control head to control the operation of these doors. Some vehicles have vacuum motors controlled by electric solenoids, while others use electric motors at the doors. There are also systems in which all the mode doors have electric motor control (Figure 9-42 and Figure 9-43).

Generally, a vacuum system problem can be traced to a cut, kinked, crimped, or disconnected vacuum hose. A faulty selector valve, vacuum actuator, storage tank, or check valve may also be the problem.

**Figure 9-44** A typical vacuum motor.

In an electric solenoid or electric motor system, an electrical system defect may be responsible for improper mode door operation. Since these systems function electrically, it is wise to consult the appropriate manufacturer's service manual for specific troubleshooting procedures. One must be extremely careful when troubleshooting electrical systems under the dash. Just one improper test point could cause serious damage to one of the onboard computers.

The area under the dash is cramped and congested—filled with wires, vacuum hoses, and ducts, as well as various electrical and mechanical components and assemblies. It is not, therefore, easy to gain access to any of the components, especially those associated with the vacuum control system. The control panel on many vehicles, however, may be pulled out far enough from the dash to gain access. Extreme caution must be exercised when gaining access to any under-dash component. Failure to do so could trigger the air bag restraint system.

## Visual Inspection

When addressing a customer complaint for poor or insufficient heating or cooling, the first step is to make a visual inspection. The following should be included in the inspection:

* **Is the case and ductwork sound?** Check for cracks or broken or disconnected ducts.
* **Are the vacuum hoses sound?** Check for disconnected, split, damaged, or kinked vacuum hoses.
* **Is the airflow restricted?** Check to ensure that mode doors are opening. Check for leaves or other debris that may block airflow, such as at the fresh air inlet screen located at the base of the windshield. Is the cabin filter clean, if equipped?
* **Are the cables secure?** Check for loose, broken, or binding mode door control cables.

**AUTHOR'S NOTE:** When checking electric actuator circuits, use only high-impedance multimeters. Never use a test light which could overload the circuits in the microprocessor. Always follow the manufacturer's recommended diagnostic procedures.

## Mode Door Adjustment

A cable or vacuum actuator is used to position one or more of the mode doors in the duct system. The cable-operated system (Figure 9-45) consists of a steel cable encased in a plastic, nylon, or steel housing. It is used to connect the mode door to the control panel. Adjustments are made on the mode door end of the cable by repositioning the cable housing in its mounting bracket. The cable is usually held in place with a clip or a retainer secured in place with a hex-head screw.

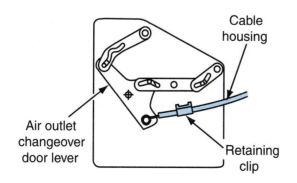

Cable housing

Air outlet changeover door lever

Retaining clip

**Figure 9-45** A typical cable-operated mode door.

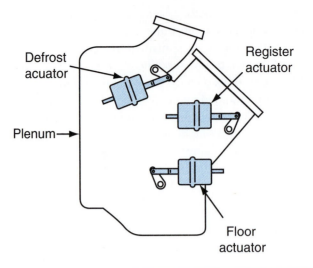

**Figure 9-46** A typical vacuum-operated mode door.

The only adjustment possible for a vacuum actuator (Figure 9-46) is in the linkage, if there are adjustment provisions. If the problem proves to be a defective vacuum motor, however, it must be replaced. First, ensure that there is a vacuum signal at the vacuum motor indicating that the vacuum system is sound. More information on troubleshooting and servicing of the vacuum and electrically operated actuators can be found in Chapter 10 of this manual as well as in Chapters 9 and 10 of the Shop Manual.

# Summary

❏ There are many variations of mode and blend door positions, as well as many case/duct system designs.

❏ Doors may be electric, vacuum, or cable operated.

❏ Some doors are either fully opened or fully closed; others are infinitely variable.

❏ Because of the many different applications and methods of control (Figure 9-47 and Figure 9-48), it is necessary to consult a particular manufacturer's manual for specifications and testing procedures.

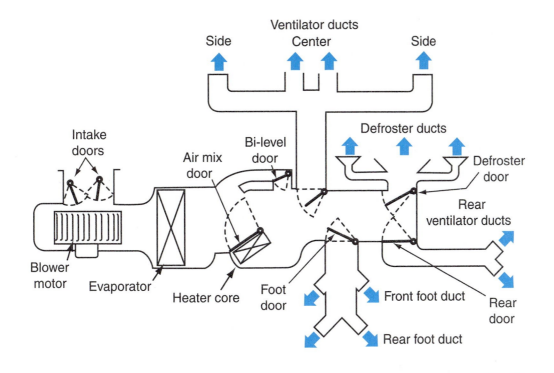

**Figure 9-47** One type of case/duct system. Compare with Figure 9-48.

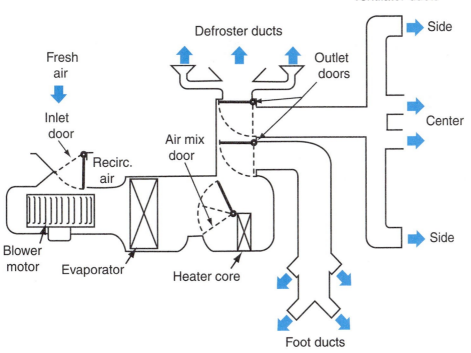

**Figure 9-48** Another type of case/duct system. Compare with Figure 9-47.

# Review Questions

## Short Answer Essays

1. What is one of the two purposes of the case/duct system?

2. How does the dealer-installed air conditioner differ from the manufacturer-installed system?

3. Where is the air taken from that is to be "conditioned" for MAX cooling?

4. What is the purpose of maintaining a slightly positive pressure in the vehicle's interior?

5. What are the main components of the plenum section?

6. How is air tempered to maintain a desired humidity?

7. Where is air directed in the distribution section?

8. Describe the airflow through the case/duct system when DEFROST is selected.

9. Describe one of the two types of control panels in use for system selection.

10. Define the term *bi-level*.

## Fill-in-the-Blanks

1. Mode doors may be _____ , cable, or _____ operated.

2. The MIX selection on some models is basically the same as the _____ selection on other models.

3. A fully automatic temperature control system relies on a _____ microprocessor.

4. A small amount of conditioned air may be directed to the _____ outlets to prevent windshield _____ .

5. The compressor may operate in the heat mode to help maintain in-vehicle _____ .

6. Cooled air is generally delivered into the passenger compartment through the _____ vents.

7. Heated air is generally delivered into the passenger compartment through the _____ _____ .

8. The air conditioning and heating system is provided to _____ the in-vehicle air.

9. There are two types of blower system: an upstream blower and a _____ _____ .

10. The case system provides a _____ for the components while the duct system provides a _____ for the airflow.

## Multiple Choice

1. The fresh air supply of 100 percent is being discussed:
   *Technician A* says it is always provided in the heating mode.
   *Technician B* says that it is always provided in the cooling mode.
   Who is correct?
   - **A.** A only
   - **B.** B only
   - **C.** Both A and B
   - **D.** Neither A nor B

2. The following statements about a typical system set to MAX cooling are true, *except*:
   - **A.** The compressor clutch is engaged.
   - **B.** The blower motor is running.
   - **C.** The outside/recirculate door is in recirculate position.
   - **D.** Return air is from vehicle exterior.

3. When VENT is selected, the fresh incoming air:
   - **A.** Is heated
   - **B.** Is cooled
   - **C.** Both A and B
   - **D.** Neither A nor B

4. During normal air conditioning system operation, the position of the system mode doors:
   - **A.** Are fully opened
   - **B.** Are fully closed
   - **C.** Are partially opened (or closed)
   - **D.** Depend on the mode selected

5. *Technician A* says that an independent case system may have an upstream blower assembly.
   *Technician B* says that an independent case system may have a downstream blower assembly.
   Who is correct?
   - **A.** A only
   - **B.** B only
   - **C.** Both A and B
   - **D.** Neither A nor B

6. Humidity control is being discussed:
   *Technician A* says that humidity control is not important in the cooling mode.
   *Technician B* says that humidity control is important in the heating mode.
   Who is correct?
   - **A.** A only
   - **B.** B only
   - **C.** Both A and B
   - **D.** Neither A nor B

7. The airflow path in the case/duct system illustrated in Figure 9-48 is being discussed:
   *Technician A* says that airflow is also through the heater core in the cooling mode.
   *Technician B* says that airflow is also through the evaporator in the heating mode.
   Who is correct?
   - **A.** A only
   - **B.** B only
   - **C.** Both A and B
   - **D.** Neither A nor B

8. *Technician A* says that up to 20 percent of fresh air provides a means to maintain a positive in-vehicle pressure when the windows are closed.
   *Technician B* says this positive pressure is necessary to provide a proper balance of air pressure within the air delivery system.
   Who is correct?
   - **A.** A only
   - **B.** B only
   - **C.** Both A and B
   - **D.** Neither A nor B

9. Definitions are being discussed:
   *Technician A* says that "ambient" refers to outside air temperature.
   *Technician B* says that "ambient" refers to inside vehicle air temperature.
   Who is correct?
   - **A.** A only
   - **B.** B only
   - **C.** Both A and B
   - **D.** Neither A nor B

10. *Technician A* says that most mode doors are either fully opened or are fully closed.
    *Technician B* says that some mode doors may be manually adjusted to provide custom air blending for individual passenger comfort.
    Who is correct?
    - **A.** A only
    - **B.** B only
    - **C.** Both A and B
    - **D.** Neither A nor B

# System Controls

Upon completion and review of this chapter, you should be able to:

❏ Understand the requirements of fuses and circuit breakers for electrical circuit protection.

❏ Recognize the components of the air conditioning and climate control system.

❏ Discuss the operation and function of a temperature control thermostat.

❏ Describe the different types of evaporator blower motors.

❏ Explain the application and function of an electromagnetic clutch assembly.

❏ Compare the difference of controlling system temperature by using pressure- and temperature-actuated controllers.

❏ Explain the difference in low- and high-pressure switches.

❏ Understand how to trace an electrical circuit using a schematic.

❏ Compare the function of gauges versus lamps for engine coolant temperature.

❏ Recognize vacuum system components and understand their function.

❏ Understand the operation and recognize the components of an automatic temperature control system.

## Introduction

The automotive air conditioning control system can be as simple as that found in aftermarket installations or as complex as that found in computer-controlled automatic factory-installed systems. The simple system usually consists of a master on/off switch, blower control, thermostat, blower motor, clutch coil, and **fuse** or **circuit breaker**.

Note in the schematic (Figure 10-1) that only one wire is shown from the battery. The other side of the battery, as well as the blower motor and clutch coil, terminate to ground. The vehicle chassis, body, and all metal parts are *common* (ground) in 12-volt, direct-current (dc) automotive electrical systems. A separate ground wire circuit is not required unless the car has fiberglass or other nonconducting body components. An electrical symbol (Figure 10-2) is used to indicate a ground connection. Examples of other wiring diagram symbols are shown in Figure 10-3.

The schematic for a factory-installed heater/air conditioner control system is more complex (Figure 10-4). Actually, the schematic in this illustration has been condensed so that it can be shown on one page. Many schematics of factory-installed heater/air conditioning systems require several pages in the shop service manual for illustration.

The air conditioning and heater electrical systems are integral and often share fuses or circuit breakers. The blower motor serves both the heater and air conditioner in factory-installed systems. Electrical circuits associated with the heating and cooling system, such as those used to warn of engine overheating conditions, may also be a part of the electrical system schematic.

A **fuse** is an electrical device used to protect a circuit against accidental overload or unit malfunction.

A **circuit breaker** is a bimetallic electrical device used to protect a circuit against accidental overload or unit malfunction. It automatically resets once it cools down.

Most factory-installed heater and air conditioner electrical schematics require two or more pages.

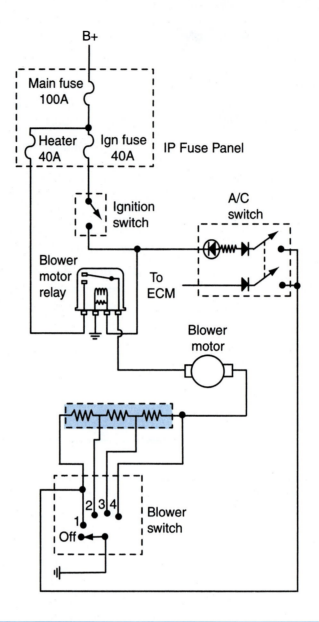

**Figure 10-1** A typical air conditioner/heater system schematic.

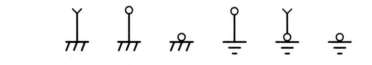

**Figure 10-2** Electrical symbols used to identify a ground connection.

| SYMBOLS USED IN WIRING DIAGRAMS | | | | |
|---|---|---|---|---|
| + | Positive | (T) | Temperature switch |
| — | Negative | ⇥ | Diode |
| ⊣⊢ | Ground | ⇥ | Zenner diode |
| ⌣ | Fuse | -⊏○⊐- | Motor |
| ⌢ | Circuit breaker | → C101 | Connector 101 |
| →⊦ | Condenser | → | Male connector |
| Ω | Ohm | ⊱ | Female connector |
| -W- | Fixed value resistor | -⦁ | Splice |
| -W- | Variable resistor | S101 | Splice number |
| WWWW | Series resistors | ⊓⊔⊓⊔ | Thermal element |
| -○○- | Coil | ⇉‖⊱ | Multiple connectors |
| 吕 | Open contacts | 88:88 | Digital readout |
| 白 | Closed contacts | -⊙- | Single filament bulb |
| ⦁→⦁ | Closed switch | ⊛ | Dual filament bulb |
| ⌁ | Open switch | ⊕ | Light emitting diode |
| ⇗ | Ganged switch (N.O.) | (T)W | Thermistor |
| ⌁ | Single pole double throw switch | ⊖K | PNP bi-polar transistor |
| ⊣⌁ | Momentary contact switch | ⊖K | NPN bi-polar transistor |
| (P) | Pressure switch | (↗) | Gauge |
| ⊣⌐ | Battery | ⊱ | Wire Crossing |

**Figure 10-3** Typical schematic symbols.

Wiring diagrams are also known as schematics.

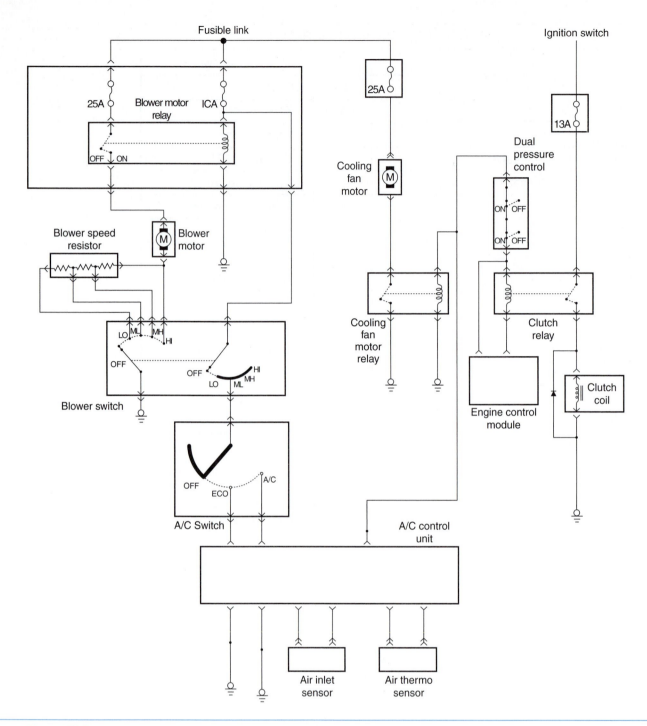

**Figure 10-4** A typical climate-control system electrical diagram.

**Shop Manual**
Chapter 10, page 364

# Fuses and Circuit Breakers

A fuse or circuit breaker (Figure 10-5) is used to protect the air conditioning and heating components and wiring. Usually rated at 20–30 amperes, they should not be replaced with one having a different rating. If a fuse or circuit breaker is rated too low, it will not carry the load and will quickly burn out (blow). If it is rated too high, the device it is intended to protect may be damaged due to excessive current.

Figure 10-5 Fuses and circuit breakers.

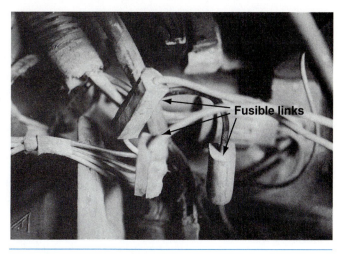

Figure 10-6 Fusible links.

The fuse or circuit breaker is usually located in the main fuse block. Major circuits are often protected by a fusible link (Figure 10-6) or a maxi-fuse. Fuses may also be located in in-line fuse holders (Figure 10-7).

Circuit breakers are constructed of a bimetallic strip and a set of contacts. Excessive current, caused by a defective component, produces heat that causes the bimetallic strip to bend. When the strip bends, the contacts open and current to the component is interrupted. When there is no current flow, the bimetallic strip cools and the contacts automatically close. This continues until the cause of the problem is corrected.

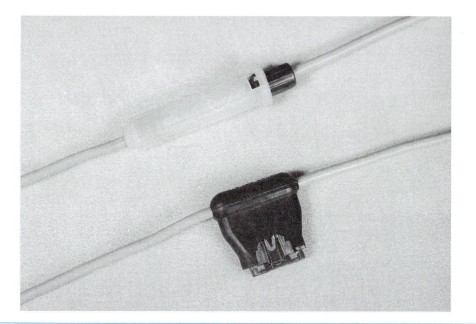

Figure 10-7 In-line fuse holders.

Another term for rheostat is potentiometer.

**Shop Manual**

Chapter 10, page 377

**Master control** is the primary or main control.

A **rheostat** is a wire-wound variable resistor with one input and one output wire.

A multiwound motor is also referred to as a tapped motor.

# Master Control

The **master control** (Figure 10-8) generally includes the blower speed control provisions. The variable (infinite) speed control, also known as a **rheostat** (Figure 10-9), is generally found on aftermarket systems. Also used are four- or five-position blower speed controls.

The four-speed five-position control (Figure 10-10) has three resistors to provide selected blower motor speed. The first position is OFF. The second position, LOW, supplies current to the motor through all three resistors. This provides maximum reduced voltage for low-speed operation. The next position, LO-MED, supplies current to the motor through two resistors to provide medium-low speed. Current is supplied to the motor through one resistor in the fourth position, HI-MED, to provide medium-high blower speed. The fifth position, HIGH, supplies full battery voltage to the motor to provide high-speed operation of the blower.

Some multiposition blower speed control switches (Figure 10-11) do not have resistors. These switches provide full battery voltage to either of several windings in the motor. These multiwound motors are covered later in this chapter.

The blower motor speed control may be a part of the master ON/OFF control (Figure 10-12). The blower switch, in either ON position, provides full battery voltage to the control thermostat. In this arrangement, the compressor clutch does not engage unless the blower motor is running.

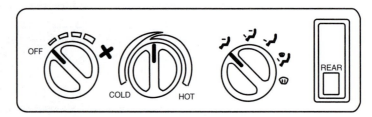

Heater control

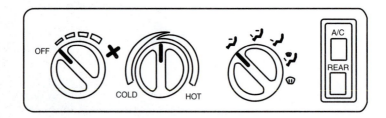

Manual A/C control

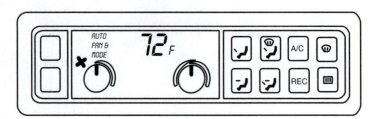

ATC control module

**Figure 10-8** Typical master controls.

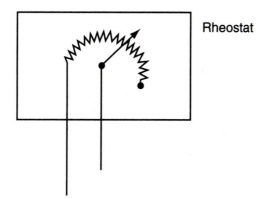

Rheostat

Figure 10-9 A rheostat is a two-wire variable resistor with no feedback signal wire, common on dashlight dimmer circuits.

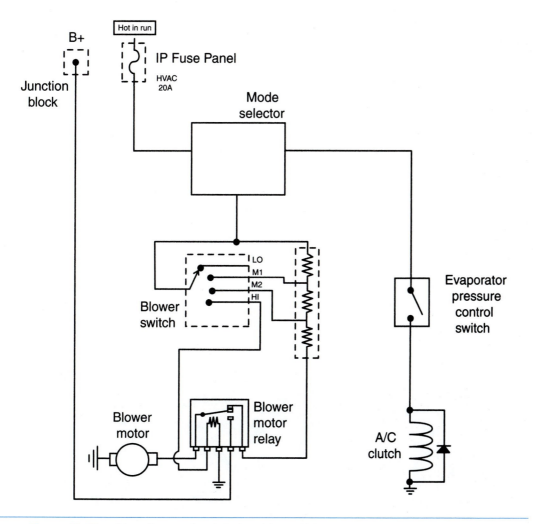

Figure 10-10 Wiring diagram for typical multispeed blower motor.

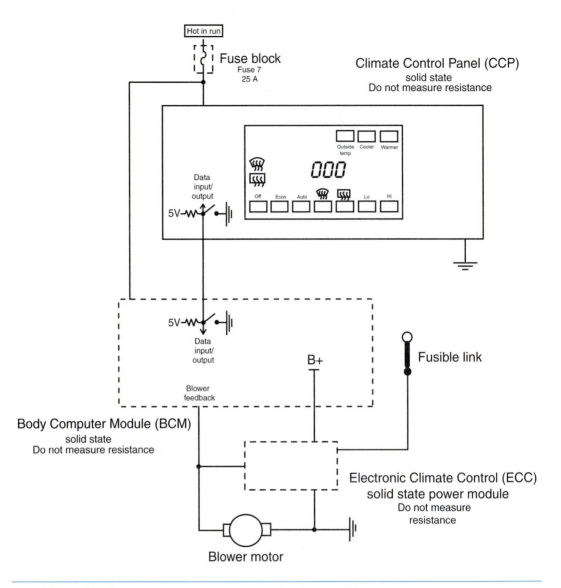

**Figure 10-11** Wiring schematic showing a pulse width modulated motor control circuit and feedback circuit to the BCM.

**Figure 10-12** A master control panel.

# Thermostat

An electromagnetic clutch is used on the compressor of all automotive air conditioning systems to turn it on when cooling is desired and off when cooling is not desired. The clutch is often used to provide a means of in-vehicle temperature control. One way to accomplish this is to control the compressor operation with a temperature-sensitive switch known as a thermostat (Figure 10-13). Another method, control with a pressure-sensitive switch, is covered later in this chapter.

The thermostat may be located in the evaporator where it senses the temperature of the air being delivered into the vehicle or it may be mounted in such a manner that its remote bulb is immersed into a well in the outlet tube (suction line) of the evaporator (Figure 10-14). The thermostat, set by the driver to a predetermined temperature, cycles the clutch on-off at the selected setting. This, in turn, controls the average in-vehicle temperature.

**Shop Manual**
Chapter 10, page 366

Some thermostat capillary tubes are inserted into a well provided in the suction line immediately after the evaporator.

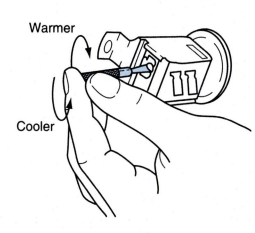

**Figure 10-13** Typical thermostat adjustment.

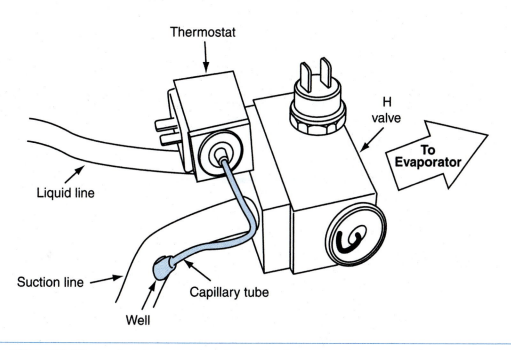

**Figure 10-14** A typical thermostat location on H-valve.

The thermostat senses the temperature of the evaporator core air or of the vapor leaving the evaporator. A temperature above that selected closes the thermostat contacts to provide current to the clutch coil. The clutch is energized and the compressor operates. A temperature at or below that selected opens the thermostat switch to interrupt current to the clutch coil. The clutch then de-energizes and compressor operation stops.

Thermostats generally have an OFF position so that the clutch can be turned off regardless of the temperature. In this way, the blower motor can be operated without a refrigerating effect.

## Thermostat Construction

A capillary tube connected to the thermostat is filled with a temperature-sensitive fluid or vapor. The capillary is attached to a **bellows** within the thermostat (Figure 10-15). This bellows, in turn, is attached to a swinging frame assembly. Two electrical contact points are provided. One contact is fastened to the swinging frame through an **insulator**, and the other electrical contact is fastened to the body of the unit, again through an insulator.

## Thermostat Operation

As the inert gas in the capillary tube expands, a pressure is exerted on the bellows. The bellows, in turn, closes the electrical contacts (Figure 10-16). The temperature selection is provided by a cam that is connected to the swinging frame via a shaft to an external control knob. When the knob is turned clockwise, the spring tension is increased against the bellows. If more pressure is required to overcome the increased spring tension, more heat is necessary. Since it is heat that is being removed from the evaporator, a lower temperature is required to open the points. On a temperature rise, the heat again exerts pressure on the bellows to close the points and allow for cooling.

The capillary tube is often filled with the same fluid used in the system, either, R-12 or R-134a.

A **bellows** is an accordion-type chamber that expands and contracts as its interior pressure is increased or decreased to create a mechanical action, such as in a thermostatic expansion valve.

An **insulator** is a nonconductive material, such as the covering on electrical wire.

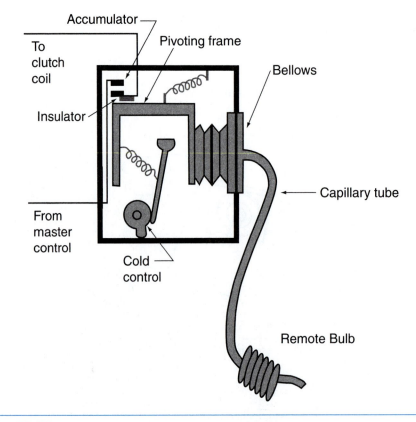

**Figure 10-15** Thermostat capillary tube shown with points open.

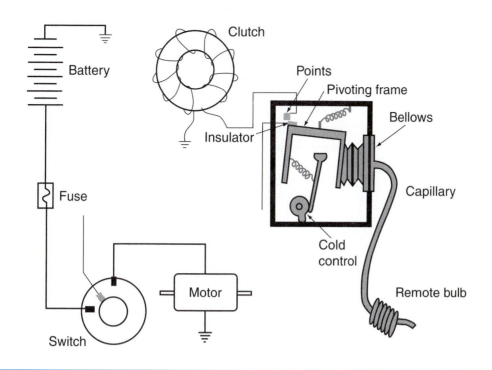

**Figure 10-16** Thermostat operation: points closed.

A second spring in the thermostat regulates the temperature interval that the points are open. This interval usually represents a temperature rise (delta T or $\Delta_T$) of 12°F (6.6°C), providing sufficient time for the evaporator to defrost.

## Thermostat Installation and Handling

As with any device containing a capillary tube, care must be exercised when handling a thermostat. There should be no sharp bends or kinks in the capillary. When a bend must be made, it should be no sharper than can be formed around the end of a thumb.

For best results, the end of the capillary tube should be inserted into the evaporator core between the fins to a depth of about 1 in. (25.4 mm). The capillary should not be inserted all the way through the fins because it may interfere with the blowers, which are often mounted behind the core. If a remote bulb prevents insertion, the remote bulb should be fastened against the evaporator core (Figure 10-17).

**Figure 10-17** Thermostat remote bulb inserted into the evaporator core.

If the capillary is damaged and has lost its charge of inert gas for any reason, the thermostat must be replaced. When there is no fluid in the capillary, the unit has no ON cycle. The capillary cannot be recharged using standard equipment. Many thermostats are adjustable.

# Blower Motor

**Shop Manual**
Chapter 10, page 367

There are many styles and types of blower motors available, depending upon their application. Blower motors may have a single or double shaft. Some have provisions for flange mounting and may also have provisions for internal cooling. Regardless of style or type, the blower motor drives a squirrel-cage blower to move air across the evaporator and/or heater core (Figure 10-18).

If motor speed control is provided by resistors, the motor will have only one winding (Figure 10-19). Speed control may also be provided by a multiwound motor (Figure 10-20). As discussed earlier, resistance for speed control is provided by the motor windings, and no external resistors are required.

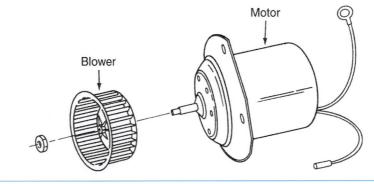

**Figure 10-18** A squirrel cage blower with motor.

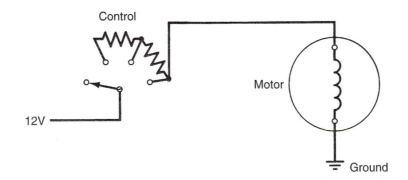

**Figure 10-19** A single-wound motor.

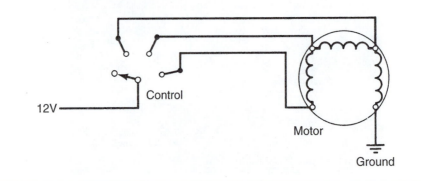

**Figure 10-20** A multiwound motor.

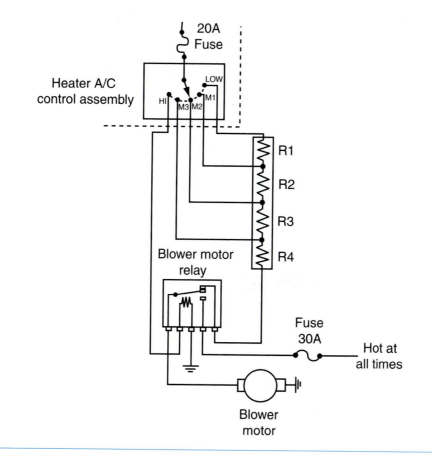

**Figure 10-21** High-speed blower motor relay.

Some blower speed control systems have a high-speed blower control relay, such as the one shown in Figure 10-21. Note that this five-speed blower has two fuses protecting the circuit: one for the first four speeds and one for high speed.

It should be noted that some replacement motors are reversible whereas most are not. It is also important to note whether the defective motor turned clockwise or counterclockwise facing the shaft end. The replacement motor selected must turn in the same direction. If the wrong motor is installed, little or no airflow will circulate through the duct system. In addition, some replacement blower motors do not come with a blower cage. In these circumstances, the old cage must be reused. Ensure that the cage fits snugly on the motor shaft and does not slip. Other abbreviations relating to the selection of blower motors include DBL (double shaft) and THD (threaded shaft) end.

**AUTHOR'S NOTE:** You may notice a small steel clip on one of the blower motor cage fins; this is a weight to balance the assembly. Do not remove this clip or vibration will result, which could also lead to premature motor bearing failure and customer complaints.

Aftermarket air conditioner motors often have two shafts.

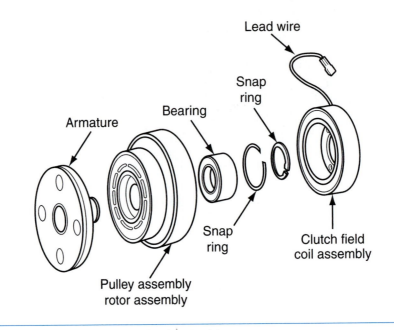

Figure 10-22 Electromagnetic clutch assembly.

# Electromagnetic Clutch

An electromagnetic clutch (Figure 10-22) is used in automotive air conditioning systems as a means of engaging the compressor when cooling is desired and disengaging it when cooling is not required. For example, the compressor is disengaged when the air conditioner is not being used or when the desired temperature is reached in the vehicle.

All clutches operate on the same basic principle—that of magnetic attraction. This is accomplished by energizing a stationary field coil. The magnetic attraction of the field coil, in turn, pulls an armature into contact with a rotating member, the pulley.

All automotive air conditioning systems have an electromagnetic clutch. Not all, however, are used to cycle the compressor for temperature control. For those that do, the electrical circuit to the clutch coil is interrupted when a set of contacts, thermostatically controlled or pressure actuated, open as the set temperature or pressure is reached. Those that do not cycle to effect the desired temperature rely on the operation of a variable displacement compressor as a means of temperature control.

## Clutch Diode

The clutch coil is an electromagnet with a strong magnetic field when current is applied. This magnetic field is constant as long as power is applied to the coil. When power is removed, the magnetic field collapses and creates high-voltage spikes. These spikes are harmful to delicate electronic circuits of the computer and must be prevented.

A **diode** placed across the clutch coil (Figure 10-23) provides a path to ground back through the clutch coil until the electrical energy is dissipated, thereby holding the spikes to a safe level. This diode is usually taped inside the clutch coil connector, across the 12-volt lead and ground lead. A diode may be checked with either an analog or digital volt ohmmeter (DVOM). Many DVOMs have provisions for diode quick-testing procedures; this is the preferred method for testing diodes.

**Shop Manual**
Chapter 10,
page 368

**Shop Manual**
Chapter 10,
page 242

A diode may be thought of as an electrical check valve.

A **diode** is an electrical one-way check valve. Current will flow in only one direction through the diode.

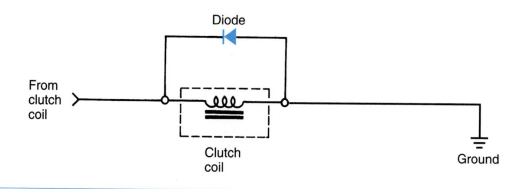

Figure 10-23 A diode is placed across the clutch coil to reduce spikes as the clutch is cycled on.

# Pressure Cutoff Switch

Some systems have a low- and/or high-pressure cutoff switch as part of the clutch circuit. These switches, which are normally closed (nc), are sensitive to system pressure and open in the event of abnormally low or high pressure. This, in turn, interrupts electrical current to the clutch coil to stop the compressor. These switches serve two purposes: temperature control and system protection.

Some pressure switches (Figure 10-24) can be replaced without having to remove the refrigerant from the system. Others, on the other hand, require that the refrigerant be recovered before the old switch can be removed. Those that do not require refrigerant removal have a valve depressor located inside the threaded end of the pressure switch (Figure 10-25). This pin presses on the Schrader-type valve stem as the switch is screwed on and allows system pressure to be expressed on the switch.

**Shop Manual**
Chapter 10,
page 373

The clutch-cycling low-pressure switch is often found on the accumulator.

A pressure cycling switch may open (close) on low or high pressure depending on application.

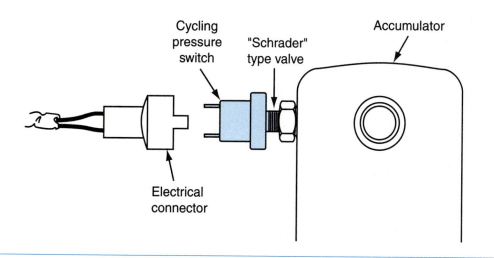

Figure 10-24 Some pressure switches can be replaced without removing the refrigerant.

Figure 10-25 A valve depressor located inside the threaded portion of the pressure switch.

## Low-Pressure Switch

Many cycling clutch orifice tube systems and fixed orifice tube cycling clutch systems use a **pressure switch** instead of a thermostat. The pressure cycling switch, which is mounted on the accumulator, senses low-side pressure to cycle the clutch off at about 24–26 psig (165–179 kPa) and cuts back in at about 40–42 psig (276–290 kPa). These pressures correspond to temperatures of 24–27°F (–4.4––2.8°C) and 43–45°F (6.1–7.2°C), respectively, for R-12. They correspond to 27.5–30°F (–2.5––1.1°C) and 45–47°F (7.2–8.3°C), respectively, for R-134a. This maintains a cold evaporator while controlling for freeze-up. The pressure/temperature relationships for R-12 and R-134a in the evaporating range is given in Figure 10-26.

The low-pressure cutoff switch (Figure 10-27) may be found in the system anywhere between the evaporator inlet and the compressor inlet. In the event of an abnormally low pressure of 8–10 psig (55.2–68.9 kPa), the switch will open to stop the compressor. This prevents further reduction of system pressure to protect the system from the possible entrance of air or moisture, as would be the case with a low-side leak.

## High-Pressure Switch

The high-pressure cutoff switch is found on some General Motors, Chrysler, and Subaru car lines. This switch is found in the system anywhere between the compressor outlet and the evaporator inlet. In the case of an abnormally high pressure of 300–500 psig (2,068.5–3,447.5 kPa), the switch will open, stopping compressor action. This prevents system damage and/or rupture that may be caused by a further increase in pressure.

The high-pressure switch is normally closed (nc) and opens if the air conditioning system pressure exceeds 425–435 psig (2,930–2,953 kPa). It closes when the system pressure drops to below 200 psig (1,379 kPa). This switch provides for system safety if, for any reason, pressures exceed safe limits. Unlike the low-pressure switch, the high-pressure switch does not provide data to the microprocessor. This switch is usually in series with the compressor clutch circuit.

| TEMPERATURE | | PRESSURE | | | |
|---|---|---|---|---|---|
| °F | °C | CFC-12 | | HFC-134a | |
| | | psig | kPa | psig | kPa |
| 20 | −6.7 | 21.0 | 144.8 | 18.4 | 126.9 |
| 21 | −6.1 | 21.7 | 149.6 | 19.2 | 132.4 |
| 22 | −5.6 | 22.4 | 154.4 | 19.9 | 137.2 |
| 23 | −5.0 | 23.2 | 160.0 | 20.6 | 142.0 |
| 24 | −4.4 | 23.9 | 164.8 | 21.4 | 147.6 |
| 25 | −3.9 | 24.6 | 169.6 | 22.0 | 151.7 |
| 26 | −3.3 | 25.4 | 175.1 | 22.9 | 157.9 |
| 27 | −2.8 | 26.1 | 180.0 | 23.7 | 163.4 |
| 28 | −2.2 | 26.9 | 185.5 | 24.5 | 168.9 |
| 29 | −1.7 | 27.7 | 191.0 | 25.3 | 174.4 |
| 30 | −1.1 | 28.4 | 195.8 | 26.1 | 180.0 |
| 31 | −0.6 | 29.2 | 201.3 | 26.9 | 185.5 |
| 32 | 0.0 | 30.1 | 207.5 | 27.8 | 191.7 |
| 33 | 0.6 | 30.9 | 213.1 | 28.7 | 197.9 |
| 34 | 1.1 | 31.7 | 218.6 | 29.5 | 203.4 |
| 35 | 1.7 | 32.6 | 224.8 | 30.4 | 209.6 |
| 36 | 2.2 | 33.4 | 230.3 | 31.3 | 215.8 |
| 37 | 2.8 | 34.3 | 236.5 | 32.2 | 220.0 |
| 38 | 3.3 | 35.2 | 242.7 | 33.2 | 228.9 |
| 39 | 3.9 | 36.1 | 248.9 | 34.1 | 235.1 |
| 40 | 4.4 | 37.0 | 255.1 | 35.1 | 242.0 |
| 41 | 5.0 | 37.9 | 261.3 | 36.0 | 248.2 |
| 42 | 5.6 | 38.8 | 267.5 | 37.0 | 255.1 |
| 43 | 6.1 | 39.8 | 274.4 | 38.0 | 262.0 |
| 44 | 6.7 | 40.7 | 280.6 | 39.0 | 268.9 |
| 45 | 7.2 | 41.7 | 287.5 | 40.1 | 276.5 |
| 46 | 7.8 | 42.6 | 293.7 | 41.1 | 283.4 |
| 47 | 8.3 | 43.6 | 300.6 | 42.2 | 291.0 |
| 48 | 8.9 | 44.6 | 307.5 | 43.3 | 298.6 |
| 49 | 9.4 | 45.7 | 315.1 | 44.4 | 306.1 |
| 50 | 10.0 | 46.7 | 322.0 | 45.5 | 313.7 |

Figure 10-26 Low-side pressure/temperature chart for R-12 and R-134a, English and metric.

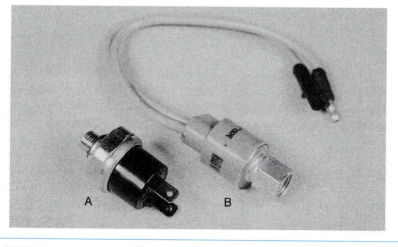

Figure 10-27 Low-pressure cutoff switch: (A) male thread; (B) female thread.

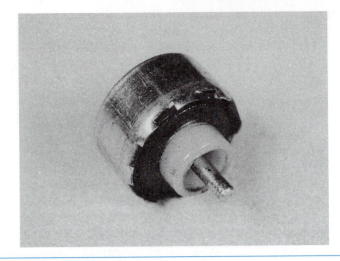

**Figure 10-28** A compressor discharge pressure switch.

# Compressor Discharge Pressure Switch

The compressor discharge pressure switch is actually a low-pressure switch.

Many factory systems use a compressor discharge pressure switch to disengage the compressor clutch electrical circuit if the refrigerant charge in the system is not adequate enough to provide sufficient circulation. The compressor discharge pressure switch is also called a no-charge switch, ambient low-temperature switch, or a low-pressure cutoff switch. The switch is designed to open electrically to shut off the compressor when high-side system pressure drops below 37 psig (255 kPa). This switch also performs the secondary function of an outside ambient air temperature sensor. When outside ambient air temperature falls below 40°F (4.4°C), the reduced corresponding refrigerant pressure, 36.9 psig (254.4 kPa), keeps the switch open.

The compressor discharge pressure switch (Figure 10-28), which is located in the compressor housing or the high-pressure discharge line from the compressor or receiver-drier, cannot be repaired. If it fails in service, it must be replaced with a new unit. Its function is to protect the compressor. That function should not be defeated, such as by bypassing it with a jumper wire.

# Factory-Installed Wiring

The electrical schematic illustrated earlier in Figure 10-4 is typical of any of the hundreds that illustrate the wiring of factory-installed air conditioning (cooling and heating) systems. When servicing a particular system, it is necessary to consult the appropriate service manual for specific information and schematic details. As previously discussed, it must be noted that various methods of temperature control are used: thermostat, pressure control, variable displacement compressor, and blend air (warm and cool).

# Coolant Temperature Warning System

When operating, the automotive air conditioning system places a high demand and an additional heat load on the engine cooling system. The condenser is located upstream (in front) of the radiator. Air intended to remove heat from the engine coolant in the radiator first passes through the condenser.

**Shop Manual**
Chapter 10,
page 373

Figure 10-29 A typical engine coolant temperature gauge.

A malfunctioning air conditioner will often affect engine coolant temperature. Conversely, an overheated engine will affect air conditioning performance. To monitor the engine coolant condition, a dash light or a dash gauge (Figure 10-29) is used. Either type has a sending unit located in the engine coolant system.

## Lamps

There are two types of engine coolant lamp systems: the one-lamp system and the two-lamp system. The one-lamp system (Figure 10-30) warns that the engine has overheated and that immediate attention is required.

The two-lamp system has one lamp to indicate cold and another lamp to indicate hot. In the two-lamp system, the cold switch is closed until the engine coolant temperature reaches its normal operating temperature, usually about 180°F (82.2°C). In both the one- and two-lamp systems, the hot contacts of the sending unit close when engine coolant temperature reaches about 250°F (121.1°C). The actual temperature at which this switch closes depends upon the engine design.

The main disadvantage of the telltale light system is obvious; the hot lamp generally is not illuminated until after there is a problem. This is probably why the telltale light is sometimes referred to as an "idiot light."

Most telltale lamp systems have one lamp: HOT. They are often referred to as an "idiot light."

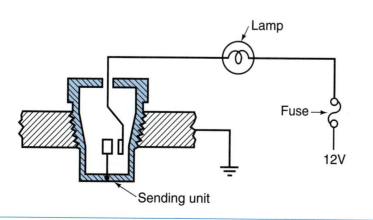

Figure 10-30 A one-lamp coolant warming system.

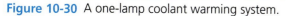

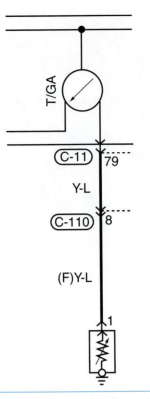

**Figure 10-31** Engine coolant temperature gauge schematic.

The higher the temperature of a thermistor, the lower its resistance.

## Gauges

The coolant temperature gauge system (Figure 10-31) consists of two parts: the dash (gauge) unit and the engine (sending) unit. The sending unit contains a sintered material known as a thermistor. A thermistor changes resistance in relation to its temperature. This material, which is sealed in a metal bulb, is screwed into a coolant passage of the engine. It has a high resistance when cold and a low resistance when hot.

The varying resistance of the sending unit regulates the amount of current passing through the coil of the dash gauge and moves the pointer accordingly.

# Control Devices

Many controls used in automotive air conditioning systems are either negative (vacuum) or positive (pressure) actuated. Others are mechanically, electrically, or electronically actuated.

## Vacuum Circuits

*Negative* refers to any pressure less than atmospheric; *positive* refers to any pressure above atmospheric.

**Delta P** (Δp) is a term used when referring to a difference in pressure.

To understand vacuum circuits, it is first essential that the term *vacuum* be defined and understood. Vacuum is defined as a space that is devoid of matter. Since all things contain matter in some form, it would seem that there is no such thing as a vacuum.

For all practical purposes, therefore, a vacuum is better thought of as a portion of space that is partially devoid of matter. For a clearer understanding, consider that a vacuum is a space in which pressure is below atmospheric pressure. A good example of a vacuum is demonstrated by a person drinking through a straw (Figure 10-32). As the person sucks on the straw, a slight vacuum is created in the straw. Atmospheric pressure, which is greater than the vacuum pressure, is exerted against the surface of the liquid. This difference in pressure, known as **delta P** (Δp), forces the liquid up the straw.

Figure 10-32 A person drinking through a straw: (A) vacuum pressure; (B) atmospheric pressure.

**Atmospheric Pressure.** Atmospheric pressure at sea level is 14.696 psia (101.328 kPa absolute). For all practical purposes, this value is usually rounded off to 14.7 psia (101.4 kPa absolute) or 15 psia (103.4 kPa absolute). At sea level, then, a pressure of 14 psia (96.5 kPa absolute) is a vacuum. Traditionally, English system vacuum pressure values are given in *inches of mercury* (in. Hg).

**Vacuum Terms.** Most automotive manufacturers' manuals give vacuum value requirements and specifications using the term *inches* only. In this manual, reference to vacuum values are given in the English and metric absolute scales of pressure. The conversion chart in Figure 10-33 may be used as an aid for comparison of inches to psia and kPa absolute.

## Vacuum-Operated Devices

Many vacuum-operated devices, such as heater coolant valves and mode doors, are activated with a **vacuum pot**, also called a vacuum motor or vacuum power unit.

**Single-Chamber Pot.** The exertion (force) of atmospheric pressure on one side of a diaphragm causes the diaphragm to move toward the lower (vacuum) pressure side (Figure 10-34). This moves the device that is to be controlled through a lever, arm, or rod linkage.

**Dual-Chamber Pots.** Dual-chamber vacuum pots (motors) operate below atmospheric pressure based on a pressure differential ($\Delta_p$) from one side to the other. A higher pressure on either side will move the diaphragm to the side with a lower pressure. This provides a push or pull effect on the vacuum pot.

| Inches of Mercury (inHg) | Pounds Per Square Inch Absolute (psia) | Kilopascals Absolute (kPa absolute) |
|---|---|---|
| 28.98 | 0.5 | 3.45 |
| 27.96 | 1.0 | 6.89 |
| 26.94 | 1.5 | 10.34 |
| 25.92 | 2.0 | 13.79 |
| 24.90 | 2.5 | 17.24 |
| 23.88 | 3.0 | 20.68 |
| 22.86 | 3.5 | 24.13 |
| 21.83 | 4.0 | 27.58 |
| 20.81 | 4.5 | 30.03 |
| 19.79 | 5.0 | 34.47 |
| 18.77 | 5.5 | 37.92 |
| 17.75 | 6.0 | 41.37 |
| 16.73 | 6.5 | 44.82 |
| 18.71 | 7.0 | 48.26 |
| 14.69 | 7.5 | 51.71 |
| 13.67 | 8.0 | 55.16 |
| 12.65 | 8.5 | 58.61 |
| 11.63 | 9.0 | 62.05 |
| 10.61 | 9.5 | 65.50 |
| 9.59 | 10.0 | 68.95 |
| 8.57 | 10.5 | 72.40 |
| 7.54 | 11.0 | 75.84 |
| 6.52 | 11.5 | 79.29 |
| 5.50 | 12.0 | 82.74 |
| 4.48 | 12.5 | 86.19 |
| 3.46 | 13.0 | 89.63 |
| 2.44 | 13.5 | 93.08 |
| 1.42 | 14.0 | 96.53 |
| 0.40 | 14.5 | 99.98 |
| | 15.0 | 103.42 |

**Figure 10-33** Conversion chart: absolute scale versus atmospheric scale.

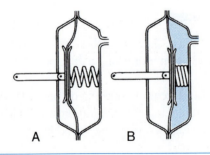

A          B

**Figure 10-34** Movement of a single-chamber vacuum motor: (A) no vacuum applied; (B) full vacuum applied.

## Vacuum Source

When running, the automobile engine provides a ready source of vacuum. This source is usually taken off the intake manifold and routed to the various components through small-diameter synthetic rubber, plastic, or nylon hoses. The engine vacuum supply source can vary from 0.01 in. Hg (14.7 psia or 101.4 kPa absolute) to 20 in. Hg (4.89 psia or 33.7 kPa absolute), or more. Actual vacuum conditions depend on certain engine conditions. The reason for the vacuum variation is not important in this discussion. It is important, however, to be aware that engine vacuum does vary.

Because of this vacuum variation, a reserve tank and check valve are used (Figure 10-35). This combination of devices provides the means to maintain maximum vacuum values to properly operate air conditioning and heater vacuum controls under all engine operating conditions. It should be noted that more than one reserve tank or check valve may be found in the air conditioning and heating system vacuum circuit. It may also be noted that the vacuum system may serve other components, such as the power brake booster.

**Reserve Tank.** Vacuum reserve tanks are provided in a variety of sizes and shapes. Some early tanks, which are made of metal, resemble a large juice can (Figure 10-36). Others (Figure 10-37) are made of plastic and resemble a sphere. Vacuum reserve tanks generally require no maintenance, but they sometimes develop pinhole-sized leaks due to exposure to the elements. When a vacuum tank is found to be leaking, it may be repaired. If the reservoir fails to a hold vacuum, the mode doors may operate sporadically or not at all. The default or normal position for the mode door when no vacuum is applied is typically in the defrost mode supplying air to the windshield on many vehicles. This is done for safety so that the windshield will stay clear even with a system failure.

The vacuum reserve tank and check valve prevent erratic operation of the vacuum motors.

**Shop Manual**
Chapter 9, page 336

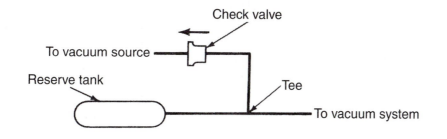

**Figure 10-35** Reserve vacuum tank and check valve.

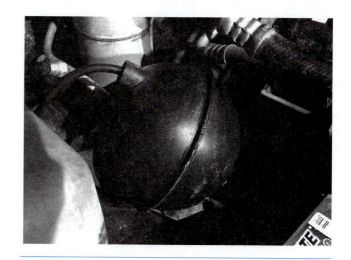

**Figure 10-36** An early vacuum reserve tank.

**Figure 10-37** A plastic vacuum reserve tank.

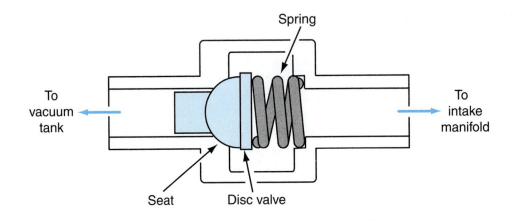

**Shop Manual**
Chapter 9,
page 334

**Shop Manual**
Chapter 9, page 284

Vacuum signal legend includes "pv" for partial vacuum, "nv" for no vacuum, and "v" or "fv" for full vacuum.

**Figure 10-38** A typical vacuum check valve.

**Check Valve.** Many types and styles of check valves are used in the automotive vacuum circuit. Essentially, a check valve (Figure 10-38) allows the flow of a fluid or vapor in one direction and blocks the flow in the opposite direction. Many systems use a check valve between the engine manifold supply vacuum hose and the reservoir tank. This ensures a consistent supply of vacuum and a source of vacuum if manifold vacuum decreases (such as under a load).

**Restrictor.** Some vacuum systems have a restrictor to provide a delay or to slow the operation of a device. Restrictors have a small orifice that sometimes becomes clogged with lint or other airborne debris. Attempts to clean a restrictor usually prove unsuccessful, and replacement is suggested. To test a restrictor, simply use a vacuum pump and gauge setup.

# Vacuum System Diagrams

The vacuum system diagram in Figure 10-39 must be considered to be typical only since it is a composite of one of hundreds of variations. The manufacturer's vacuum system diagram for a specific year/model car must be followed. Basically, the vacuum system is used to open, close, or position the heater coolant valve and mode doors to achieve a desired preselected temperature and humidity level. Pressure differentials provide a source of power to perform the mechanical movement of devices.

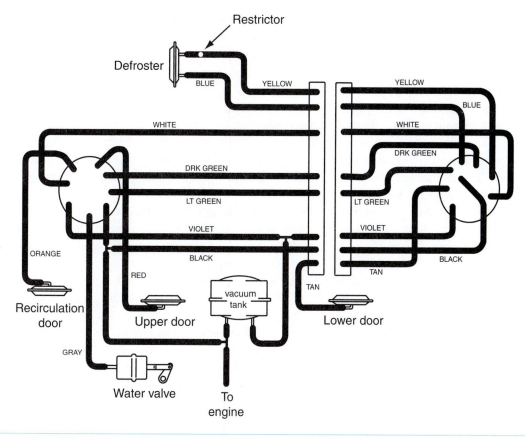

**Figure 10-39** A typical vacuum system diagram.

# Pressure Controls

Within the range of 20 psig (137.9 kPa) and 80 psig (551.6 kPa), the temperature of refrigerant R-12 has a very close relationship to its operating pressure. For refrigerant R-134a, this relationship exists from about 10 psig (68.9 kPa) through 70 psig (482.6 kPa).

Liquid refrigerant is metered into the evaporator by the metering device—either a thermostatic expansion valve or an orifice tube. The amount of refrigerant required is determined by the heat load on the evaporator. As the heat load decreases, there is a corresponding decrease in the amount of refrigerant that is metered into the evaporator by the metering device. In this discussion of pressure controls, recall that water droplets that accumulate on the surface of the evaporator freeze when the temperature drops below 32°F (0°C).

**Classroom Manual**
Chapter 10,
page 378

### A BIT OF HISTORY

In 1964, Cadillac introduced the first automatic air conditioning climate control system. This was one of the most significant advancements in available options for the luxury car market.

# Automatic Temperature Controls

**Shop Manual**
Chapter 10,
page 377

Many different types of semiautomatic and automatic temperature control systems are used today—so many that it is not possible to cover each system individually in this manual. Systems are modified or changed from year to year and from car model to car model.

Many solid-state components are so sensitive that even the 1.5-volt battery used in an analog ohmmeter may destroy them. A digital ohmmeter, then, must be used whenever a manufacturer's specifications suggest that component resistance measurements be taken. Some components and circuits are so sensitive to outside influence, however, that some schematics are labeled "Do not measure resistance." Heed this caution when it is noted to avoid damage to delicate electronic components.

The average person is comfortable at a temperature of 78°F to 80°F with a relative humidity (rh) of 45–50 percent.

Though systems differ in many respects, all are designed to provide in-car temperature and humidity conditions at a preset level (within system limitations), regardless of the temperature conditions outside the car. The temperature control also functions to hold the relative humidity within the car to a healthful level and to prevent window fogging.

For example, if the desired temperature is 75°F (23.89°C), the automatic control system will maintain an in-car environment of 75°F (23.89°C) at 45–55 percent humidity, regardless of the outside weather conditions.

In even the hottest weather, a properly operating system can rapidly cool the automobile interior to the predetermined temperature (75°F or 23.89°C). The degree of cooling then cycles to maintain the desired temperature level. In mild weather conditions, the passenger compartment can be held to this same predetermined temperature (75°F or 23.89°C) without resetting or changing the control.

During cold weather, the system rapidly heats the passenger compartment to the predetermined 75°F (23.89°C) level, and then automatically maintains this temperature level.

The intent of this text is to give an overall understanding of the components of the various systems, not to cover any particular system in detail. These components include, but are not limited to:

- ❏ Coolant temperature sensor
- ❏ In-car temperature sensor
- ❏ Outside temperature sensor
- ❏ High-side temperature switch
- ❏ Low-side temperature switch
- ❏ Evaporator thermistor
- ❏ Low-pressure switch
- ❏ High-pressure switch
- ❏ Vehicle speed sensor
- ❏ Throttle position sensor
- ❏ Sunload sensor
- ❏ Power steering cutout switch

Many automotive electronic temperature control systems have self-diagnostic test provisions whereby an onboard microprocessor-controlled subsystem will display a code. This code (number, letter, or alphanumeric) is displayed to tell the technician the cause of the malfunction. Some systems also display a code to indicate which computer detected the malfunction. The manufacturer's specifications must be followed to identify the malfunction display codes.

It is possible for the air conditioning system to malfunction even though self-check testing indicates there are no problems. It is then necessary to follow a manufacturer's step-by-step procedure to troubleshoot and check the system.

# Sensors

Although they may vary in physical appearance, sensors all have the same general operating characteristics. That is, they are extremely sensitive to slight changes in temperature. The change in resistance value of each sensor is inversely proportional to a temperature change. For example, when the temperature decreases, the resistance of the sensor increases; and when the temperature increases, the sensor resistance decreases.

The sensor is actually a resistor whose resistance value is determined by its temperature. This type of resistor is called a thermistor (Figure 10-40). Although the theory of thermistor operation is not covered in this manual, a good understanding is possible from the description illustrated in Figure 10-41.

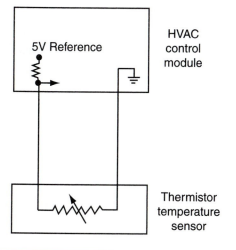

**Figure 10-40** Wiring diagram for a typical thermistor.

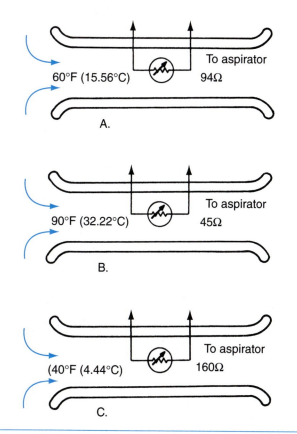

**Figure 10-41** The resistance of a thermistor changes as temperature changes.

In Figure 10-41A, one thermistor is installed in a duct. With air at a temperature of 60°F (15.56°C) passing through the duct, the resistance value of the thermistor is 94 ohms. Refer to the thermistor value given in the chart (Figure 10-42). If the temperature in the duct is 90°F (32.22°C), as in Figure 10-41B, then the resistance of the thermistor decreases to about 45 ohms. If, however, the temperature is decreased to 40°F (4.44°C), the thermistor resistance is increased to 160 ohms (Figure 10-41C).

A graph of individual sensor values at various temperatures (Figure 10-43) may be compared with the examples given to this point. Note that each sensor has a different value for a particular temperature.

| Temperature* °F | °C | Resistance Ohms | Temperature* °F | °C | Resistance Ohms |
|---|---|---|---|---|---|
| 50 | 10.0 | 120 | 66 | 18.9 | 83 |
| 51 | 10.6 | 117.5 | 67 | 19.4 | 81 |
| 52 | 11.1 | 115 | 68 | 20.0 | 79 |
| 53 | 11.7 | 112.5 | 69 | 20.6 | 77 |
| 54 | 12.2 | 110 | 70 | 21.1 | 75 |
| 55 | 12.8 | 107 | 71 | 21.7 | 73.5 |
| 56 | 13.3 | 104 | 72 | 22.2 | 72 |
| 57 | 13.9 | 101.5 | 73 | 22.8 | 70.5 |
| 58 | 14.4 | 99 | 74 | 23.3 | 69 |
| 59 | 15.0 | 96.5 | 75 | 23.9 | 67.5 |
| 60 | 15.6 | 94 | 76 | 24.4 | 66 |
| 61 | 16.1 | 92.5 | 77 | 25.0 | 64.5 |
| 62 | 16.7 | 91 | 78 | 25.6 | 63 |
| 63 | 17.2 | 89 | 79 | 26.1 | 61.5 |
| 64 | 17.8 | 87 | 80 | 26.7 | 60 |
| 65 | 18.3 | 85 | 81 | 27.2 | 58.5 |

*Temperature of ambient air passing across the thermistor

**Figure 10-42** Thermistor values.

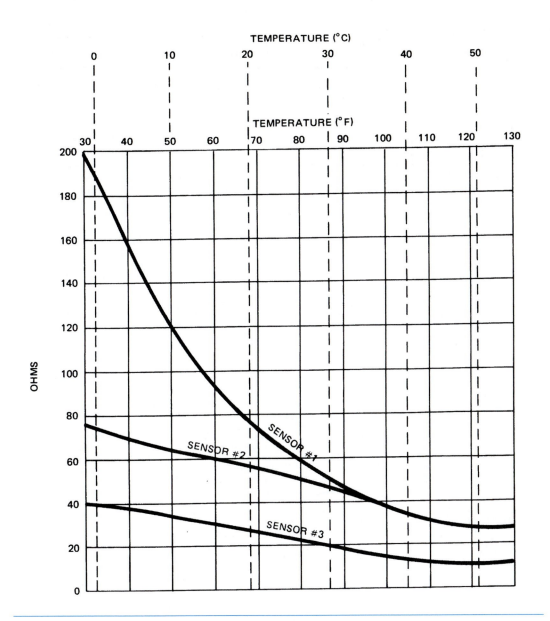

**Figure 10-43** Individual sensor values graphed.

# Electronic Temperature Control Systems

Many types of electronic temperature control systems are in use. The flowcharts shown in Figure 10-44 illustrate two typical systems. The following information relates to many of the components found in an electronic temperature control system. Not all components, however, are found in all systems.

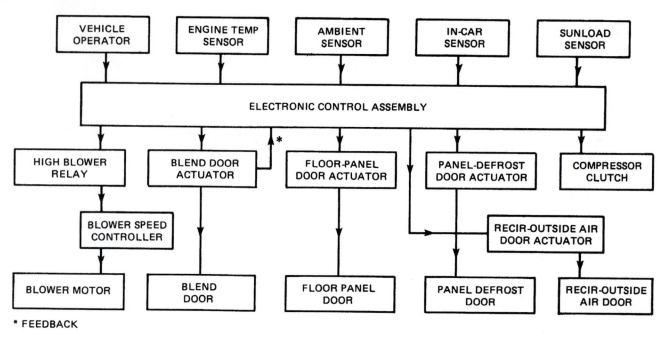

**A**

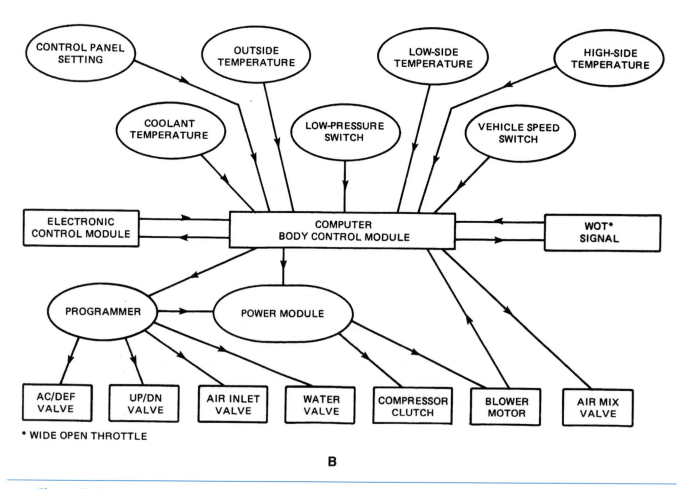

**B**

**Figure 10-44** Electronic temperature control flowcharts with five inputs (A) and nine inputs (B).

# Control Panel

The control panel is found in the instrument panel at a convenient location for both driver and front-seat passenger access. Two types of control panel (Figure 10-45) may be found: manual and pushbutton. All serve the same purpose: to provide operator input control for the air conditioning and heating system. Some control panels have features that other panels do not have, such as provisions to display in-car and outside air temperature in English or metric units.

Provisions are made on the control panel for operator selection of an in-car temperature, generally between 65°F (47.2°C) and 85°F (56.6°C) in one-degree increments. Some have an override feature that provides for a setting of either 60°F (42.2°C) or 90°F (72.2°C). Either of these two settings will override all in-car temperature control circuits to provide maximum cooling or heating conditions.

A microprocessor is usually located in the control head to input data to the **programmer**, based on operator-selected conditions. When the ignition switch is turned off, a memory circuit will remember the previous setting. These conditions will be restored each time the ignition switch is turned on. If the battery is disconnected, however, the memory circuit is cleared and must be reprogrammed.

In-car comfort may dictate a temperature setting other than that determined to be ideal for the average person.

A **programmer** is the part of an automatic temperature control system that controls the blower speed, air mix doors, and vacuum or electrical actuators.

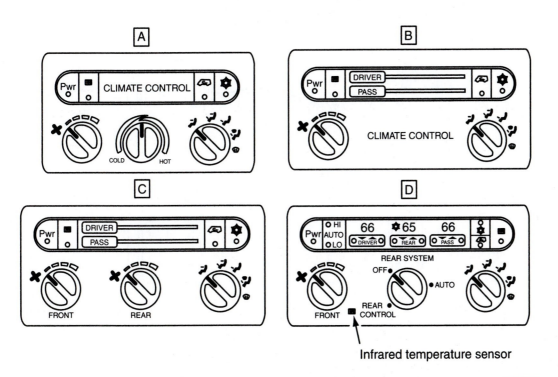

Infrared temperature sensor

Figure 10-45 Examples of typical control panel for HVAC systems. (A) is a typical single zone, (B) is a typical zone system, (C) is a typical three zone system, and (D) is a typical three zone system with automatic temperature control (ATC).

# Master Control Heads

**Dual systems**
usually refers to systems with two evaporators in an air conditioning system, one in the front and one in the rear of the vehicle, driven off a single compressor and condenser system.

The master control head (Figure 10-46) is found in the instrument panel where it is easily accessed by the driver or front-seat passenger. Some **dual systems** also have a control panel in the rear of the vehicle (Figure 10-47) for the comfort and convenience of the rear-seat passengers.

A mini-microprocessor is found in the control head to input temperature and humidity data selected by the operator to the programmer. Most electronic temperature control heads have provisions for self-testing, known as onboard diagnostics (OBD). This system provides a number, letter, or alphanumeric code to provide the technician information relative to the problem. Manufacturers' charts must be consulted to interpret a particular code. For example Ford's "09" or

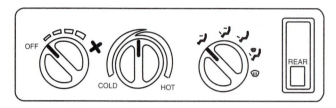

Heater control

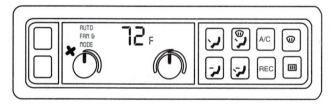

Manual A/C control

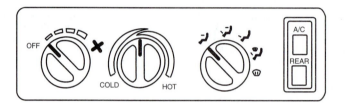

ATC control module

**Figure 10-46** A typical master control head.

**Figure 10-47** A typical rear control panel.

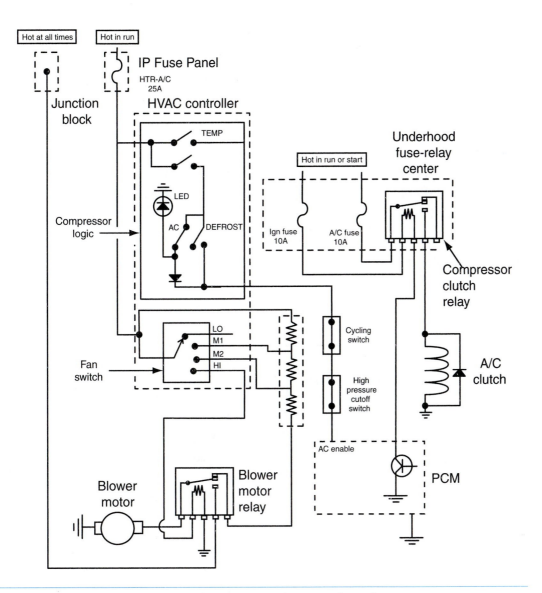

**Figure 10-48** A typical electronic climate control system schematic.

"88," a no-trouble code, corresponds to General Motors' ".7,0." Another example, code "14," indicates "control head defective" in a Ford system while "36" indicates "ATC head communications failure" in a Chrysler system.

Note, too, that some electronic climate control (ECC) programmers (Figure 10-48) have an "ECC diagnostic connector" provision for the connection of an external readout.

## Automatic (Electronic) Temperature Controls

Comfort of those in the passenger compartment is maintained by mixing cooled and ambient or heated air in the plenum section of the heater-air conditioning duct system. In the AUTO mode, the operator sets the desired comfort level, often humidity as well as temperature. Both the quality as well as the quantity of air delivered to the passenger compartment is then controlled automatically. The blower speed and air delivery can, however, be manually controlled if desired.

The control panel in Figure 10-45D is typical for an automatic temperature control (ATC) system. The control panel may be used to select a predetermined temperature level that will automatically be maintained at all times. If desired, the operator can override the automatic provisions of the control head by selecting MAX A/C or MAX heat. Manual modes are also available for selecting BI-LEVEL, DEF, VENT, and DEFOG operation. Check the heater and A/C function test chart (Figure 10-49) for the proper system response for the various control settings.

## Programmer

The programmer (Figure 10-50) receives electrical input signals from sensors and the main control panel. Based on all inputs, the programmer provides output signals to turn on/off the compressor clutch, open/close the heater water valve, determine blower speed, and position all mix/blend and fresh/recirculate mode doors.

## Power Module

The blower motor power module is a solid-state device that takes the place of the stepped resistor for blower speed control. It is typically found on automatic temperature control (ATC) systems

| STEP | CONTROL SETTINGS | | | | SYSTEM RESPONSE | | | |
|------|------|------|------|------|------|------|------|------|
| | Mode control | Temp control | Fan control | Blower speed | Heater outlet | A/C outlets | Defrost outlets | Remarks |
| 1 | OFF | 60 | Does not function | OFF | No airflow | No airflow | No airflow | A |
| 2 | AUTO | 60 | LO | LO | Min. airflow | Airflow | No airflow | A |
| 3 | AUTO | 60 | LO to HI | LO to HI | Small airflow | Airflow | No airflow | D |
| 4 | BI-LEVEL | 60 | LO to HI | LO to HI | Airflow | Airflow | Small airflow | A,D |
| 5 | AUTO | 60 | HI | HI | Airflow | No airflow | Small airflow | A,B,C,D |
| 6 | DEF FRT | 90 | HI | HI | Small airflow | No airflow | Airflow | A,D |
| 7 | DEF REAR | 90 | Does not change system response | | | | | A |

REMARKS:

A. The word "AUTO" must appear in L/H upper corner of display when in automatic mode.
   Mode arrows in display must indicate flow from appropriate outlet.
   LEDs must light above mode buttons when selected.

B. Listen for air noise reduction as recirculation door closes.

C. During transition from A/C outlets to heater outlets there will be a period of time when one half of the air will be directed from the defroster outlets.

D. Check for airflow at side window defogger outlets in all modes but OFF.

**Figure 10-49** A typical heater and air conditioning function test chart.

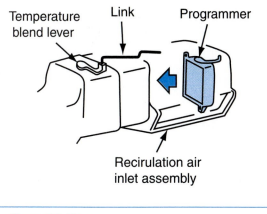

Temperature blend lever  Link  Programmer

Recirulation air inlet assembly

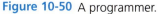

**Figure 10-50** A programmer.

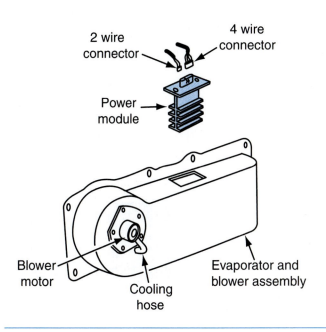

2 wire connector  4 wire connector

Power module

Blower motor  Cooling hose  Evaporator and blower assembly

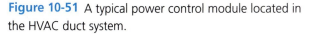

**Figure 10-51** A typical power control module located in the HVAC duct system.

and is typically bolted into the duct system (Figure 10-51). It is a solid-state electrical device and is housed in a heat sink to keep it cool. The power control module amplifies the blower-driver signal from the programmer; its output signal is proportional to its input signal. The power control module sends a pulse width modulated signal to the blower motor to regulate blower speeds. By varying the duty cycle (Figure 10-52) of the motor, an infinite number of speeds can be achieved.

If the in-car temperature is considerably higher than the selected temperature when using the air conditioning, the power control module will increase blower motor speed until the temperature within the vehicle begins to drop. Once the temperature begins to drop, the power control module will reduce the blower speed to a level that will maintain the temperature selected at the control panel.

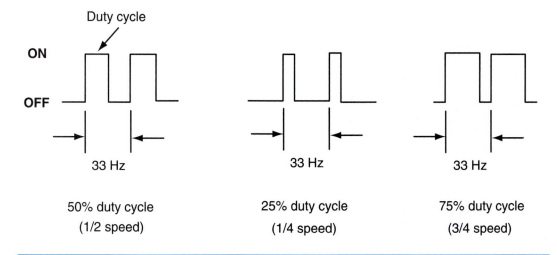

Duty cycle

ON

OFF

33 Hz    33 Hz    33 Hz

50% duty cycle    25% duty cycle    75% duty cycle
(1/2 speed)    (1/4 speed)    (3/4 speed)

**Figure 10-52** Typical duty cycle patterns, as viewed with an oscilloscope, to achieve various blower motor speed through the use of pulse width modulation.

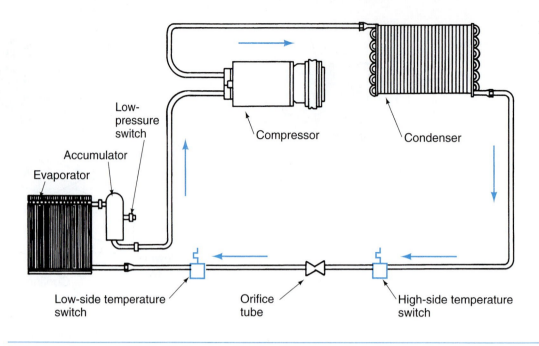

**Figure 10-53** Location of the low- and high-side temperature switch.

### High-Side Temperature Switch

The high-side temperature switch is located in the air conditioning system liquid line between the condenser outlet and the orifice tube inlet (Figure 10-53). Though it is a temperature-sensing device, it provides air conditioner system pressure data to the processor. System temperature is determined by system pressure based on the temperature/pressure relationship of the refrigerant.

### Low-Side Temperature Switch

The low-side temperature switch is located in the air conditioning system line between the orifice tube outlet and the evaporator inlet. Its purpose is to sense low-side refrigerant pressure and to provide this information to the microprocessor.

### Low-Pressure Switch

Conditions such as a loss of refrigerant may cause abnormally low low-side pressures.

The low-pressure switch is located in the low side of the air conditioning system, usually on the accumulator (Figure 10-54). This normally closed (nc) switch opens when system low-side pressure drops below 2–8 psig (13.8–55.2 kPa). An open low-pressure switch signals the microprocessor to disengage the compressor clutch circuit to prevent compressor operation during low-pressure conditions. Low-pressure conditions may result due to a loss of refrigerant or a clogged metering device.

### Pressure Cycling Switch

The pressure cycling switch is found on some systems. It is used as a means of temperature control by opening and closing the electrical circuit to the compressor clutch coil. On cycling clutch systems, this switch usually opens at a low pressure of 25–26 psig (172.4–179.3 kPa) and closes at a high pressure of 46–48 psig (317.2–331 kPa). On some systems, this switch may be in line with the compressor clutch coil. On other systems, it may send data to the microprocessor to turn the compressor on and off.

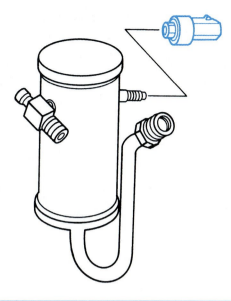

Figure 10-54 The low-pressure switch is usually located on the accumulator.

## Sensors

A sensor is a general name given to a transducer, which is short for "transfer inductor." In automotive terms, a sensor is a device that is capable of sensing a change in pressure, temperature, or other controlled variables.

## Sun Load Sensor

The sun load sensor (Figure 10-55) is usually found atop the dashboard, adjacent to one of the radio speaker grilles. The sunload sensor is a photovoltaic diode that sends an appropriate signal to the microprocessor to aid in regulating the in-car temperature. The sun load sensor can also be found under the defrost grille at about the center of the windshield. It is a thermistor that is sensitive to the heat load of the sun on the vehicle.

The BCM compares the sun load values with in-car temperature values to determine how much cooling is required in order to maintain selected in-vehicle temperature conditions (Figure 10-56).

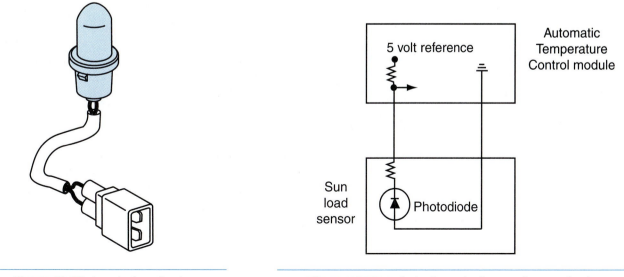

Figure 10-55 A typical sun load sensor.

Figure 10-56 Typical schematic diagram for a sunload sensor.

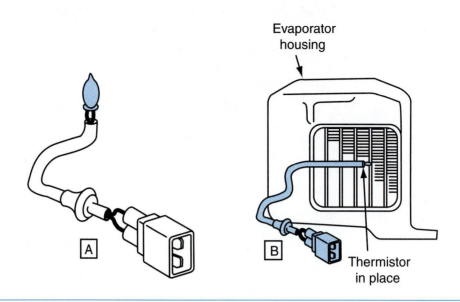

Figure 10-57 A typical evaporator thermistor (A), in position (B) between evaporator cooling fins.

## Evaporator Thermistor

The evaporator thermistor (Figure 10-57) is used on some systems to control evaporator temperature. A variable resistor, it electrically connects to the compressor clutch microprocessor circuit to turn the compressor off when the evaporator temperature drops to 34°F (1.1°C). This prevents the formation of frost and ice on the fins of the evaporator.

## Outside Temperature Sensor

The ambient temperature sensor (ATS), also referred to as the outside temperature sensor (OTS), is a thermistor found in a protective housing just behind the radiator grille (Figure 10-58). Data from the ATS is processed by the BCM and is displayed on the ECC. Through a rather complicated process, the ATS provides information regarding outside ambient temperature that is essen-

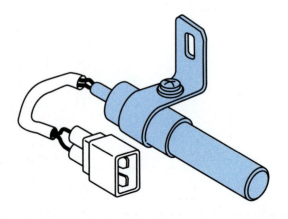

Figure 10-58 The outside temperature sensor is located behind the grille.

tial for the proper operation of an electronic automatic temperature control (EATC) system. The outside temperature sensor, also called an ambient temperature sensor, is usually located just behind the radiator grille and in front of the condenser. Its purpose is to sense outside ambient temperature conditions to provide data to the microprocessor.

This sensor circuit has several programmed memory features to prevent false ambient temperature data input during periods of low-speed driving or when stopped close behind another vehicle, such as when waiting for a traffic signal. If ambient air temperature is below the minimum preprogrammed level, the control module will not allow the air conditioning compressor clutch to engage. Air conditioning is not generally required at temperatures below 50°F (10°C). This is due to the low relative moisture content contained in air at that temperature, even at the saturation point.

## In-Car Temperature Sensor

The in-car temperature sensor, also called an in-vehicle sensor (Figure 10-59), is located in a tubular device called an **aspirator**. A small amount of in-car air is drawn through the aspirator across the in-car sensor to provide average in-car temperature data to the microprocessor.

The aspirator is a small duct system that is designed to cause a small amount of in-car air to pass through it. The main airstream causes a low pressure (suction) at the inlet end of the aspirator. This causes in-car air to be drawn into the in-car sensor plenum. The in-car sensor, located in the plenum, is continuously exposed to average in-car air to monitor the in-car air temperature.

An **aspirator** is a device that uses suction to move air, accomplished by a differential in air pressure.

## Infrared Temperature Sensor

Some vehicles with automatic temperature control are equipped with an infrared temperature sensor (ITS) to determine passenger compartment temperature. It may be located in the temperature control assembly or near the dash discharge outlets at the center of the dash. Infrared temperature sensors measure surface temperatures rather than air temperature and thus can adjust

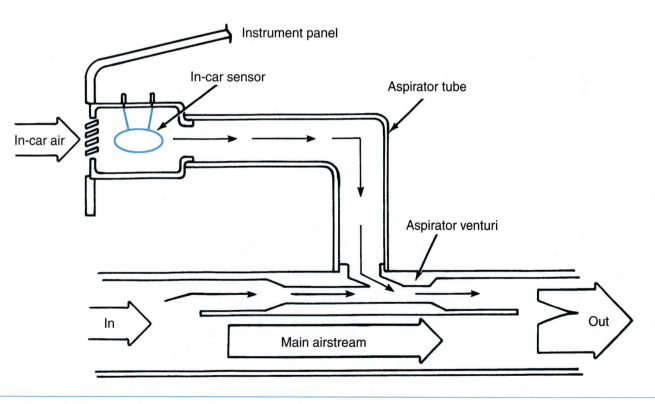

**Figure 10-59** A typical in car temperature sensor and aspirator assembly.

passenger compartment temperatures based on the perceived temperature (caused by ultraviolet radiation from the sun or evaporative heat loss) of the passenger instead of actual air temperature. The temperature control module interprets the data received by the ITS and evaporator temperature sensor to adjust blower speed and the amount of refrigerant flowing through the evaporator core to maintain the selected temperature level of the passenger compartment. If an infrared sensor is found to be defective, it must be replaced as an assembly.

## Coolant Temperature Sensor

The coolant temperature sensor is a thermistor that provides engine coolant temperature information to the microprocessor. This sensor also provides input information to other onboard computers to provide data for fuel enrichment, ignition timing, exhaust gas recirculate operation, canister purge control, idle speed control, and closed loop fuel control.

A defective coolant temperature sensor will cause poor engine performance, which will probably be evident before poor air conditioning performance is noticed.

## Vehicle Speed Sensor

The vehicle speed sensor is a pulse generator that is usually located at the transmission output shaft. It provides actual vehicle speed data to the microprocessor as well as other subsystems, such as the electronic control module (ECM).

## Throttle Position Sensor

The throttle position sensor is actually a potentiometer with a voltage input from the processor. The processor, then, determines throttle position based on the return voltage signal. At the wide-open throttle (WOT) position, the compressor clutch is disengaged to provide maximum power for acceleration. This device is often called the WOT sensor and is most often found on diesel engine-equipped vehicles.

## Heater Turn-On Switch

The heater turn-on switch is usually a bimetallic snap-action switch found in the coolant stream of the engine. Its purpose is to prevent blower operation when engine coolant temperature is below 118–122°F (48.9–50°C), if heat is selected.

If cooling is selected, the programmer will override this switch to provide immediate blower operation, regardless of engine coolant temperature.

## Brake Booster Vacuum Switch

The brake booster vacuum switch is a low-pressure switch.

The brake booster vacuum switch is found on some cars. Its purpose is to disengage the air conditioning compressor whenever braking requires maximum effort. This switch, which is usually in series with the compressor clutch electrical circuit, does not provide data to the microprocessor.

## Power Steering Cutoff Switch

The power steering cutoff switch is a high-pressure switch.

The power steering cutoff switch, which is found on some cars, is used to disengage the air conditioning compressor whenever power steering requires maximum effort. This switch, on some cars, is in series with the compressor control relay and does not provide data to the programmer. On other applications, this switch is in the electronic control module and provides feedback data to the microprocessor.

# Scan Tool

A scan tool (Figure 10-60) is a microprocessor that is designed to communicate with the vehicle's computer. When connected to the computer, through diagnostic connectors, a scan tool accesses diagnostic trouble codes (DTCs), runs tests to check system operations, and monitors the activity of the system. Both trouble codes and test results are displayed on a light-emitting diode (LED) screen or are printed out on the scanner printer.

A scan tool receives its information from several sources. Some scan tools use cartridges containing programmable read-only memory (PROM) chips. Each chip contains all of the information needed to diagnose problems in a specific model line, and the appropriate cartridge for whatever vehicle is being worked on is inserted into the tool accordingly.

LED displays on some are generally only large enough to display four short lines of information, limiting the technician's ability to compare test data. Today, most scan tools have large screens with many lines of information and graphing capabilities. Many may be interfaced with a laptop or desktop computer for increased data display and graphing, as well as enabling service technicians to store information and create their own data and waveform library. Most scan tools can store the test data in a random access memory (RAM) that can be accessed by a printer, personal computer, or an engine analyzer to retrieve the information.

Trouble codes set by the computer help the technician identify the cause of the problem. Most diagnostic work on computer control systems should be based on a description of symptoms to help locate any technical service bulletins that refer to the problem. One can also use the symptom description to locate the appropriate troubleshooting sequence in the manufacturer's service manuals.

The average person is comfortable at 78–80°F (25.6–26.7°C) at a relative humidity (rh) of 45–50 percent.

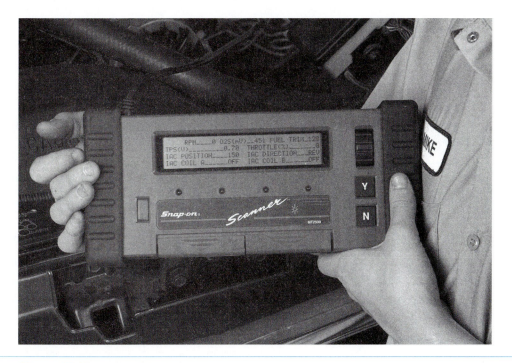

**Figure 10-60** A typical handheld scan tool.

# Summary

❑ Many of the components of an automatic temperature control system are covered in this chapter.

❑ Because of the complexity of the automatic control system and its number of variations, it is essential that manufacturers' specifications, manuals, and schematics be consulted for any specific year/model car to be serviced.

# Review Questions

## Short Answer Essay

1. What is the purpose of the clutch diode?
2. Explain the meaning of the term *delta P* ($\Delta_p$).
3. Describe the purpose of an aspirator.
4. Compare the difference between a temperature-controlled switch and a pressure-controlled switch.
5. What type of a warning device is an "idiot" light?
6. What is the definition and function of a CCOT?
7. Identify the difference between a fuse and a circuit breaker.
8. What is the purpose of a capillary tube?
9. Where is a field coil found in an automotive air conditioning system?
10. Why are insulators and insulation necessary in an electrical system?

## Fill-in-the-Blanks

1. The vehicle _____ , body, and all other _____ _____ are common (ground).

2. A _____-speed blower motor speed control module will have three _____ .

3. A thermostat capillary tube, filled with a _____ , is attached to the _____ of the thermostat.

4. A(n) _____ _____ is used to engage and disengage a compressor.

5. If there is too little space between the armature and rotor, the clutch will _____ when off; if there is too much, it will _____ when on.

6. The FOTCC system uses a_____-sensitive compressor cycling switch instead of a _____-sensitive switch.

7. A vacuum circuit relies on pressure _____ atmospheric.

8. A vacuum _____ _____ ensures system component operation during brief periods of little or no manifold vacuum.

9. An automatic air conditioning system should provide selected in-car _____ and _____ at all times.

10. A self-diagnostic readout is usually presented in _____ , _____ , or alphanumeric values.

## Multiple Choice

1. *Technician A* says that most electronic control circuits may be measured with an analog ohmmeter. *Technician B* says that any electronic control circuit may be measured with a digital ohmmeter. Who is correct?
   - **A.** A only
   - **B.** B only
   - **C.** Both A and B
   - **D.** Neither A nor B

2. *Technician A* says that a high-pressure control is used as a means of temperature control on some air conditioners. *Technician B* says a thermostat is used for temperature control on some air conditioners. Who is correct?
   - **A.** A only
   - **B.** B only
   - **C.** Both A and B
   - **D.** Neither A nor B

3. All of the following statements are correct, *except*:
   - **A.** A low-pressure cutoff switch opens at a predetermined low pressure.
   - **B.** Atmospheric pressure at sea level is 14.696 psia.
   - **C.** A clutch coil resistor is used to prevent high voltage spikes.
   - **D.** A sensor is an electrical input device which may be used to sense temperature and/or pressure.

4. *Technician A* says that 16 psia is a vacuum pressure. *Technician B* says that 179 kPa (absolute) is a vacuum pressure. Who is correct?
   - **A.** A only
   - **B.** B only
   - **C.** Both A and B
   - **D.** Neither A nor B

5. *Technician A* says that the purpose of the rheostat is to provide infinite fan speed control. *Technician B* says its purpose is to provide 2-, 3-, 4-, or 5-speed fan control. Who is correct?
   - **A.** A only
   - **B.** B only
   - **C.** Both A and B
   - **D.** Neither A nor B

6. *Technician A* says that resistors are used to reduce voltage. *Technician B* says that resistors are used to control blower speed. Who is correct?
   - **A.** A only
   - **B.** B only
   - **C.** Both A and B
   - **D.** Neither A nor B

7. The following may be used to maintain in-vehicle temperature, *except*:
   - **A.** Evaporator thermistor
   - **B.** Variable displacement compressor
   - **C.** Coolant temperature sensor
   - **D.** Pressure cycling switch

8. *Technician A* says that three dropping resistors may be required for a three-speed blower motor. *Technician B* says that not all motors require dropping resistors for speed control. Who is correct?
   - **A.** A only
   - **B.** B only
   - **C.** Both A and B
   - **D.** Neither A nor B

9. The clutch diode is being discussed: *Technician A* says that it assures that 12 volts are supplied to the clutch coil. *Technician B* says that it prevents reverse polarity of the clutch coil. Who is correct?
   - **A.** A only
   - **B.** B only
   - **C.** Both A and B
   - **D.** Neither A nor B

10. The effects of atmospheric pressure on vacuum motors are being discussed: *Technician A* says that atmospheric pressure does not affect single-chamber vacuum motors. *Technician B* says that atmospheric pressure does not affect dual-chamber vacuum motors. Who is correct?
    - **A.** A only
    - **B.** B only
    - **C.** Both A and B
    - **D.** Neither A nor B

# Retrofit and Future Trends (R-12 to R-134a)

Upon completion and review of this chapter, you should be able to:

❏ Discuss the various refrigerants approved to replace R-12.

❏ Identify the refrigerant approved to replace R-12 in automotive air conditioning systems.

❏ Understand the problems associated with contaminated refrigerant.

❏ Compare components used in R-134a systems with those used in R-12 systems.

❏ Discuss the prospect of R-744 as the next automotive refrigerant.

## Introduction

When speaking about an automotive air conditioning system, the term *retrofit* is used to describe the process of converting an R-12 system to one using an **alternative refrigerant**. In this text, it will be assumed that the conversion refrigerant is R-134a because the automotive industry, worldwide, chose this refrigerant to be the replacement in new as well as retrofitted automotive air conditioning systems.

Most automobile manufacturers have developed retrofit kits and/or procedures for some of their late 1980 through early 1990 model vehicles. These kits and information are intended to provide the best level of performance with R-134a refrigerant with no regard for costs. Vehicle owners, however, generally do not want to pay the high cost for a retrofit and are, therefore, often the target of the independent technician offering an inexpensive solution—the "magic bullet," so to speak.

### The Inexpensive Retrofit

The procedures for an inexpensive retrofit are relatively simple and generally do not require major component replacements. The process usually only requires removal of the R-12 refrigerant, new fittings, new label, and the addition of the proper lubricant. For many, this simple inexpensive retrofit will provide the owner with an air conditioning system performance that is comparable to the former R-12 system. Even if the retrofit results in slightly reduced performance, it is usually sufficient for customer satisfaction.

The Environmental Protection Agency (EPA) has an ongoing program intended to educate car owners on matters concerning retrofit options. Many car owners, however, rely on their service technician for their education. When recommending a retrofit to a customer, the "three C's" should be discussed: cost, climate, and components.

**Cost.** What is the value of the car? How long will the customer continue to drive it? Is it a refrigerant leaker or is this the first time the air conditioning system has been serviced? How much is the customer willing to spend?

**Climate.** Does the customer live in the North and require minimal air conditioning performance because the car is only used for occasional short pleasure trips, or does the customer live in the South and need maximum performance because the car is used five or six days a week for business?

**Retrofit** is the process of modifying equipment that is already in service by installing updated parts and/or materials made available after the time of original manufacturing.

**Alternative refrigerant** is a refrigerant that can be used to replace an existing refrigerant, such as ozone-friendly R-134a that is used to replace ozone-depleting R-12.

**Components.** Are the air conditioning system components in good working order? Are they compatible with the new refrigerant, R-134a? Are there any indications of leaking hoses, restrictions in the system, or a noisy compressor? If not operational, did the system cool satisfactorily when it was last working? If R-12 system performance is no more than marginally satisfactory, retrofitting will not make it better. To the contrary, owners should be prepared for a slight reduction in system performance.

## Retrofit Problems

In older cars, it is often necessary that worn air conditioning system components be replaced. R-134a operates at a higher pressure than R-12 and will put additional stress on system components. Older, somewhat worn components not designed for R-134a service may not withstand the higher pressures and are more likely to fail.

There is no such thing as a universal retrofit kit that can be purchased nor is there a set procedure for a technician to follow that will ensure a successful retrofit for every car. Even within a given vehicle model, the retrofit requirements will vary. For example, a vehicle driven 90,000 miles (144,810 kilometers) in southern Florida may require a more extensive retrofit than an identical car driven, say, 25,000 miles (40,225 kilometers) in northern Minnesota.

According to EPA regulations, any alternate refrigerant used to replace R-12 requires the following:

> **Cross-contamination** is when one refrigerant is contaminated with another. This usually occurs due to improper or incomplete service procedures.

❑ Unique service fittings (Figure 11-1) must be used on both the high side as well as the low side of the system. This requirement is intended to reduce the likelihood of **cross-contamination** of the air conditioning system or the repair facility's refrigeration service equipment.

❑ Use of the new refrigerant must be noted on a uniquely colored label (Figure 11-2) to distinguish the type refrigerant and lubrication used in the system.

❑ All R-12 must be properly removed from the system before filling the system with an alternative refrigerant.

❑ To prevent release of refrigerant to the atmosphere, a high-pressure compressor shutoff switch must be installed on any system equipped with a pressure relief device.

❑ Separate, dedicated EPA-approved equipment must be used to recover R-12 refrigerant from the system.

❑ Barrier hoses must be used with alternative refrigerant blends that contain HCFC-22.

**Figure 11-1** An R-134a system uses unique hose fittings.

**Figure 11-2** A label identifies the type of refrigerant in the system.

# The Replacement Refrigerant of Choice

Several refrigerants in addition to R-134a are now listed by the EPA as acceptable for motor vehicle air conditioner (MVAC) use under their Significant New Alternatives Policy (SNAP) plan. Others are under SNAP review. The SNAP program tests and evaluates substitute refrigerants for their effect on human health and the environment. SNAP does not test and evaluate refrigerants for performance or durability. Except for R-134a, no refrigerant has been endorsed by vehicle manufacturers for use in MVACs. While some alternate refrigerants are being marketed as "drop-ins," there is by definition no such thing as a refrigerant that can literally be "dropped in" on top of existing R-12 in a system.

The current refrigerant of choice—R-134a—is considered to be one of the safest refrigerants based on toxicity data. Extensive tests indicate that R-134a does not pose cancer or birth defect hazards, is not corrosive on steel, aluminum, or copper samples, and is not flammable at ambient temperatures at atmospheric pressure. Service equipment and vehicle air conditioning systems, however, should not be pressure or leak tested using compressed air. Some mixtures of air and R-134a have been known to be combustible at elevated pressures.

As with any other chemical, R-134a should be handled with respect; work in a well-ventilated area, wear adequate personal protection, avoid open flames, and do not inhale any vapor.

## System Charge

The amount of R-134a charged into the system should initially be 80–90 percent of the charge of R-12. Most manufacturers provide guidelines regarding the amount of R-134a to be used.

## Lubricants

The mineral oil used with R-12 cannot be adequately transported through the system by R-134a. Most, but not all, automobile manufacturers chose polyalkaline glycol (PAG) lubricants for use in new and retrofitted air conditioning systems charged with R-134a. PAGs are very hygroscopic; they draw water from the atmosphere when exposed to open air. Some specialists choose to use polyol ester (POE) lubricants (Figure 11-3), believing that PAG's hygroscopic nature limits its lubricating ability and causes corrosion in a system. Although it is less hygroscopic than PAG, care must still be taken with POE to ensure that excess moisture does not enter the system.

Personal protection such as PVC-coated gloves or barrier creams and OSHA-approved safety goggles should be used when handling these lubricants. Prolonged skin contact or eye contact can cause irritations such as stinging and burning. One should avoid breathing any vapors produced by these lubricants, and only use them in a well-ventilated area. They should be stored in tightly sealed containers to prevent contamination by humidity and to ensure that the vapors do not escape.

**Figure 11-3** A small container of POE lubricant.

**Flushing.** The amount of mineral oil that can remain in a system after retrofitting without affecting performance is still being debated. The technician should always remove as much of the mineral oil as possible, however. Removal may require draining components such as the compressor and accumulator. Tests have shown that any residual R-12 remaining in the system will not have a significant effect on system performance. If the vehicle manufacturer does not recommend flushing the system during the retrofit procedure, it can be assumed that flushing is not necessary.

**Hoses and O-Rings.** Tests have shown that lubricant used in an automotive air conditioning system is absorbed into the hose to create a natural barrier to R-134a permeation. In most cases, R-12 nonbarrier hoses will perform well for R-134a service, provided they are in good condition. Any replacement hose, however, should be of the barrier type.

If the fittings were not disturbed during retrofit, replacing them should not be necessary. Most retrofit instructions suggest lubricating replacement green or blue R-134a O-rings with mineral oil to provide protection since the mineral oil also provides a natural barrier.

**Compressors.** Most compressors that function satisfactorily in an R-12 system will continue to function after retrofitting an R-134a system. When a compressor is first operated with R-12, a thin film of metal chloride forms on bearing surfaces to serve as an antiwear agent. This protection continues even after the system has been retrofitted to R-134a. This may explain why new R-12 compressors often fail when installed in an R-134a system without the benefit of a break-in period with R-12.

Some older compressors have seals made of Viton® that are not compatible with R-134a or the new lubricants and must be replaced. Also, any compressor that is not in good working order should be replaced during the retrofit procedure with one designed for R-134a service.

**Desiccants.** R-12 systems often use silica gel or a desiccant designated XH-5, while R-134a systems use either XH-7 or XH-9. Some recommend replacement during the retrofit procedure of the accumulator or receiver-drier to one having XH-7 or XH-9 desiccant. It is generally agreed, however, that the accumulator or receiver-drier should be replaced if the vehicle has over 70,000 miles (112,630 kilometers), is five years or more old, or is opened up for major repair.

**Condensers and Evaporators.** It is generally accepted that if an R-12 system is operating within the manufacturer's specifications, there may be no need to replace the condenser or evaporator. The higher vapor pressures associated with R-134a, however, may result in lost condenser capacity. When planning a retrofit, the technician should consider the airflow and condenser design.

A pusher-type cooling fan mounted in front of the condenser often has improved the performance of a retrofitted air conditioning system. Bent, misshapen, or improperly positioned airflow dams and deflectors also affect performance. Hood seal kits are often recommended for retrofit procedures.

**Pressure Cutout Switch.** Systems not equipped with a high-pressure cutout switch should have one installed to prevent damage to air conditioning system parts and to prevent refrigerant emissions. The high-pressure cutout switch will disengage the compressor clutch during high-pressure conditions, thereby reducing the possibility of venting refrigerant and engine cooling system overheating.

**Metering Devices.** Orifice tubes, thermostatic expansion valves, pressure cycling switches, or other pressure controls may have to be changed during the course of a retrofit.

With the exception of R-134a, all approved alternate refrigerants are blends; they contain two or more refrigerants. In addition to R-134a, the following alternate refrigerants are available. One must be cautioned that not all are approved by the EPA for use in motor vehicle air conditioners (MVAC) and MVAC-like appliances. Some are considered by the EPA to be dangerous, and heavy penalties are imposed on those who use them. The EPA makes no exceptions and its rules are simple: Use it—get caught—pay the penalty. There are no excuses. There are one or more questions in the certification exam that test whether the technician "knows the law." If there are any doubts, call the EPA hotline and ask. Their toll-free number is included in the Appendix.

# Other Refrigerants

The Mobile Air Conditioning Society (MACS) has warned on many occasions that several refrigerant products are being offered as substitutes for R-12. Many of these refrigerants contain butane (R-600), ethane (R-170), and/or propane (R-290). While they are all refrigerants, they are also very flammable materials.

By the close of 1993, 13 states and the District of Columbia had established laws that prohibited the use of any flammable refrigerant in mobile air conditioning equipment. The first states to enact the law were Arkansas, Connecticut, Idaho, Indiana, Kansas, Louisiana, Maryland, North Dakota, Oklahoma, Texas, Utah, Virginia, and Washington.

In early 1994, Florida was first to pass a law to make it illegal to use any flammable refrigerant in an automobile air conditioning system. It is now a violation of federal law to use any refrigerant, flammable or otherwise, in a mobile air conditioning system if it has not been approved by a department of the Environmental Protection Agency (EPA) known as the Significant New Alternatives Policy (SNAP) program. Currently, there are five refrigerants that are not approved. Although there are ten refrigerants that are approved for use, only one, R-134a, has been universally accepted by the automotive industry. All refrigerants used in a mobile air conditioning system must have unique fittings and be identified by labels. There are also requirements for compressor high-pressure cutoff switches to prevent venting to the atmosphere.

Everyone is looking for the "magic bullet," a drop-in replacement for R-12. So far, it does not exist. MACS warns:

❏ Use only R-12 in an R-12-equipped system.
❏ Use only R-134a in an R-134a-equipped system.
❏ Follow retrofit procedures to use R-134a in an R-12 system.
❏ Do not use refrigerants that contain a toxic substance.
❏ Do not use a refrigerant that contains a flammable substance.
❏ The use of unauthorized refrigerants will void the manufacturer's warranties.
❏ Talk to your customer about prior automotive air conditioning service. Take no chances with health and safety. Use extreme caution if an unknown refrigerant has been introduced into the system.
❏ Protect yourself, your equipment, and your refrigerant. Use a refrigerant identifier on every job.

# Substitute Refrigerants

Five of the ten substitute refrigerants found acceptable for automotive use by the EPA contain HCFC-22 as a main component. The use conditions for these refrigerants—R-406/GHG/McCOOL, GHG-X4/Autofrost/Chil-it, Hot Shot/Kar Kool, GHG-HP, and GHG-X5—in addition to unique fittings, labels, and compressor shutoff switch, require barrier hoses. The other five refrigerants accepted by the EPA—R-134a, FRIGC FR-12, Free Zone RB-276, Ikon-12, and Freeze-12—have the same use conditions except they do not require barrier hoses.

Currently, with the exception of R-134a, no vehicle manufacturer approves the use of any of these refrigerants for use in any of their air conditioning systems as a substitute refrigerant for R-12.

There are three refrigerants at present that are not acceptable to the EPA due to their flammability. These refrigerants are OZ-12, HC-12A®, and Duracool-12. Also, refrigerant R-176 is not acceptable because it contains R-12, and R-405A is unacceptable because of its potential association with global warming and high stratospheric lifetime.

The EPA last accepted a substitute refrigerant in mid 1997. It must be noted that the EPA accepts refrigerant for use in certain applications, such as motor vehicle air conditioners (MVACs). However, this does not mean that the EPA recommends or otherwise endorses any particular refrigerant for any particular use. The agency, however, does recognize that R-134a is currently the accepted refrigerant for vehicle use by the industry.

Dedicated service and storage equipment is required by the EPA for each type of refrigerant used in a service facility. For the average facility, that means two systems: one for R-12 and one for R-134a. If one decides to service vehicles using, for example, FREEZE-12, a third set of service and storage equipment must be purchased for use. This is required even though FREEZE-12 contains 80 percent R-134a. The other 20 percent contains HCFC-142b, and it would contaminate the R-134a equipment.

For the latest update and information on refrigerant approval or any other stratospheric ozone issue, one may contact the EPA. Contact information, toll-free numbers, FAX numbers, and Web site addresses are found in the Appendix.

### Freeze 12

Freeze 12 (Figure 11-4)—a blend of 80 percent R-134a and 20 percent HCFC-142b—is acceptable for automotive use subject to having proper fittings, labeling, and a compressor shutoff switch. It is not a drop-in replacement for R-12 or R-134a. The high-side service port must be 3/8-24 right-hand thread and the low-side service port must be 7/16-20 right-hand thread. The label background color is required to be yellow.

### Free Zone/RB-276

Free Zone/RB-276 (Figure 11-5)—a blend of 79 percent R-134a, 19 percent HCFC-142b, and 2 percent lubricant—is acceptable for automotive use subject to having proper fittings, labeling, and a compressor shutoff switch. It is not a drop-in replacement for R-12 or R-134a. The high-side service port must be 1/2-13 right-hand thread and the low-side service port must be 9/16-18 right-hand thread. The label background color is required to be light green.

### Hot Shot/Kar Kool

Hot Shot—a blend of 50 percent HCFC-22, 39 percent HR-124, 9.5 percent HCFC-142b, and 1.5 percent R-600a—is acceptable for automotive use subject to having proper fittings, labeling, bar-

**Figure 11-4** Typical Freeze 12 containers.

**Figure 11-5** A Free Zone/RB-276 refrigerant cylinder.

rier hoses, and a compressor shutoff switch. It is not a drop-in replacement for R-12 nor R-134a. Although this refrigerant contains **hydrocarbons** (R-600a, Isobutane), it is not flammable as blended. The high-side service port must be 5/8-18 left-hand thread and the low-side service port must be 5/8-18 right-hand thread. The label background color is required to be medium blue.

**Hydrocarbons** are organic compounds containing only hydrogen (H) and carbon (C).

## GHG-HP

This refrigerant is a blend of 65 percent HCFC-22, 31 percent HCFC-142b, and 4 percent R-600a. It is acceptable for automotive use subject to having proper fittings, labeling, barrier hoses, and a compressor shutoff switch. Although it contains hydrocarbons (R-600a, Isobutane), it is not considered flammable as blended. It is not a drop-in replacement for R-12 nor R-134a. The required fitting sizes and label background color were undetermined at the time of this writing. Contact the EPA for this information.

## GXG-X4/Autofrost/Chil-It

This refrigerant—a blend of 51 percent HCFC-22, 28.5 percent HCFC-124, 16.5 percent HCFC-142b, and 4 percent R-600a—is acceptable for automotive use subject to having proper fittings, labeling, barrier hoses, and a compressor shutoff switch. Although it contains hydrocarbon (R-600a, Isobutane), it is not flammable as blended. It is not a drop-in replacement for R-12 nor R-134a. The high-side service port must be 0.305-32 right-hand thread and the low-side service port must be 0.368-26 right-hand thread. The label background color is required to be red.

## GXG-X5

GXG-X5—a blend of 41 percent HCFC-22, 15 percent HCFC-142b, 40 percent HFC-227ea, and 4 percent R-600a—is acceptable for automotive use subject to having proper fittings, labeling, barrier hoses, and a compressor shutoff switch. This refrigerant contains 4 percent Isobutane, a hydrocarbon, but it is not considered flammable as blended. It is not a drop-in replacement for R-12 nor R-134a. The high-side service port must be 1/2-20 left-hand thread and the low-side service port must be 9/16-18 left-hand thread. The label background color is required to be orange.

## R-406A/GHG

This refrigerant is a blend of 55 percent HCFC-22, 41 percent HCFC-142b, and 4 percent R-600a. It is acceptable for automotive use subject to having proper fittings, labeling, barrier hoses, and a compressor shutoff switch. It is not considered flammable as blended, although it contains Isobutane (R600a), a hydrocarbon. It is not a drop-in replacement for R-12 nor R-134a. The high-side service port must be 0.305-32 left-hand thread and the low-side service port must be 0.368-26 left-hand thread. The label background color is required to be black.

## Ikon-12

This refrigerant was approved for automotive air conditioning system use in mid-1996. The manufacturer, Ikon Corporation, claims that the composition of this refrigerant is confidential business information. Requirements relating to fitting sizes and label color are not developed at the time of this writing. Nor is it yet known whether barrier hoses are required. Contact the EPA or the manufacturer for more information.

## FRIGC FR-12

This refrigerant is a blend of 39 percent HR-124, 59 percent R-134a, and 2 percent R-600. It is acceptable for automotive use subject to having proper fittings, labeling, and a compressor shutoff switch. It is not considered flammable as blended, though it contains a hydrocarbon, Butane (R-600). It is not a drop-in replacement for R-12 nor R-134a. The high-side and low-side service ports must be a quick disconnect-type, but they are different from the R-134a service ports. The label background color is required to be grey.

## OZ-12®

This refrigerant, a hydrocarbon Blend A, is not SNAP-approved by the EPA. The agency claims that it contains a flammable blend of hydrocarbons and that insufficient data was submitted to demonstrate its safety.

## R-176

This refrigerant contains R-12, HCFC-22, and HCFC-142b. It is not SNAP-approved by the EPA, which claims that it is not appropriate to use an R-12 blend as an R-12 substitute.

## HC-12a®

This refrigerant, a hydrocarbon Blend B, is not SNAP-approved by the EPA, which claims that it contains a flammable blend of hydrocarbons and that insufficient data was submitted to demonstrate its safety.

## Duracool 12a

This refrigerant is not SNAP-approved by the EPA. It is identical to HC-12a® in composition, but it is produced by a different manufacturer.

## R-405A

This refrigerant is not SNAP-approved by the EPA because it contains perfluorocarbons which are implicated in global warming.

## MT-31

This blend proposed as an R-12 substitute is not approved by the EPA for use in any application because of the toxicity of one of its components.

# The Do-It-Yourselfer

Although the Clean Air Act (CAA) amendments prevent the sale of small containers of R-12 to the general public, it is not unusual to find small cans of R-12, R-22 (Figure 11-6), and R-134a on the shelves of automotive parts shops. Nor is it at all uncommon for do-it-yourselfers (DIYer) to somehow acquire refrigerant and install it in their personal vehicles. If asked by friends to purchase refrigerant for them, be aware that you may be subject to the wrath of the EPA for doing so, and act accordingly. Some refrigerants are flammable under certain conditions. Refrigerants are not compatible with each other and will contaminate the system.

Water ($H_2O$), a refrigerant, is unwanted in an air conditioning system.

# Contaminated Refrigerant

Mixing two or more different refrigerants in an air conditioning system contaminates the refrigerant. The refrigerant is contaminated in that it is no longer *"pure"* and will not react chemically and physically as intended. Not only will the system not function properly, if it functions at all, but also contaminated refrigerant can damage expensive equipment, such as a recovery/recycle unit.

Do not put any additional refrigerant in a recovery cylinder if the present date is five years or more past the test date stamped on the cylinder shoulder or collar. There are no exceptions to the rule that recovery cylinders must be inspected every five years. There is no "grace period." Using a recovery cylinder beyond the reinspection date can result in heavy penalties.

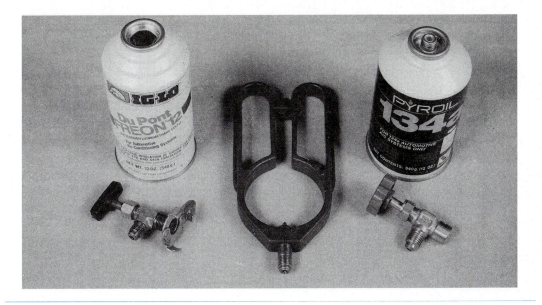

**Figure 11-6** A small container and can tap of both R-12 and R-134a, notice the different style of can taps.

If there is any doubt as to the purity of the refrigerant in the vehicle, do not service the air conditioning system unless you are properly equipped.

With the transition to CFC-free air conditioning systems, the likelihood of cross-mixing refrigerants is a growing concern. Different refrigerants, as well as their lubricants, are not compatible and should not be mixed. It is possible, however, for the wrong refrigerant to be mistakenly charged into an air conditioning system or for refrigerants to be mixed in the same recovery tank. Also, since recovery/recycling equipment is generally designed for a particular refrigerant, inadvertent mixing can cause damage to the equipment.

A refrigerant identifier tester is far superior to pressure/temperature comparisons because, at certain temperatures, the pressures of R-12 and R-134a are too similar to differentiate with a standard gauge. This is easily noted in the chart shown in Figure 11-7. For example, at 90°F (32.2°C), both 95 percent R-12 and 95 percent R-134a have about the same pressure—111 and 112 psig, respectively. Given that this chart is accurate to plus/minus 2 percent, there is really no way of determining which type refrigerant is in the air conditioning system or tank. Also, because other substitute refrigerants and blends may have been introduced into the automotive air condi-

The thermometer should be placed in an area where it can "sense" free air.

| AMB TEMP | | R-12/R-134a PERCENT BY WEIGHT | | | | | | | | | | |
|---|---|---|---|---|---|---|---|---|---|---|---|---|
| °F | °C | 100/0 | 98/2 | 95/5 | 90/10 | 75/25 | 50/50 | 25/75 | 10/90 | 5/95 | 2/98 | 0/100 |
| 65 | 18.3 | 64 | 67 | 71 | 74 | 83 | 84 | 78 | 73 | 70 | 67 | 64 |
| 70 | 21.1 | 70 | 74 | 79 | 82 | 90 | 92 | 87 | 81 | 77 | 74 | 71 |
| 75 | 23.9 | 77 | 81 | 85 | 91 | 99 | 101 | 96 | 89 | 85 | 83 | 79 |
| 80 | 26.7 | 84 | 88 | 93 | 99 | 107 | 110 | 105 | 98 | 95 | 92 | 87 |
| 85 | 29.4 | 92 | 96 | 101 | 108 | 116 | 120 | 114 | 106 | 103 | 100 | 95 |
| 90 | 32.2 | 100 | 105 | 111 | 116 | 125 | 130 | 125 | 116 | 112 | 109 | 104 |
| 95 | 35.0 | 108 | 114 | 119 | 126 | 135 | 140 | 135 | 126 | 122 | 119 | 114 |
| 100 | 37.8 | 117 | 123 | 127 | 135 | 145 | 151 | 145 | 136 | 133 | 130 | 124 |
| 105 | 40.6 | 127 | 132 | 138 | 146 | 158 | 164 | 159 | 149 | 144 | 141 | 135 |
| 110 | 43.3 | 136 | 142 | 147 | 156 | 170 | 176 | 173 | 164 | 157 | 152 | 146 |
| 115 | 46.1 | 147 | 152 | 159 | 166 | 183 | 192 | 184 | 175 | 168 | 163 | 158 |
| 120 | 48.9 | 158 | 164 | 170 | 177 | 195 | 205 | 196 | 187 | 181 | 176 | 171 |

CFC-12/HFC-134a Cross Contamination Chart. All pressures are given in psig. For kPa, multiply psig by 6.895. For example, 100% R-12 at 95°F (35°C) is 108 psig or 744.7 kPa.

**Figure 11-7** Temperature/pressure chart of R-12 and R-134a mixed refrigerants.

tioning system, they can contaminate a system or tank and may not be detected by the pressure/temperature method. A refrigerant identifier would conclude the refrigerant in our example to be UNKNOWN.

The purity of refrigerants has been set by SAE purity standards for both R-12 and R-134a. The purity standard for recycled R-12 is J1991 and the specified limits are 15 parts per million (ppm) by weight for water, 4,000 ppm by weight for refrigerant oil, and 330 ppm by weight for non-condensable gases (air). The purity standard for recycled R-134a is J2099 and the specified limits are 15 parts per million (ppm) by weight for water, 500 ppm by weight for refrigerant oil, and 150 ppm by weight for non-condensable gases (air). Refrigerant should test at least 98 percent pure when tested with a purity tester. If the refrigerant is less than 98% pure it should be considered contaminated refrigerant and treated as such.

## Proper Equipment

Being properly equipped means that you have access to and use "recovery only" equipment (Figure 11-8) that meets SAE's J2209 standards. You must also have proper recovery cylinders that meet rigid Department of Transportation (DOT) specifications. These cylinders should be marked "CONTAMINATED REFRIGERANT" for identification. Only contaminated refrigerant should be recovered into this cylinder.

Disposable cylinders, known as DOT 39s (Figure 11-9), must not be used for recovered refrigerant. Federal law prohibits refilling these cylinders.

Recovery cylinders must be inspected every five years.

## Don't Take Chances

If there is any doubt about the purity of the refrigerant, question the customer. Ask the customer such questions as:

❏ When is the last time the system was serviced?

❏ Who worked on it?

❏ What parts were replaced?

❏ Do you have a copy of the work order?

**Figure 11-8** A typical refrigerant recovery unit.

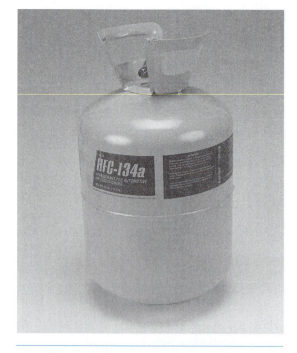

**Figure 11-9** Disposable R-134a cylinder.

Remember, under the CAA, anyone performing repairs for consideration (pay) to a motor vehicle air conditioning system must be certified, must use recovery/recycle equipment, and must comply with all rules and regulations.

Be very suspicious if the customer's response to "Who worked on it?" is something like, "Well, my neighbor works at a shop and he did it over the weekend as a favor to me." You should then ask, "Where?" Chances are the customer will reply, "At my home."

The good-intentioned neighbor may have simply been trying to do a favor. Whatever the reason, he could have contaminated the system. After all, the air conditioner still doesn't work. If it worked, your customer wouldn't have brought it to you for service.

Don't take a chance. Test a sample of the refrigerant with a purity tester as covered in Chapter 6 of this manual and Chapter 6 of the Shop Manual. If a purity tester is not available and there is even the slightest doubt, turn the vehicle away. An alternative is to keep the vehicle overnight, a period of 12 hours or more, and check for refrigerant purity according to a temperature/pressure chart, before attempting repairs.

*If in doubt, hold the purity test.*

## Purity Test

A determination of the purity of the refrigerant in the vehicle is possible while allowing for reasonable inaccuracies of the gauge, the thermometer, and the reader. After a 12-hour period, the pressure should nearly match that expected for any given temperature if the refrigerant is pure.

There are other factors to be considered, however, when testing refrigerants. For example, if there is air in the system, an accurate reading may not be noted. If there is any doubt, do not run the risk of contaminating a good tank of refrigerant.

## Disposal of Contaminated Refrigerant

Contaminated refrigerant may be reclaimed to ARI-700-88 standards, or it may be destroyed by fire. This is usually accomplished at an off-site reclamation facility that is equipped to handle such problems. Remember, however, that it is your responsibility to legally *dispose* of contaminated refrigerant.

*Make no attempt to destroy refrigerant without the proper equipment.*

## Use of Alternate Refrigerants

Many new alternative refrigerants marketed for use in motor vehicle air conditioning systems are being touted by their manufacturers and distributors. Whether employed by a nationwide repair chain or a one-person service facility, the technician should take time to determine how well an alternative refrigerant will perform and whether it may pose any problems for customers or raise liability issues.

### Health and the Environment

The EPA's Significant New Alternatives Policy (SNAP) program determines what risks to human health and the environment are posed by R-12 alternatives. The EPA evaluates the alternative refrigerant's ozone-depleting potential (ODP), global warming potential (GWP), flammability, and toxicity. The SNAP evaluation, however, does not determine if the alternate refrigerant will provide adequate performance or if it will be compatible with the components of the system.

### Use Conditions

The EPA places conditions or restrictions on how an alternative can be used. Under SNAP, for example, an R-12 substitute requires the use of a new label and new fittings unique to the alternative. There are no exemptions of the rule for do-it-yourself (DIY) mechanics.

Because of the vast range of equipment types and designs, the EPA does not issue retrofit procedures. The manufacturer of the system is the best source of information about how well a given substitute will perform. Additionally, one must determine whether charging a system with a particular "new" refrigerant will void any manufacturer's warranty.

## Clean Air Act (CAA)

The CAA requires that the EPA establish standards for recovery, recycling, and reclamation of refrigerants, including alternatives, accepted under SNAP. If standards have not been published by the EPA for a particular alternative, they may be under development. Ensure that the refrigerant manufacturer intends to work with the EPA to develop uniform methods for extraction, recycling, and reclamation.

## Standards

The Air Conditioning and Refrigeration Institute (ARI), a manufacturers' trade association, develops standards for the industry. ARI's standard 700 specifies acceptable levels of refrigerant purity for R-12, as well as for certain refrigerant blends. The purpose of the standard is to enable end users to evaluate and accept or reject any refrigerant.

The American Society of Heating, Refrigerating and Air-Conditioning Engineers (ASHRAE), a trade association, sets many of the standards and guidelines to provide a uniform method of rating refrigerants for toxicity and flammability and to assign refrigerant numbers. In fact, before ARI determines that its standard 700 should apply to a particular refrigerant, it must receive a classification from ASHRAE. However, ASHRAE classification is not required for SNAP acceptability.

## Flammability

Both ASHRAE and the EPA evaluate refrigerants for flammability. The EPA requires that a new refrigerant be analyzed according to a test of the American Society of Testing Materials (ASTM). This test determines the concentrations in the air at which a substance is flammable at normal atmospheric pressure. Some hydrocarbons, for example, ignite at concentrations as low as 2 percent by volume. If a blend contains a flammable component, the EPA requires leak testing to ensure that the blend does not change and become flammable.

If a system is charged with an alternative refrigerant that later becomes unavailable, the system may have to be retrofitted again, a service the customer may feel is unfair and be unwilling to pay for.

## Grace Period

A refrigerant manufacturer must submit information on a new refrigerant for SNAP review at least 90 days before marketing. The CAA, however, does not prohibit the sale and use of that refrigerant after the 90-day period. If the agency is still engaged in its review after 90 days, the refrigerant can be sold and used even though it is not formally approved. The EPA may later determine that the refrigerant is unacceptable, and you may be stuck with an inventory of refrigerant that cannot be legally used.

## Use versus Sale

The CAA granted to the EPA authority to regulate the *use* of alternative refrigerants, not the *sale* of them. If, for example, the EPA determines that an alternative is unacceptable for automotive service, it is still legal to sell it to the automotive trade. Using it in a customer's air conditioning system, however, is considered illegal, and the technician who serviced the air conditioning system may be fined $25,000 and have to serve up to five years in prison.

# Retrofit Components

Following is an overview of some of the problems and conditions associated with components, listed in no particular order, when retrofitting an automotive air conditioning system from R-12 to R-134a refrigerant.

## Access Valves

There is a distinct difference between the access valves used on R-134a systems (Figure 11-10) and those used on R-12 systems (Figure 11-11). Adapters (Figure 11-12) are available that are to be used on R-12 fittings during retrofit procedures to make them compatible with R-134a equipment. A special adapter, called a saddle clamp access valve (Figure 11-13) is available for installation where space does not permit the R-134a adapter to convert the R-12 valve.

Saddle clamp access valves have been used to gain access to domestic "hermetic" air conditioners for many years.

**Figure 11-10** Access valve port on an R-134a system.

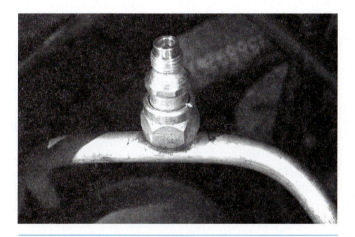

**Figure 11-11** Access valve port on an R-12 system hose.

**Figure 11-12** Adapter fittings for retrofitting R-12 access valve fittings over to R-134a access valve fittings.

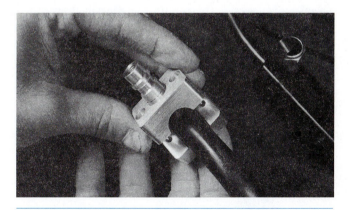

**Figure 11-13** A saddle clamp access valve.

Do not attempt to screw a metric fitting into an English fitting.

## Accumulator

Accumulators (Figure 11-14) in R-12 systems typically have a desiccant designated as XH5. This desiccant is not compatible with R-134a refrigerant. The desiccant to be used in R-134a systems is designated XH7 or XH9. This desiccant is found in accumulators and receivers designated for R-134a service. General Motors and Ford do not recommend that their accumulator be changed since the desiccant used is compatible with R-134a. Both XH7 and XH9 desiccants are compatible with R-12 as well as R-134a.

If a clutch cycling pressure switch (CCPS) is to be changed, however, the accumulator may have to be replaced to accommodate the metric threads found on the switch. In some retrofit packages, an adapter may be included for English-to-metric thread conversion.

## Compressor

Compressors are being redesigned to withstand the slight increase in pressures associated with R-134a. Most compressor rebuilders are also incorporating these design changes into their rebuilding procedures. When purchasing a new or rebuilt compressor for an R-134a system, make sure that it has been identified for that application.

It is not recommended that a compressor be replaced as a matter of course for retrofitting. The compressor should only be replaced if it is defective. Do not replace a compressor simply because the system is being retrofitted.

## Condenser

Engine performance is often affected by the increased load created by the air conditioner.

To change any part of an original design is to change the performance of the equipment. This may be especially true for the condenser. The engine cooling system may also be affected by the slight increase in pressure (and temperature) of the condensing R-134a refrigerant. A dam may be considered to reduce the problems. Some manufacturers recommend replacing the condenser assembly during the retrofit procedure with one designed for use with R-134a, or system performance may suffer after retrofitting. Always refer to the manufacturer's recommendations prior to performing retrofit procedures or quoting the cost of the service to your customer.

**Dams.** A dam, loosely identified, is the sealing provision located between the radiator and condenser that helps to direct ambient and ram air through both components. It is critical that all condenser and radiator seals be in place. All holes, regardless of how small, that could allow air to bypass either component should be blocked off to ensure maximum airflow.

Do not overload the circuit by adding a second motor to the original relay.

In some installations, the condenser will be changed. Since the mounting space is limited, this usually means a condenser with more fin area, fins-per-inch (FPI). A higher rpm cooling fan motor may be used to replace the original motor. In other cases, a second motor and fan, a pusher-type, may be placed in front of the condenser. The idea is to improve or increase airflow to remove more heat.

If a fan and motor are added, a relay should also be added. This is to ensure that the electrical system is not overloaded. The coil of the relay may be wired in with the compressor clutch circuit (Figure 11-15) to ensure that the fan is running when the air conditioning system is turned on. An in-line fuse is included to protect the circuit.

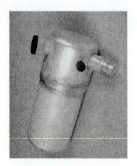

**Figure 11-14** A typical accumulator.

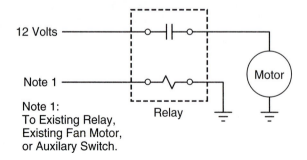

**Figure 11-15** Schematic for adding an auxiliary condenser fan motor.

## Evaporator

The evaporator is not replaced unless it is found to be leaking. There have been no problems reported when using R-12 evaporators for an R-134a retrofit.

Minor changes are necessary for evaporators designated for use with R-134a refrigerant to accommodate the slightly higher pressure that may be expected.

## Hoses

Generally, hoses (Figure 11-16) used for automotive air conditioning service on 1989 and later year/model vehicles need not be replaced when retrofitting from R-12 to R-134a. The exception is if the hose is found to be leaking during retrofit procedures.

## O-Rings and Seals

While O-rings made of epichlorohydrin and designated for R-12 service are not compatible with R-134a, it is not recommended that they be replaced when retrofitting an air conditioning system. The exception is if the fitting is found to be leaking. In that case, use only O-rings and seals (Figure 11-17) designated for the refrigerant being used in the system. Generally, O-rings and seals for R-12 systems are black. Unfortunately, some manufacturers prefer black R-134a O-rings and seals as well. Many, however, color code the O-rings and seals designated for R-134a service. When in doubt, use color-coded neoprene or HSN/HNBR O-rings or seals; they are also compatible with R-12.

If O-rings are to be replaced, use components designated for use with R-134a.

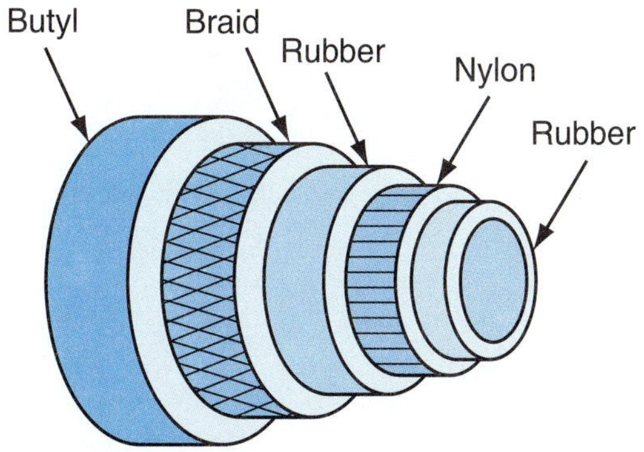

**Figure 11-16** Construction detail of a barrier hose.

**Figure 11-17** Typical A/C O-rings and seals.

# Metering Devices

Metering devices should not be changed as a matter of practice when retrofitting a system. There are two types of metering devices used in the modern automotive air conditioning system: the thermostatic expansion valve (TXV) and the fixed orifice tube (FOT).

**Thermostatic Expansion Valve.** The thermostatic expansion valve (TXV) (Figure 11-18) does not have to be replaced when retrofitting a system from R-12 to R-134a. If, however, a TXV is found to be defective, it should be replaced with a model designed for use with the system refrigerant. An R-12 TXV used in an R-134a system will result in higher superheat and improved overall evaporator temperature. An R-134a valve used in an R-12 system will have reduced superheat and will not perform as well. Since superheat has a direct effect on performance, it is not advisable that the superheat be allowed to increase more than 3°F (1.7°C) over that of the operating R-12 system.

If a new TXV is required, use one that is designed for the specific refrigerant in the system. As a rule of thumb: R-12 valves should not be used on automobiles originally equipped with R-134a systems and, conversely, R-134a valves should not be used on R-12 systems.

**Orifice Tube.** With the exception of one automobile manufacturer, it is not recommended that the orifice tube (Figure 11-19) be replaced when retrofitting an air conditioning system. Volvo recommends changing the orifice tube to one that has a 0.002-in. (0.0508-mm) smaller orifice. If it is changed, however, a slight increase in high-side pressure may be noted.

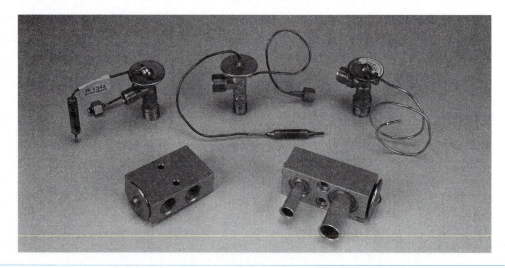

**Figure 11-18** Typical thermostatic expansion valves.

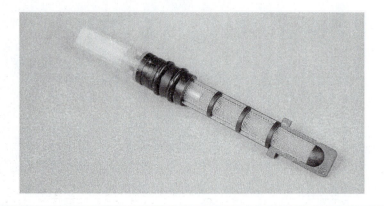

**Figure 11-19** An orifice tube.

# Pressure Switch

Either or both of two switches may be recommended for change during some retrofit procedures. These switches are the clutch cycling pressure switch (CCPS) and the refrigerant containment device. A brief description follows.

Do not bypass system protective switches.

**Clutch Cycling Pressure Switch.** The clutch cycling pressure switch (CCPS) (Figure 11-20) may be changed for some R-134a retrofits. The difference is that the R-134a switches are calibrated for slightly lower clutch cycling pressures. Also, the mounting threads are metric to prevent the connection of an English-thread R-12 switch in an R-134a system.

**Refrigerant Containment Device.** This device, which is new for 1994 and later model/year vehicles, may also be included in some retrofit kits for earlier model year vehicles. The refrigerant containment device includes models for single- and dual-function refrigerant containment switches and the air conditioner high-pressure transducer.

Each have their specific applications. The single switch is in general use, controlling the compressor clutch; the dual switch also includes provisions to control the condenser fan. The transducer is in some solid-state temperature control systems.

# High-Pressure Switch

The EPA requires the installation of a high-pressure cutout switch, also called a refrigerant containment switch. Its purpose is to interrupt the clutch coil circuit, thereby stopping the compressor before high-side pressure reaches the point at which it would open the high-pressure relief valve and release refrigerant into the environment.

One such switch designed for retrofit (Figure 11-21) is included with a tee-fitting service valve and is actually a dual-pressure switch. It opens the compressor clutch circuit at a high pressure of about

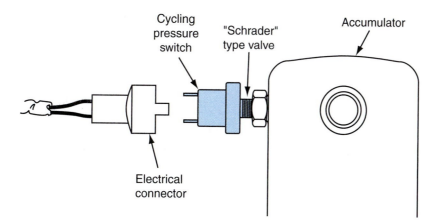

**Figure 11-20** A cycling clutch pressure switch.

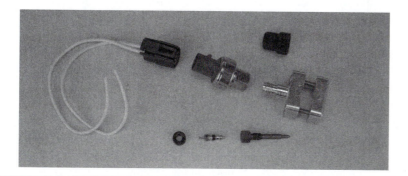

**Figure 11-21** A high-pressure cutout switch with saddle clamp.

**Figure 11-22** A typical receiver-drier.

390–400 psig (2,689–2,758 kPa) and closes the circuit at about 310–315 psig (2,137–2,172 kPa). For low-pressure protection, the switch opens the clutch circuit at a low pressure of about 28 psig (193 kPa), a condition that would not exist on the high side of the system unless the refrigerant had leaked out. This, then, would prevent the compressor from running when the air conditioning system is first turned on.

### Receiver-Drier

The receiver-drier (Figure 11-22) used in R-12 systems typically has XH5 desiccant. This desiccant is not compatible with R-134a refrigerant. To be sure, the receiver-drier should be replaced during retrofit procedures with a unit designated for R-134a service and PAG or ester lubricants. This desiccant, designated XH7 or XH9, is also compatible with R-12 refrigerant and mineral oils.

## System Flushing

Little is written about flushing because "the jury is still out" on the subject. Some claim that flushing is necessary to "clean" an air conditioning system, while others claim flushing causes more harm than good. There is no need to **flush** an air conditioning system to remove refrigerant. Refrigerant removal is accomplished with the use of a proper refrigerant recovery machine. Flushing, then, is only performed in an attempt to clean the system of excess debris and lubricant. Actually, during the flushing procedure, a great deal of the debris will be caught in the screens of the metering device and dehydrator (receiver or accumulator). Also, the lubricant will be trapped in the bottom tank of the evaporator and dehydrator. Little, if anything, will be removed by flushing if the individual components are not removed from the vehicle and flushed individually.

General Motors (GM), as a general rule, does not recommend flushing an air conditioning system. There are but two possible exceptions to the rule: a lubricant overfill or lubricant contamination. Even then, GM recommends removing and draining the accumulator in an effort to remove the lubricant before considering flushing the air conditioning system. If flushing is determined to be necessary, the only flushing chemical approved by GM is to use the same refrigerant that the air conditioning system was originally charged with.

Accordingly, flushing procedures are not specifically covered in this manual. If it is found, however, that an automotive air conditioning system needs flushing, one should follow the specific instructions included with the flushing equipment. Several flushing systems are available. Robinair, for example, has air conditioning flushing kits (Figure 11-23), an accessory that connects to their recovery/recycle machines and uses recovered refrigerant as a flushing agent.

Figure 11-23 Typical flush system.

The time is at hand to seriously consider the retrofit market for automotive air conditioning systems. According to a report made by the International Trade Commission, the agency that tracks refrigerant production, only about half as much R-12 was produced in 1994 as in 1993. They also caution us that production of all CFCs ended January 1, 1996. That means that the only R-12 now available for automotive use is that which has been recovered and recycled or was produced prior to production being banned by the Clean Air Act.

# New Refrigerant Systems on the Horizon

## CO₂ (R-744) Refrigerant Systems

Air conditioning systems, which where once considered a luxury, are now considered standard equipment on most passenger vehicles. However, with this increased popularity came environmental hazards. We have already discussed the environmental hazards and dangers of an R-12 system, but there are also dangers associated with R-134a. R-134a is not an ozone-depleting refrigerant, but it is a greenhouse gas. The concern in the world community has shifted from the threat of ozone-depleting chemicals to a concern over global warming. In 1997, the U.S. government decided not to sign the Kyoto Protocol, an international agreement that, among other things, set reduction quotas for the production of greenhouse gases that contribute to global warming. The U.S. government did agree with the principle of the agreement and decided to implement a voluntary U.S. policy to limit the production of greenhouse gases.

**R-744** is the refrigerant gas designation given to carbon dioxide ($CO_2$).

One alternative that is being considered is the development of a new mobile air conditioning system (**R-744**) that uses carbon dioxide ($CO_2$), a naturally occurring gas, as the refrigerant. A $CO_2$ system is similar to today's systems, but the operating pressures are extremely high, seven to ten times greater than R-134a systems. Currently, the efficiency of the overall system is much lower than R-134a systems. Less efficient systems require more power to perform the same job, and since we still rely on the internal combustion engine, the overall benefits of the $CO_2$ system are negated. As research continues, R-744 systems are becoming more efficient.

Though further refinements and improvements in the efficiency of R-744 systems are needed, R-744 refrigerant systems show the most promise as the next generation of air conditioning advances and may change the map of automotive air conditioning forever. This is the century of global environmental concern and lessening our dependence on fossil fuels.

What makes R-744 better than R-134a systems used today? Carbon dioxide shows the most potential as the next refrigerant because the properties of the gas make it ideal for small portable refrigeration systems. Although technically $CO_2$ is a greenhouse gas, its release into the atmosphere is harmless because there is enough $CO_2$ occurring naturally or obtained through natural chemical reaction that no new $CO_2$ would have to be created. The new R-744 refrigerant systems could greatly benefit automotive manufacturers who could, for the first time since R-12 systems, offer a system that cools better than the current R-134a systems and poses no environmental hazard that could affect costs through government regulations.

One large hurdle that automotive manufacturers must first overcome is the extreme line pressure that the system must operate at. The average high-side pressure will be in the range of 2000 psig (13789.5 kPa), which means system components like the compressor and lines must be strengthened. On the other hand, the new R-744 systems require about half the refrigerant capacity of current R-134a systems, with better cooling results.

There are some differences in the R-744 system compared to the R-134a system. The R-744 system (Figure 11-24) has a gas cooler instead of a condenser to reduce the temperature of the R-744 gas but not condense it. Instead, some of the gas condenses as it passes through the expansion valve

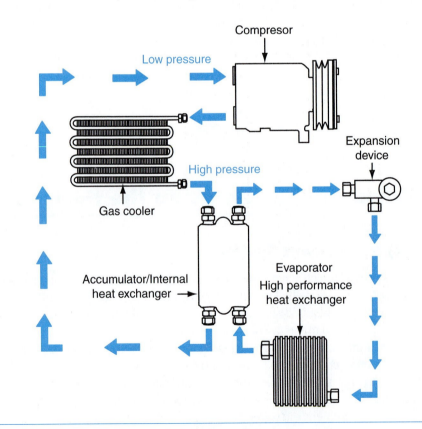

**Figure 11-24** A typical R-744 ($CO_2$) refrigerant system.

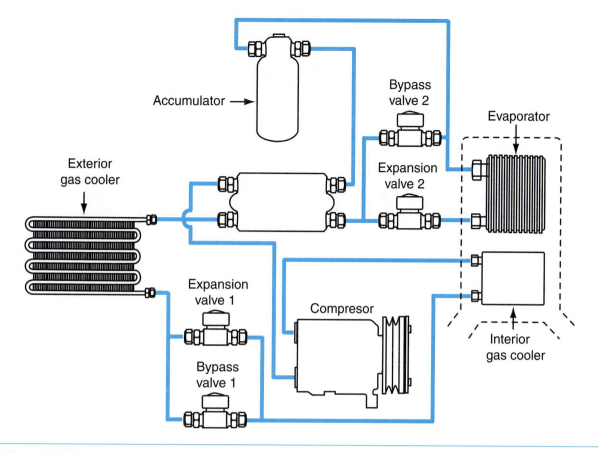

**Figure 11-25** An R-744 system with heat pump for passenger compartment heating.

as a result of **adiabatic expansion**. Further cooling occurs by exchanging heat with the inner heat exchanger, which is between the gas cooler and evaporator on the low side of the system.

The R-744 system can also serve as a source of heat for the passenger compartment through the use of an integrated heat pump (Figure 11-25), a special heat exchanger that uses the heat created in the air conditioning system to provide heat for the passenger compartment. This will be a very useful system for both passenger compartment heating and cooling, especially on electric- or fuel cell-powered vehicles (which have little or no waste heat). In addition, with smaller, more fuel-efficient internal combustion engines, the need for a supplemental heater is also growing, especially in the compact diesel market. This system will enable both heating and cooling simultaneously by regulating refrigerant gas flow through both expansion valves in the system. One expansion valve will regulate refrigerant flow to the evaporator for cooling, while the second expansion valve will regulate refrigerant flow to the interior gas cooler (heater core) for heating.

As for the near future, we will see more electronics integrated into the automotive air conditioning system. The use of computer-controlled variable displacement compressors will increase, and electric-driven compressors will become commonplace on vehicles with start-stop technology (idle shutoff systems). There will also be increased use of electronic expansion valves and orifice tubes. The future looks bright and exciting for the automotive air conditioning industry.

**Adiabatic expansion** is a process that occurs without the loss or gain of heat.

# An Industry Study

A paper sponsored by Elf Atochem, a leading manufacturer of refrigerants, was presented in the winter of 1994 at the International CFC and Halon Alternatives Conference. Written by a staff engineer and a senior technician at Elf Atochem's fluorochemicals research and development center, the paper revealed that retrofitting is simpler than originally believed.

The report was the result of a study of a fleet of 17 employee-volunteered vehicles retrofitted in 1993 to R-134a and polyalkaline glycol (PAG) lubricant. In early 1994, 20 more vehicles were retrofitted with R-134a and polyol ester (POE) lubricant. Only refrigerant and lubricant were replaced; no system components were replaced. Some were power flushed to remove as much of the mineral oil as possible, others were simply drained and refilled. The study involved a random selection of both domestic and imported cars and light trucks.

Regardless of the procedure, flush or no flush, there was little or no noticeable difference in the performance of any of the vehicles. There were only two reported failures; both lost their complete R-134a charge due to O-ring failure. Another vehicle lost 6 percent of its charge of R-134a due to a leak. The worst "leaker" in the study was actually a control vehicle that had not been retrofitted at all. This vehicle lost 38 percent of its R-12 charge due to a leak.

**AUTHOR'S NOTE:** If after retrofitting a system from R-12 to R-134a and the high-side head pressure is excessive, the installation of an auxiliary cooling fan will help lower this pressure. The auxiliary fan should be wired so that it will run continuously when air conditioning is selected.

## Summary

❏ Follow appropriate manufacturer's retrofit procedures.

❏ After retrofit, appropriate decals must be affixed to identify the type of refrigerant in the system.

❏ A light blue (the industry color code for R-134a), decal is placed over the current R-12 decal (Figure 11-26).

❏ A yellow (the color used for caution), decal may be placed around the hoses at the service fittings.

## Terms to Know

Adiabatic expansion

Alternative refrigerant

Cross-contamination

Flushing

Hydrocarbons

Retrofit

R-744

## Review Questions

### Short Answer Essays

1. Describe the meaning of the term *retrofit*.

2. Why are the DIYers generally unable to service their own vehicles?

3. What are some of the problems that may result if an inexperienced person services an automotive air conditioning system?

4. Describe the proper disposal of contaminated refrigerant.

5. Summarize the retrofit procedures for a General Motors vehicle.

6. Describe the difference in application for an XH9 drier compared to an XH5 drier.

7. Explain what desiccant is and where it is to be found in an automotive air conditioning system.

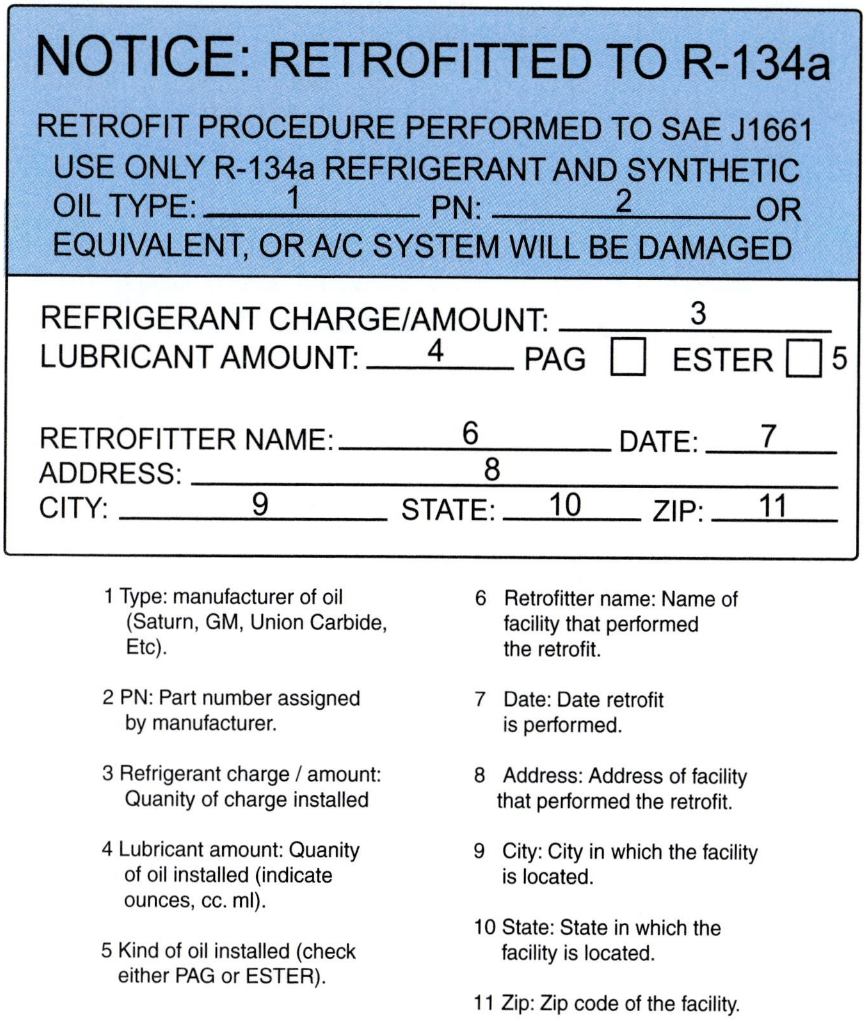

**NOTICE: RETROFITTED TO R-134a**

RETROFIT PROCEDURE PERFORMED TO SAE J1661
USE ONLY R-134a REFRIGERANT AND SYNTHETIC
OIL TYPE: _____1_____ PN: _____2_____ OR
EQUIVALENT, OR A/C SYSTEM WILL BE DAMAGED

REFRIGERANT CHARGE/AMOUNT: _____3_____
LUBRICANT AMOUNT: ___4___ PAG ☐ ESTER ☐ 5

RETROFITTER NAME: _____6_____ DATE: ___7___
ADDRESS: _____8_____
CITY: _____9_____ STATE: ___10___ ZIP: ___11___

1 Type: manufacturer of oil (Saturn, GM, Union Carbide, Etc).

2 PN: Part number assigned by manufacturer.

3 Refrigerant charge / amount: Quanity of charge installed

4 Lubricant amount: Quanity of oil installed (indicate ounces, cc. ml).

5 Kind of oil installed (check either PAG or ESTER).

6 Retrofitter name: Name of facility that performed the retrofit.

7 Date: Date retrofit is performed.

8 Address: Address of facility that performed the retrofit.

9 City: City in which the facility is located.

10 State: State in which the facility is located.

11 Zip: Zip code of the facility.

**Figure 11-26** A typical retrofit label.

8. What is an important consideration for the condenser/radiator during retrofit procedures?

9. Describe the conditions under which hoses and/or O-rings should be replaced during retrofit procedures.

10. Identify and describe either of the components that are included on R-134a systems but are not found on R-12 systems.

## Fill-in-the-Blanks

1. The _____ _____ _____ is the agency that tracks refrigerant production.

2. Volvo recommends replacing the _____ _____ with a smaller _____ when retrofitting.

3. If a hose is found to be _____ during retrofitting, it should be _____ .

4. Two types of threads that are not interchangeable are _____ and _____ .

5. Volvo recommends _____ lubricant while most other manufacturers recommend _____ lubricant.

6. R-12 receiver-driers containing _____ desiccant must be replaced with receiver-driers containing _____ or _____ desiccant when retrofitting to R-134a.

7. State and local laws and regulations often override _____ laws.

8. Gauge and meter reading errors are generally due to the inaccuracies of the _____ and the _____ _____ .

9. _____ _____ , known as DOT 39s, must not be used for _____ _____ .

10. MACS is an acronym for _____ _____ _____ _____ .

## Multiple Choice

1. All of the following alternate refrigerants are approved for automotive use, *except*:
   A. Freeze-12
   B. FRIGC FR-12
   C. Ikon-12
   D. Duracool 12a

2. Replacement of hoses during retrofit procedures is being discussed:
   *Technician A* says hoses need not be replaced unless they are the old-style nonbarrier type.
   *Technician B* says hoses need not be replaced unless they are equipped with the old-style O-rings and fittings.
   Who is correct?
   A. A only
   B. B only
   C. Both A and B
   D. Neither A nor B

3. Refrigerant contamination is being discussed:
   *Technician A* says that R-12 with a 5 percent trace of R-22 is considered contaminated.
   *Technician B* says that R-12 with a 5 percent trace of R-134a is considered contaminated.
   Who is correct?
   A. A only
   B. B only
   C. Both A and B
   D. Neither A nor B

4. *Technician A* says barrier hoses are required for replacement refrigerants that contain HCFC-22.
   *Technician B* says that refrigerant containment switches are required on all retrofit automotive air conditioning systems.
   Who is correct?
   A. A only
   B. B only
   C. Both A and B
   D. Neither A nor B

5. *Technician A* says that a DOT 39 cylinder may be used to temporarily store contaminated refrigerant.
   *Technician B* says that, if they are used, DOT 39s must be marked "CONTAMINATED REFRIGERANT" for identification.
   Who is correct?
   A. A only
   B. B only
   C. Both A and B
   D. Neither A nor B

6. *Technician A* says that immersing the recovery cylinder in an ice bath will help hasten recovery.
   *Technician B* says that heating the receiver-drier or accumulator-drier will help hasten recovery.
   Who is correct?
   A. A only
   B. B only
   C. Both A and B
   D. Neither A nor B

7. *Technician A* says that Ford does not recommend draining the mineral oil for retrofit.
*Technician B* says that Ford recommends replacing the receiver-drier or accumulator-drier for retrofit.
Who is correct?
   A. A only
   B. B only
   C. Both A and B
   D. Neither A nor B

8. *Technician A* says that a red label is required to identify R-134a in an automotive air conditioning system.
*Technician B* says that a yellow label is used to identify PAG lubricant in an automotive air conditioning system.
Who is correct?
   A. A only
   B. B only
   C. Both A and B
   D. Neither A nor B

9. *Technician A* says that the accumulator may have to be changed for retrofit to accommodate the metric threads of a new thermostatic control.
*Technician B* says that an adapter may be available for some of these new controls.
Who is correct?
   A. A only
   B. B only
   C. Both A and B
   D. Neither A nor B

10. *Technician A* says that O-rings designated for R-12 service need not be changed for retrofit.
*Technician B* says that O-rings designated for R-134a service may also be used for R-12 service.
Who is correct?
   A. A only
   B. B only
   C. Both A and B
   D. Neither A nor B

# GLOSSARY

**Absolute zero** The complete absence of heat, believed to be –459°F (–273.15°C). This is shown as 0° on the Rankine and Kelvin temperature scales.

**Cero absoluto** Ausencia completa de calor, lo cual se cree ser –459°F (–273.15°C). Se indica como 0° en las escalas de temperatura Rankine y Kelvin.

**Absorb** To take in or to suck up; to become a part of itself.

**Absorber** Admitir o aspirar; llegar a ser una parte de si mismo.

**Accumulator** A tank-like vessel located at the outlet (tailpipe) of the evaporator to receive all of the refrigerant that leaves the evaporator. This device is constructed to ensure that no liquid refrigerant enters the compressor.

**Acumulador** Recipiente parecido a un tanque ubicado en la salida (tubo de escape) del evaporador para recibir todo el refrigerante que sal del evaporador. Dicho dispositivo esta disenado de modo que asegure que el refrigerante liquido no entre en el compresor.

**Additive** A substance added to another substance, expected to increase its quality or performance. Antifreeze, for example, is an additive that may be added to water ($H_2O$) to raise its boiling point and lower its freezing point.

**Aditivo** Sustancia que se agrega a otra sustancia para mejorar su calidad o rendimiento. Por ejemplo, el anticongelante es un aditivo que puede agregarse al agua ($H_2O$) para elevar su punto te ebullicion y disminuir su punto de congelacion.

**Adiabatic expansion** The process of expansion without the gain or loss of heat.

**Expansión adiabiático** El proceso del expansión sín un gano o pérdida del calor.

**Adsorb** To take up and hold a thin layer of vapor or liquid molecules on the surface of a solid substance.

**Adsorber** Recoger y retener una capa delgada de moleculas de vapor o liquido en la superficie de una sustancia solida.

**Aftermarket** A term generally given to a device or accessory that is added to a vehicle by the dealer after original manufacturer, such as an air conditioning system.

**Postmercado** Termino dado generalmente a un dispositivo o accesoria que el distribuidor de automoviles agrega al vehiculo despues de la fabricacion original, como por ejemplo un sistema de acondicionamiento de aire.

**Air conditioning** The process of adjusting and regulating by heating or refrigerating; the quality, quantity, temperature, humidity, and circulation of air in a space or enclosure; to condition the air.

**Acondicionamiento de aire** Proceso de ajustar y regular al calentar o enfriar, la calidad, cantidad, temperatura, humedad, y circulacion de aire en un espacio o encerramiento; para acondicionar el aire.

**Allotrope** A structurally different form of an element. For example, though different in structure, the properties of graphite and diamond are the same as the element carbon (C).

**Aliotropo** Una forma de un elemento que es diferente en estructura. Por ejemplo, aunque son diferentes en estructura, las propiedades del grafito y diamante son las mismas del elemento carbon (C).

**Alternative refrigerant** A refrigerant that can be used to replace an existing refrigerant, such as ozone friendly R-134a that is used to replace ozone depleting R-12.

**Refrjerante alternativa** Un refrigerante que se puede usar para reemplazar un refrigerante actual, tal como el R-134 que no agota el ozono del medio ambiente para reemplazar el R-12 que si lo agota.

**Ambient** All around, surrounding, or encompassing.

**Amblente** El area circundante o los alredededores.

**Antifreeze** A commercially available additive solution used to increase the boiling temperature and reduce the freezing temperature of engine coolant. A solution of 50 percent water and 50 percent antifreeze is suggested for year-round protection.

**Anticongelante** Solucion aditiva comercialmente disponible utilizada para elevar la temperatura de ebullicion y disminuir la temperatura de congelacion del enfriador del motor. Se sugiere una solucion de un 50 percent de agua y un 50 percent de anticongelante para proveer protection durante todo el ano.

**Arid** Dry.

**Arido** Seco.

**Aspirator** A device that uses suction to move air, accomplished by a differential in air pressure.

**Aspirador** Dispositivo que aspira para mover el aire; dicho movimiento se debe a una diferencia en la presion del aire.

**ATC** Abbreviation for automatic temperature control.

**ATC** Abreviatura de control automatico de temperatura.

**Atmosphere** Air.

**Atmosfera** El aire.

**Atom** The smallest possible particle of matter.

**Atomo** Particula mas pequena de materia.

**Automatic** A self-regulating system or device that adjusts to variables of a predetermined condition.

**Automatico** Sistema o dispositivo con regulacion automatica que se adjusta a estador variables de una condicion predeterminada.

**Auxiliary** A backup component or system. The rear evaporator in a dual air conditioning system is often referred to as an "auxiliary evaporator."

**Auxiliar** Un componente o sistema auxiliar. El evaporador trasero en un sistema del aire acondicionado muchas veces se refiere como un evaporador auxiliar.

**Axial** Pertaining to an axis; a pivot point.

**Axial** Perteneciente a un eje; punto de giro.

**Axial plate** That part of an automotive air conditioner compressor piston assembly that rotates as a part of the driven shaft.

**Placa axial** La parte del conjunto del piston de un compresor del acondicionador de aire automortriz que gira como parte del arbol mandado.

**Barrier** A term given to something that stands in the way, separates, keeps apart, or restricts; an obstruction.

**Barrera** Termino dado a algo que impide, separa, mantiene separado, o restrinje; una obstruccion.

**Bellows** An accordian-type chamber that expands and contracts as its interior pressure is increased or decreased to create a mechanical action, such as in a thermostatic expansion valve.

**Fuelles** Camara en forma de acordeon que se dilata y se contrae cuando su presion interior se aumenta o se disminuye para crear una accion mecanica, como por ejemplo en una valvula de expansion termostatica.

**Bi-level**  A condition whereby air is delivered at two levels in the vehicle, generally to the floor and dash outlets.

**Bilevel**  Condicion por medio de la cual se envia el aire a dos nieveles en el vehiculo, generalmente al piso y a las salidas del tablero de instrumentos.

**Blend air door**  A door in the duct system that controls temperature by blending heated and cooled air.

**Puerta de aire mezclado**  Puerta en el sistema de conductos que regula la temperatura al mezclar el aire calentado y enfriado.

**Blend door**  See Blend air door.

**Puerta de mezcla**  Ver Blend air door [Puerta del aire mezclado].

**Block valve**  A type of thermostatic expansion valve utilizing an internal sensing bulb.

**Valvula de bloque**  Tipo de valvula de expansion termostatica que utiliza una bombilla sensora interior.

**Bowden cable**  A wire cable inside a metal or rubber housing used to regulate a valve or control from a remote place.

**Cable Bowden**  Cable trenzado de alambre que esta envuelto por una cubierta de metal o de caucho y que se utiliza para regular una valvula o regulador desde un sitio a distancia.

**British thermal unit (Btu)**  A measure of heat energy; one Btu is the amount of heat necessary to raise one pound of water 1°F.

**Unidad termica britanica (Btu)**  Medida de energia calorifica; un Btu es igual al calor necesario para elevar la temperatura de una libra de agua en 1°F.

**Butane**  A colorless gas ($C_4H_{10}$) that is used as a fuel.

**Butano**  Gas incoloro ($C_4H_{10}$) utilizado como combustible.

**Bypass**  A passage or hose which directs coolant around thermostat when thermostat is closed and back to the water pump.

**Desviado**  Un pasaje o manguera que dirije el refrigerante alrededor del termostato cuando esta cerrado y lo dirije a la bomba de agua.

**Capillary tube**  A tube with a calibrated inside diameter and length used to control the flow of refrigerant. In automotive air conditioning systems, the tube connecting the remote bulb to the expansion valve or to the thermostat is called the capillary tube.

**Tubo capilar**  Tubo cuyo diametro y longitud interiores son calibrados; se utiliza para regular el flujo de refrigerante. En sistemas automotrices para el acondicionamiento de aire, el tubo que conecta la bombilla a distancia a la valvula de expansion o al termostato se llama el tubo capilar.

**Case**  A thing used to hold, cover, or contain something, such as the evaporator and heater cores of an air conditioning system.

**Caja**  Cosa utilizada para guardar, cubrir, o contener algo, como por ejemplo lo nucleos del evaporador y del calentador de un sistema de acondicionamiento de aire.

**CCOT**  Cycling-clutch orifice tube.

**CCOT**  Tubo de onificio del embrague con funcionamiento ciclico.

**CCPS**  Cycling-clutch pressure switch.

**CCPS**  Automata manometrico del embrague con funcionamiento ciclico.

**CDPS**  Compressor discharge pressure switch.

**CDPS**  Automata manometrico de discarga del compresor.

**Centrifugal**  Moving away from the center or axis; to develop a force that is progressively away or outward from the axis.

**Centrífugo**  Moviendose hace afuera del centro o el eje; desarrollar una fuerza que se mueva progresivamente hace afuera del eje.

**Centrifugal impeller**  Rotating water pump impeller uses centrifugal force to force water drawn in from the center outward to the outlet passage.

**Impulsor centrífugo**  Un impulsor giratorio de la bomba de agua que usa la fuerza centrífuga para forzar el agua proveniente del centro hacia afuera al pasaje de salida.

**Centrifugal pump**  A type of pump used to circulate coolant by centrifugal force in an automotive cooling system.

**Bomba centrifuga**  Tipo de bomba utilizada para la circulacion del enfriante por medio de la fuerza centrifuga en un sistema automortiz para el acondicionamiento de aire.

**CFCs**  See chlorofluorocarbon.

**CFCs**  Véase clorofluorocarbono.

**Change of state**  Rearrangement of the molecular structure of matter as it changes between any two of the three physical states: solid, liquid, or gas.

**Cambio de estado**  Reordenamiento de la estructura molecular de materia al cambiarse entre cualquier de los tres estados fisicos solido, liquido, o gas.

**Check valve**  A one-way valve that only allows flow in one direction and restricts flow in the opposite direction.

**Válvula de retención**  Una válvula de una vía que solo permite fluir en una dirección y restrinje el flujo de la dirección opuesta.

**Chlorine (CI)**  A poisonous greenish-yellow gas used in some refrigerants and known to be harmful to the ozone ($O_3$).

**Cloro (CI)**  Gas venenoso de color verdusco amarillo utilizado en algunos refrigerantes; conocido como una sustancia nociva al ozono ($O_3$).

**Chloroflourocarbon (CFC)**  A manufactured compound used in refrigerants such as R-12, more accurately designated CFC-12.

**Clorofluorocarbono**  Compuesto sintetico utilizado en refrigerantes como por ejemplo el R 12; designado con mas presicion como CFC 12.

**Circuit breaker**  A bimetallic device used instead of a fuse to protect a circuit.

**Disyunto**  Dispositivo bimetalico utilizado en vez de un fusible para la proteccion de un circuito.

**Clean Air Act (CAA)**  A Title IV amendment signed into law in 1990, which established national policy relative to the reduction and elimination of ozone-depleting substances.

**Ley para Aire Limpio**  Enmienda Titulo IV firmado y aprobado en 1990 que establecio la politica nacional relacionada con la reduction y eliminacion de sustancias que agotan el ozono.

**Clutch**  An electromechanical device used to engage and disengage the compressor in an automotive air conditioning system.

**Embrague**  Un dispositivo electromecánico que sirve para embragar y desembragar el compressor en un sistema del aire acondicionado automotivo.

**Clutch diode**  A diode placed across the clutch coil to prevent unwanted electrical spikes as the clutch is engaged and disengaged.

**Diodo de embrague**  Diodo que cruza la bobina del embrague para evitar impulsos afilados electricos no deseados al engranarse y desengranarse el embrague.

**Clutch field**  Consists of many windings of wire and is fastened to the front of the compressor. Current applied to the field sets up a magnetic field that pulls the armature in to engage the clutch.

**Campo del embrague**  Consists de muchos devanados de alambre y se fija a la parte delantera del compresor. La corriente aplicada al campo produce un campo magnetico que tira la armadura para engranar el embrague.

**Cold**  The absence of heat.

**Frio**  Ausencia de calor.

**Collector** A tank located in the radiator to collect coolant.
**Colector** Tanque ubicado en el radiador para acumular enfriante.

**Compression** The act of reducing volume by pressure.
**Compresion** Accion de disminuir el volumen por efectos de la presion.

**Compression stroke** That part of the compressor piston that travels from the bottom of its stroke to the top of its stroke.
**Carrera de compresion** Parte del movimiento del piston del compreor desde la posicion inferior de su carrera hasta la posicion superior de su carrera.

**Compressor** A component of the refrigeration system that pumps refrigerant and increases the pressure of the refrigerant vapor.
**Compresor** Componente del sistema de refrigeracion que bombea el refrigerante y eleva la presion del vapor del mismo.

**Condenser** The component of a refrigeration system in which refrigerant vapor is changed to a liquid by the removal of heat.
**Condensador** Componente de un sistema de refrigeracion en el que el vapor del refrigerante se convierte en un liquido debido, a la eliminacion de calor.

**Conduction** The transmission of heat through a solid.
**Coduccion** Transferencia de calor a traves de un solido.

**Contaminated** Not being of pure form. Refrigerant is considered contaminated when it contains greater than 2 percent of one or more other gases.
**Contaminado** El no ser de una forma pura. El refrigerante se considera ser contaminado cuando contiene uno o más gases en una cantidad de 2 porciento o más.

**Contamination** A matter rendered unpure due to the production of foreign matter.
**Contaminacion** Una materia hecha impura debido a la introduccion de materia extrana.

**Control thermostat** A temperature-actuated electrical switch used to cycle the compressor clutch on and off, thereby controlling the air conditioning system temperature.
**Termostato de control** Un interruptor eléctrico actuado por la temperatura que sirve en los ciclos de apagado y prendido del embrague del compresor, asi controlando la temperatura del sistema del aire acondicionado.

**Control valve** A mechanical, pneumatic, or electric valve used to control the flow of coolant into the heater core.
**Valvula de regulacion** Valvula mecanica, neumatica, o electrica utilizada para regular el flujo de enfriante al nucleo del calentador.

**Convection** The transfer of heat by the circulation of a vapor or liquid.
**Conveccion** Transferencia de calor mediante de la circulacion de un vapor o liquido.

**Coolant pump** A term often used when referring to a water pump.
**Bomba del enfriante** Termino utilizado con frecuencia al refrirse a una bomba de agua.

**Crankshaft** That part of a reciprocating compressor on which the wobble plate or connecting rods are attached to provide for an up-down or to-fro piston action.
**Ciguenal** Parte de un compresor reciproco sobre la cual se fijan las bielas a la placa oscilante para permitir el movimiento de arriba abajo o el de un lado para otro.

**Cross-contamination** Contamination that can occur when a system is retrofitted to an alternative refrigerant and not the entire original refrigerant is removed or when one piece of equipment is used for more than one type of refrigerant.

**Contaminación cruzada** La contaminación que puede ocurrir cuando un sistema se equipa después de fabricacion para aceptar un refrigerante alternativo y no se remueva todo el refrigerante original o cuando una pieza del equipo se usa para más de un tipo del refrigerante.

**Cycling clutch** A clutch that is turned on/off to control temperature.
**Embrague con funclonamlento ciclico** Embrague que se pone en marcha y se spaga para regular la temperatura.

**Cylinder** A circular tubelike opening in a compressor block or casting in which the piston moves up and down or back and forth; a circular drum used to store refrigerant.
**Gilindro** Apergtura circular parecida a un tubo en un bloque del compresor o una pieza en los que el piston se mueve de arriba abajao o de un lado a otro; un tambor circular utilizado para el almacenaje de refrigerante.

**DC** See Direct current (dc).
**CC** Ver Direct current [Corriente continua (cc)].

**Deep-tissue temperature** The sub-surface temperature, such as the internal temperature of the human body of 98.6°F.
**Temperatura interna** La temperatura bajo la superficie, tal como la temperatura interna del cuerpo humano que es el 98.6°F.

**Defrost** To remove frost.
**Decongelar** Deshelar.

**Deice** To remove ice or heavy frost.
**Deshelar** Derretir hielo o una gran cantidad de escarcha.

**Delta P** A term used when referring to a difference in pressure.
**P delta** Termino utilizado al referirse a una diferencia en presion.

**Delta T** A term used when referring to a difference in temperature.
**T delta** Termino utilizado al referirse a una diferencia en temperatura.

**Desiccant** A drying agent used in refrigeration systems to remove excess moisture. The deciccant is located in the receiver-drier or accumulator.
**Desecante** Agente secador utilizado en sistemas de refrigeracion para eliminar un exceso de humedad. El desecante esta ubicado en el receptor/secador o en el acumulador.

**Diode** An electrical check valve. Current flows only in one direction through a diode.
**Diodo** Valvula electrica de retencion. La corriente fluye en una sola direccion a traves de un diodo.

**Direct current (dc)** A type of electrical power used in mobile applications. A unidirectional current of substantially constant value.
**Corriente continua (cc)** Tipo de potencia electrica utilizada en circunstancias cuando el objeto va a ser movil. Una corriente de un solo sentido de un valor substancialmente constante.

**Discharge** Bleeding some or all of the refrigerant from a system by opening a valve or connection and permitting the refrigerant to escape slowly.
**Descarga** Desangramiento de una porcion o de todo el refrigerante de un sistema al abrir una valvula o conexion y permitir su escape gradual.

**Discharge line** Connects the compressor outlet to the condenser inlet.
**Linea de descarga** Conecta la salida del compresor a la enstrada del condensador.

**Discharge stroke** See Compression stroke.
**Carrera de descarga** Ver Compression stroke [Carrera de compresion].

**Discharge valve** The outlet valve.
**Válvula de descarga** La válvula de salida.

**Disposal** Get rid of something.
**Eliminacion** Eliminar algo.

**Distilled water** One hundred percent pure $H_2O$.
**Agua destilada** El $H_2O$ cien por ciento puro.

**DIY** Do-it-yourself.
**"DIY"** Expresion en jerga que significa que una persona hace algo por su propia cuenta.

**Dobson unit (DU)** A measure of ozone density level, named after Gordon Dobson, a British meteorologist who was the inventor of the measuring device (called a spectrophotometer).
**Unedad Dobson (DU)** una medida el nivel de densidad del ozono, nombrado pr Gordon Dobson, un meteorologista inglés que fue el inventor del un dispositivo de medida (llamado el espectrofotómetro).

**DOT** U.S. Department of Transportation.
**DOT** Departamento de Transportes de los Estados Unidos de America.

**Drier** A device containing desiccant; a drier is placed in the liquid line to absorb moisture in the system.
**Secador** Dispositivo que contiene un desecante; se ubica un secador en la linea de liquido para absorber is humedad presente en el sistema.

**Dual systems** Two systems.
**Sistemas dobles** Dos sistemas.

**Electrolysis** The decomposition of a compound caused by the action of an electric current passing through it.
**Electrólisis** La decomposición de un compuesto causada por la acción de un corriente eléctrica que pasa por en medio.

**Electromagnet** A soft iron core surrounded by a coil of wire that will temporarily become a magnet when an electrical current is passed through it.
**Electroimán** Un núcleo de hierro blando rodeado por una bobina de alambre que se convierte brevamente en un imán cuando es atravesado por un corriente eléctrico.

**Electromagnetic clutch** An electrically controlled device used to start and stop compressor action.
**Embrague electromagnetico** Dispositivo controlado electronicamente y utilizado para arrancar y detener la accion del compresor.

**Ethylene glycol** Is a colorless liquid used in the production of antifreeze $HOCH_2CH_2OH$.
**Glicol etileno** Es un líquido sín color que se usa en la producción del anticongelante $HOCH_2CH_2OH$.

**Evacuate** To create a vacuum within a system to remove all air and moisture.
**Evacuar** Dejar un vacio dentro de un sistema para eliminar todo aire y humedad.

**Evaporation** The changing of a liquid to a vapor while picking up heat.
**Evaporacion** La conversion de un liquido en vapor al acumular el calor.

**Evaporator** The component of an air conditioning system that conditions the air.
**Evaporador** Componente en un sistema de acondicionamiento de aire que acondiciona el aire.

**Exhaust** A pipe through which used gases or vapors pass. See also Discharge.
**Escape** Tubo por el cual pasan los gases o vapores gastados. Ver tambien Discharge [Descarga].

**Expansion tank** An auxiliary tank that is usually connected to the inlet tank or a radiator to provide additional storage space for heated coolant; often called a coolant recovery tank.

**Tanque de expansion** Tanque auxiliar que normalmente se conecta al tanque de entrada o a un radiador para proveer almacenaje adicional del enfriante calentado. Llamado con frecuencia tanque para la recuperacion de enfriante.

**Expansion tube** A metering device used at the inlet of some evaporators to control the flow of liquid refrigerant into the evaporator core. Also see Fixed orifice tube (FDT).
**Tubo de expansion** Dispositivo para la dosificacion y utilizado a la entrada de algunos evaporadores para regular el flujo de refrigerante liquido dentro del nucleo del evaporador. Ver tambien Fixed orifice tube (FDT) [Tubo de orificio fijo].

**Expansion valve** A term often used when referring to a thermostatic expansion valve.
**Válvula de expansión** Un término que se usa comunmente para referirse a una válvula de expansión termoestática.

**Fan** A device that has two or more blades attached to the shaft of a motor. The fan is mounted in the evaporator and causes air to pass over the evaporator. A fan is also a device that is mounted on the water pump and has four or more blades that cause air to pass through the radiator and condenser.
**Ventilador** Dispositivo provisto de dos aletas o mas fijadas al arbol de un motor. El ventilador esta montado en el evaporador y hace que el aire pase sobre el evaporator. Un ventilador tambien puede set un dispositivo montado en la bomba de agua y que tiene cuatro aletas o mas que hacen que el aire pase por el radiador y el condensador.

**Fan clutch** A device used on engine-driven fans to limit their terminal speed, reduce power requirements, and lower noise levels.
**Embrague de ventilador** Dispositivo utilizado en ventiladores accionados por motores para limitar su velocidad terminal, disminuir requisitos de potencia, y bajar los niveles de ruino.

**Field coil** See Clutch Field and Electromagnet.
**Bobina del campo** Ver Clutch field [Campo del embrague] y Electromagnetic [Electroiman].

**Fixed orifice tube (FOT)** A refrigerant metering device used at the inlet of evaporators to control the flow of liquid refrigerant allowed to enter the evaporator.
**Tubo de orificio fijo** Dispositivo para la dosificacion de refrigerante utilizado a la entrada de los evaporadores para regular el flujo de refrigerante liquido permitido entrar en el evaporador.

**Flooded** See Flooding.
**Inundado** Ver Flooding [Inundacion].

**Flooding** A condition caused by too much liquid refrigerant being metered into the evaporator.
**Inundacion** Condicion ocasionada por una cantidad excesiva de refrigerante liquido dosificado al evaporador.

**Flush** To remove solid particles such as metal flakes or dirt. Refrigerant passages are purged with a clean dry gas such as nitrogen (N).
**Limpiar por inundacion** Remover las particulas solidas, como por ejemplo escamas metalicas o polvo. Se purgan los pasajes de refrigerante con un gas limpio y seco, como por ejemplo el nitrogeno (N).

**FOTCC** Fixed orifice tube cycling clutch.
**FOTCC** Tubo de orificio fijo del embrague con funcionamiento ciclico.

**FPI** Feet per inch or fins per inch.
**FPI** Pies por pulgada o aletas por pulgada.

**Fuse** An electrical device used to protect a circuit against accidental overload or unit malfunction.
**Fusible** Dispositivo electrico utilizado para proteger un circuito contra una sobrecarga imprevista o una disfunction de la unidad.

**Gas** A state of matter. A vapor that has no particles or droplets of liquid.

**Gas** Estado de materia. Vapor desprovisto de particulas o gotitas de liquido.

**Gauge** A device used to measure pressure or force scaled in English and/or metric values.

**Calibrador** Dispositivo utilizado para medir la presion o fuerza; provisto de una escale en valores ngleses y/o metricos.

**Global warming** The gradual warming of the earth's atmosphere due to the greenhouse effect. See Greenhouse effect.

**Calentamiento mundial** Calentamiento gradual de la atmosfera de la Tierra debido al efecto de invermadero. Ver Greenhouse effect [Efecto de invernadero].

**Greenhouse effect** A greenhouse is warmed because glass allows the sun's radiant heat to enter but prevents radiant heat from leaving. Global warming is caused by some gases in the atmosphere that act like greenhouse glass; hence, the term greenhouse effect.

**Efecto de invernadero** Se calienta un invernadero porque el vidrio permite la entrada del calor radiante del sol pero impide la salida del calor radiante de la Tierra. El calentamiento mundial es ocasionado por algunos gases en la atmosfera que actuan como el vidrio de un invernadero; por eso, se utiliza el termino efecto de invernadero.

**Halide** Any compound of a halogen with another element such as refrigerant.

**Halogenuro** Cualquier compuesto de un halogenuro y otro elemento, como por ejemplo el refrigerante.

**Halogen** Refers to any of the five chemical elements—astatine (At), bromine (Br), chlorine (Cl) fluorine (F), and iodine (I)—that may be found in some refrigerants.

**Halogeno** Se refiere a cualquier de lost cinco elementos quimicos—astatinio (At), bromo (Br), cloro (Cl), fluor (F), y yodo (I)—que pueden estar presentes en algunos refrigerantes.

**Head pressure** Pressure of the refrigerant from the discharge reed valve through the lines and condenser to the expansion valve orifice.

**Altura piezometrica** Presion del refrigerante de la valvula de la lamina de descarga a traves de las lineas y el condensador al orificio de la valvula de expansion.

**Heat** Energy; any temperature above absolute zero.

**Calor** Energia; cualquier temperatura superior al cero absoluto.

**Heater core** A heat exchanger which extracts the heat from coolant warmed by the engine to heat the passenger compartment.

**Núcleo de calor** Un cambiador de calor que extrae el calor del refrigerante calentado por el motor para calentar el compartimento del pasajero.

**Heat load** The load imposed on an air conditioner due to ambient temperature, humidity, and other factors that may produce unwanted heat.

**Carga de calor** Carga impuesta sobre un acondicionador de aire debido a la temperatura ambiente, humedad, y otros factores que pueden producir calor no deseado.

**High pressure** A relative term to describe excessive refrigerant pressure in the high side of an air conditioning system.

**Alta presión** Un término relativo que describe una presión excesiva del refrigerante en el lado alto de un sistema de aire acondicionado.

**High-pressure cutoff switch** An electrical switch that is activated by a predetermined high pressure. The switch opens a circuit during high-pressure periods.

**Interruptor de cierre de alta presion** Interruptor electrico que es accionado por una alta presion predeterminada. El interruptor abre un circuito durante periodos de alta presion.

**High-pressure switch** See High-pressure cutoff switch.

**Automata manometrico de alta presion** Ver High-pressure cutoff switch [Interruptor de cierre de alta presion].

**High side** That part of an air conditioning system extending from the compressor outlet to the metering device inlet.

**Lado alto** Esa parte de un sistema de aire acondicionado que se extiende de la salida del compresor a la entrada del dispositivo medidor.

**HL/LO** A term often used to refer to bi-level.

**HI/LO (alto/bajo)** Termino utilizado con frecuencia para referirse a binivel.

**Hot gas line** A line that carries hot gas such as the discharge line from the compressor to the condenser.

**Linea de gas caliente** Linea que conduce el gas caliente, como por ejemplo la linea de descarga, desde el compresor hasta el condensador.

**Humid** Damp.

**Humedo** Que contiene humedad.

**Humidity** See Moisture. See also Relative humidity.

**Humedad** Ver Moisture [Humedad]. Ver tambien Relative humidity [Humedad relativa].

**HVAC** The abbreviation used for heating ventilation and air conditioning.

**HVAC** La abreviación que se usa para la ventilación del calor y el aire acondicionado.

**H-valve** An expansion valve with all parts contained within that is used on some Chrysler and Ford lines.

**Valvula H** Valvula de expansion que contiene todas las partes dentro de si misma; se utiliza dicha valvula en algunos modelos de vehiculos de las companias automotrices Chrysler y Ford.

**Hydrocarbon** An organic compound containing only hydrogen (H) and carbon (C).

**Hidrocarbono** Compuesto organico que contiene solo el hidrogeno (H) y el carbono (C).

**Hydrochloric acid** A corrosive acid produced when water and R-12 are mixed as within an automotive air conditioning system.

**Acido hidroclorico** Acido corrosivo producido cuando se mezcla el agua con el R 12, como por ejemplo dentro de un sistema automotriz para el acondicionamiento de sire.

**Hydrogen** The lightest of all known substances and is colorless, odorless, flammable (H).

**Hidrógeno** La más ligera de todas las substancias conocidas que es sín color, sín olor y es inflamable.

**Hydrolysis** The chemical reaction with water whereby a substance is changed into one or more other substances.

**Hidrólisis** La reacción química con el agua en el cual una sustancia se cambia a una o más substancias.

**Hydrostatic pressure** The pressure exerted by a fluid.

**Presion hidrostatica** Presion ejercida por un fluido.

**Hygroscopic** Readily absorbing and retaining moisture.

**Higroscopico** Que absorbe y conserve facilmente la humedad.

**"Idiot light"** Slang term often used for engine coolant and/or oil pressure warning lights.

**Luz para idiotas** Termino en jerga utilizado con frecuencia para las luces de advertencia de enfriante de motor y/o de presion de aceite.

**Impeller** A rotating member with fins or blades used to move liquid, for example, the rotating part of a water pump.

**Impulsor** El elemento rotativo provisto de aletas utilizadas para mover liquido, p.e., la parte giratoria de una bomba de agua.

**Inject**  To insert, usually by force or pressure.
**Inyectar**  Insertar, normalmente por medio de la fuerza o presion.

**Insulator**  A nonconductor such as the covering of a wire (electrical) or a tube (thermal).
**Aislador**  Elemento no conductor, como por ejemplo la cubierta de un alambre (electrico) o un tubo (termico).

**Intake**  See Suction.
**Toma**  Ver Suction [Succion].

**KiloPascal absolute**  See kPa absolute.
**KiloPascal absoluto**  Ver kPa absolute [kPa absoluto].

**kPa**  An abbreviation for the metric pressure measure "kilopascal," sometimes written "kiloPascal," equivalent to 0.145 psi on the English scale.
**KPa**  Una abreviación de la medida métrica de presión "kilopascal" que a veces se escribe "kilopascal", equivalente a 0.145 libras por pulgada cuadrada en la gama inglesa.

**kPa absolute**  A metric unit of measure for pressure measured from absolute zero.
**kPa absoluto**  Unidad metrica de medida para presion medida del cero absoluto.

**Latent heat**  The amount of heat required to cause a change of state of a substance without changing its temperature.
**Calor latente**  La cantidad de calor requerida para ocasionar un cambio de estado de una sustancia sin cambiar su temperatura.

**Liquid line**  The line connecting the drier outlet with the expansion valve inlet. The line from the condenser outlet to the drier inlet is sometimes called a liquid line.
**Linea de liquido**  Linea que conecta la salida del secador con la entrada de la valvula de expansion. La linea de la salida del condensador a la entrada del secador a veces se llama una linea de liquido.

**Low pressure**  A relative term to describe below-normal pressure in the low side of an air conditioning system.
**Baja presión**  Un término relativo para describir una presión bajo lo normal en el lado bajo de un sistema del aire acondicionado.

**Low-pressure cut-off switch**  An electrical switch that is activated by a predetermined low pressure. This switch opens a circuit during certain low-pressure periods.
**Interruptor de cierre de baja presion**  Interruptor electrico que es accionado por una baja presion predeterminada. Dicho interruptor abre un circuito durante ciertos periodos de baja presion.

**Low-pressure switch**  See Low-pressure cutoff switch.
**Automata manometrico de baja presion**  Ver Low-pressure cutoff switch [Interruptor de cierre de baja presion].

**Low side**  That part of the air conditioning system extending from the inlet of the evaporator metering device to the inlet of the compressor.
**Lado bajo**  Esa parte del sistema del aire acondicionado que se extiende de la entrada del dispositivo medidora del evaporador a la entrada del compresor.

**Low-side service valve**  A device located on the suction side of the compressor that allows the service technician to check low-side pressures or perform other necessary service operations.
**Valvula de servicio del lado de baja presion**  Dispositivo ubicado en el lado de succion del compresor; dicha valvula permite que el mecanico verifique las presiones en el lado de baja presion o que lleve a cabo ontras funciones de servicio necesarias.

**Lubricant**  A substance, more commonly referred to as "oil," thought of as a petroleum-based product that is used to coat moving parts to reduce friction between them. The term generally refers to the new synthetic lubricants, such as polyalkaline glycol (PAG) and polyol ester (POE) that are used with HFC refrigerants.

**Lubricante**  Una substancia, comunmente referido como "aceite" que se suele definir como un producto a base de petroleo que se usa para cubrir las partes en movimiento para reducir la fricción entre ellas. El término generalmente se refiera a los lubricantes nuevos sintéticos, tal como el glicol polialcalino (PAG) y el poliol ester (POE) que se usan con los refrigerantes HFC.

**Malfunction**  Failure to work or perform.
**Disfuncion**  Dejar de funcionar correctamente.

**Master control**  A primary or main control.
**Regulador maestro**  Control primario o principal.

**Matter**  Anything that occupies space and possesses mass. All things in nature are composed of matter.
**Materia**  Todo lo que ocupe espacio o tenga masa. Todas las cosas en la naturaleza se componen de materia.

**Metering device**  A device for metering the proper amount of refrigerant into an evaporator. The two types for automotive air conditioning system service are thermostatic expansion valve (TXV) and orifice tube (OT).
**Dispositivo medidora**  Un dispositivo para medir la cantidad adecuada del refrigerante entrando al evaporador. Los dos tipos en el servicio del sistema aire acondicionador automotivo son la válvula de expansión termostático (TXV) y el tubo del orificio (OT).

**Miscible**  Another word for mixable.
**Miscible**  Otra palabra que significa que se puede mezclar.

**MIX**  A term often used when referring to HI/LO.
**MEZCIA**  Termino utilizado con frecuencia al referirse a HI/LO (alto/bajo).

**Mode**  Manner or state of existence of a thing; for example, hot or cool.
**Modo**  Manera o estado de existencia de una cosa; p.e., calor o fresco.

**Mode door**  A diverter door within the duct system for directing air through the heater and/or evaporator core.
**Puerta de modo**  Puerta desviadora dentro del sistema de conductos para conducir el aire a traves del nucleo del calentador y/o del evaporador.

**Moisture**  Droplets of water in the air; humidity, dampness, or wetness.
**Humedad**  Gotitas de agua en el aire.

**Molecule**  Two or more atoms chemically bound together.
**Molecula**  Dos o mas atomos quimicamente ligados.

**Negative  Minus, less than zero.** The ground (–) side of a battery or dc electrical circuit. A pressure below atmospheric; a vacuum.
**Negativo**  Menos de cero. El lado puesto a tierra (–) de un acumulador o corriente electrica de corriente continua. Una presion inferior a la de la atmosfera; un vacio.

**Nitrogen (N)**  An odorless, tasteless, and colorless element that composes over 80 percent of the atmosphere and is essential for all animal and plant life.
**Nigrogeno (N)**  Elemento inodoro, insipido e incoloro que compone mas de un 80% de la atmosfera y es esencial para toda vida vegetal y animal.

**Normally closed (nc)**  A switch or device that is closed in its relaxed (normal) position.
**Normalmente cerrado**  Conmutador o dispositivo que esta cerrado en su posicion relajada (normal).

**Normally open (no)**  A switch or device that is open in its relaxed (normal) position.
**Normalmente cerrado**  Conmutador o dispositivo que esta cerrado en su posicion relajada (normal).

**Organic acid technology** The term used to describe the chemical additive package in extended life coolant.

**Tecnología de ácidos orgánicos** El término que se usa para describir el paquete de aditivos de químicas del refrigerante de larga vida.

**Orifice** A small hole of calibrated dimensions for metering fluid or gas in exact proportions.

**Orificio** Un hoyo pequeño de dimensiones calibradas para medir los fluidos o los gases en proporciones exactas.

**Orifice tube** See Expansion tube and Fixed orifice tube (FDT).

**Tubo de orificio** Ver Expansion tube [Tubo de expansion] y Fixed orifice tube [Tubo de orificio fojo (FDT)].

**Overcooling** A general term used if the engine does not reach design operating temperature in a predetermined time period, such as would be the case if the thermostat were removed.

**Sobreenfriamlento** Termino general utilizado si el motor no alcanza la temperatura de functionamiento de diseno dentro de un periodo predeterminado de tiempo, como por ejemplo si se removara el termostato.

**Overflow tank** Another term used when referring to the coolant recovery tank which allows for both coolant expansion and contraction from the cooling system of the engine..

**Tanque de derrame** Otro término que se usa cuando se refiere al tanque de rescate del refrigerante que permite la expansión y contracción del refrigerante debido al sistema refrigerante del motor.

**Overheating** A general term used if the engine exceeds design operating temperature.

**Sobrecalentamiento** Termino general utilizado si el motor excede la temperatura de funcionamiento de diseno.

**Oxygen (O)** An odorless, tasteless, colorless element that forms about one-fifth of our atmosphere. An essential element for animal and plant life.

**Oxigeno (O)** Elemento inodoro, insipido e incoloro que forma mas o menos la quinta parte de nuestra atmosfera. Es un elemento esencial para toda vida vegetal y animul.

**Ozone (O₃)** An unstable pale-blue gas with a penetrating odor; it is an allotropic form of oxygen (O) that is usually formed by a silent electrical discharge in the air.

**Ozono (O₃)** Gas inestable de color azul palido que tiene un olor penetrante; es una forma alotropica de oxigeno (O) normalmente producido por una descarga electrica silenciosa en el aire.

**Ozone depletion** The reduction of the ozone layer due to contamination, such as the release of CFC refrigerants into the atmosphere.

**Agotamiento del ozono** La reducción de la capa de ozono debido a la contaminación, tal como los refrigerantes CFC a la atmósfera.

**Performance** The way in which something functions.

**Ejecución** La manera en la cual algo funciona.

**Perspiration** The salty fluid secreted by sweat glands through the pores of the skin.

**Sudor** Fluido salado secretado por las glandulas sudoriparas a traves de los poros de la piel.

**Pitch** Set at a particular degree or angle.

**Inclinacion** Puesto a un grado o angulo especifico.

**Plenum** See Plenum chamber.

**Pleno** Ver Plenum chamber [Camara impelente].

**Plenum chamber** An area filled with air at a pressure that is slightly higher than the surrounding air pressure, such as the chamber just before the blower motor.

**Camara impelente** Area en la cual existe una condicion de sobrepresion, como por ejemplo la camara justo enfrente del motor del soplador.

**PM** Preventive maintenance.

**PM** Mantenimiento preventivo.

**POE** An abbreviation for the synthetic lubricant polyol ester.

**POE** Abreviatura del lubrificante sintetico polioliester.

**Positive** The hot (+) side of a battery or electrical circuit. Also, a pressure above atmospheric.

**Positivo** El lado cargado (+) de un acumulador o circuito electrico. Tambien una presion superior a la de la atmosfera.

**Power train control module** Generally abbreviated PCM and is the computer system for the engine management and emission systems.

**Módulo de contro del tren motriz** Generalmente abreviado de PCM y es el sistema de computador de los sistemas de regulación del motor e emisiones.

**Predetermined** The preset parameters used.

**Predeterminado** Los parámetros prescritos que se usan.

**Pressure cap** A radiator cap that increases the pressure of the cooling system and allows higher operating temperatures.

**Tapa de presion** Tapa de radiador que eleva la presion del sistema de enfriamiento y permite un funcionamiento a temperaturas mas altas.

**Pressure switch** An electrical switch that is actuated by a predetermined low or high pressure. A pressure switch is generally used for system protection.

**Automata manometrico** Interruptor electrico accionado por una alta o baja presion predeterminada. Generalmente se utiliza un automata manometrico para la proteccion del sistema.

**Price leader** An item that a merchant may sell at cost or near cost to attract customers.

**Artículo en venta** Un artículo que un negociante puede vender en costo o casi en costo para atraer a la clientela.

**Programmer** The part of an automatic temperature control system that controls the blower speed, air mix doors, and vacuum diaphragms.

**Programador** Parte de un sistema de regulacion automatica de temperatura que regula la velocidad del soplador, puertas de mezcla de aire, y diafragmas al vacio.

**Propylene glycol** A colorless liquid used in the production of antifreeze, $C_3H_8O_2$, and is considered a low toxicity anti-freeze..

**Propileno glicol** Un líquido sín color que se usa en la producción del anticogelante, $C_3H_8O_2$, y que se considera un anticongelante de baja toxicidad.

**Pump** The compressor. Also refers to the vacuum pump.

**Bomba** El compresor. Se refiere tambien a la bomba de vacio.

**Pump down** See Evacuate.

**Vaciar** Ver Evacuate [Evacuar].

**Pure** Not mixed with anything else.

**Puro** Quo no se ha mezclado con ninguna otra cosa.

**R-12** An abbreviation to identify the chlorofluorocarbon family of ozone-depleting refrigerants. R-12, or CFC-12, was a popular refrigerant for automotive air conditioning systems service until it was phased out of production.

**R-12** Una abreviación para identificar la familia de los refrigerantes clorofluorocarburo que agotan la capa de ozono. El R-12, o CFC-12, fue un refrigerante de sistemas de aire acondicionado automotivos muy popular hasta que su producción fue restringida.

**R-134a** An abbreviation to identify the ozone-friendly hydrofluorocarbon family of refrigerants. R-134a, or HFC-134a, is the refrigerant of choice for replacing R-12 in automotive air conditioning systems.

**R-134a** Una abreviación para identificar la familia de los refrigerantes clorofluorocarburo que no agotan la capa de ozono. El R-134a, o HFC-34a, es el refrigerante que más se usa para reemplazar el R-12 en los sistemas de aire acondicionado automotivo.

**R-744** The trade name for carbon dioxide, $CO_2$, gas and is considered to be one of the alternative refrigerant gases that will be used for refrigerant systems.

**R-744** El nombre registrado del gas carbónico , $CO_2$, que se considera ser uno de los gases refrigerantes alternativos que seran usados para los sistemas refrigerantes.

**Radiation** The transfer of heat without heating the medium through which it is transmitted.

**Radiación** La transferencia del calor sín calentar el medio por el cual se esta transmitiendo.

**Radiator** A coolant-to-air heat exchanger. The device that removes heat from coolant passing through it.

**Radiador** Intercambiador de calor del enfriante al aire. El dipositivo que remueve calor del enfriante que pasa por el.

**Ram air** The term used to describe the flow of air striking the front of a vehicle as it travels in a forward direction.

**Aire admitido en marcha** El término que se usa para describir el flujo del aire que golpea la parte delantera del vehículo mientras que éste viaja en un movimiento delantera.

**RCD** Refrigerant containment device.

**RCD** Dipositivo para contener refrigerante.

**Receiver** A container for the storage of liquid refrigerant.

**Receptor** Recipiente para el almacenaje de refrigerante liquido.

**Receiver-dehydrator** A combination container for the storage of liquid refrigerant and a desiccant.

**Receptor-deshidratador** Recipiente de combinacion para el almacenaje del refrigerante liquido y un desecante.

**Receiver-drier** See Receiver-dehydrator.

**Receptor-secador** Ver Receiver-dehydrator [Receptor/deshidratador].

**Reciprocating** To move to and fro, fore and aft, or up and down.

**Movimiento alternativo** Moverse de un lado para otro, de atras para adelante, o de arriba para abajo.

**Reciprocating piston(s)** A compressor assembly that uses the back and forth movement of a piston to cause a rotary motion of the compressor crankshaft.

**Pistonos recíprocos** Una asamblea de compresor que usa el movimiento oscilante de un pistón para causar un movimiento rotario del cigueñal del compresor.

**Recirculate** To reuse. To circulate a fluid or vapor over and over again.

**Recircular** Utilizar de nuevo. Hacer circular un fluido o vapor repetidamente.

**Reclaim** To process used refrigerant to new product specifications by means that may include distillation. This process requires that a chemical analysis of the refrigerant be performed to determine that appropriate product specifications are met. This term implies the use of equipment for processes and procedures usually available only at a reprocessing facility.

**Recuperar** Procesar refrigerante gastado a nuevas especificaciones para productos por un medio que puede incluir la distilacion. Este proceso require que se realice un analisis quimico del refrigerante para determinar si se pueden cumplir con las especificaciones apropiadas para dicho producto. Este termino implica la utilizacion de equipo para procesos y proced-imientos normalmente disponibles solo en una instalacion de reprocesamiento.

**Recover** To remove refrigerant in any condition from a system and to store it in an external container without necessarily testing or processing it in any way.

**Recobrar** Remove refrigerante en cualquier condicion de un sistema y almacenarlo en un recipiente externo sin necesariamente probarlo o procesarlo.

**Recovery cylinder** A recovery cylinder for R-12 and/or R-134a must meet DOT specifications 4BA-300. These cylinders are characterized by a combined liquid/vapor valve located at the top. A dip tube is used to feed liquid refrigerant from the bottom so it can be dispensed without inverting the cylinder. A recovery cylinder should be painted gray with a yellow shoulder.

**Cilindro de recuperacion** Un cilindro de recuperacion para R 12 y/o R 134a tiene que cumplir con las especificaciones 4BA-300 del DOT. Se caracterizan estos cilindros por una valvula combinada de liquido y vapor ubicada en la parte superior. Se utiliza un tubo probador para alimentar el refrigerante liquido desde la parte inferior para que pueda dispensarse sin invertir el cilindro. Un cilindro de recuperacion debe ser pistado el color gris con un resalto amarillo.

**Recovery tank** See Recovery cylinder and Expansion tank.

**Tanque de recuperacion** Ver Recovery cylinder [Cilindro de recuperacion] y Expansion tank [Tanque de expansion].

**Recycle** To clean refrigerant for reuse by oil separation and to pass through other devices such as filter-driers to reduce moisture, acidity, and particulate matter. Recycling applies to procedures usually accomplished in the repair shop or at a local service facility.

**Reciclar** Limpiar el refrigerante para ser utilizado de nuevo por medio de la separacion de aceite y del pasaje a traves de otros dispositivos, como por ejemplo filtro-secadores, para disminuir la humedad, acidez, y materia particula. El reciclamiento se aplica a lost procedimientos normalmente realizados en el taller de reparacion o en la instalacion de servicio local.

**Reed valve** The leaves of steel located on the valve plate of a compressor. The suction reed valve opens to admit refrigerant on the intake stroke of the compressor and closes to block refrigerant flow on the exhaust stroke. The discharge reed valve, on the other hand, is closed to block refrigerant flow on the intake stroke and opens to expel refrigerant on the exhaust stroke.

**Válvula de lámina vibrante** Las láminas del acero ubicados en la placa de la válvula del compresor. La válvula succión de lámina abre para admitir al refrigerante en la carrera de entrada del compresor y cierre para bloquear el flujo del refrigerante en la carrera de escape. La válvula de descarga de lámina, en cambio, es cerrado para bloquear el flujo del refrigernate en la carrera de entrada y abre para expeller el refrigerante en la carrera de escape.

**Refrigerant** The chemical compound used in a refrigeration system to produce the desired cooling.

**Refrigerante** Compuesto quimico utilizado en un sistema de refrigeracion para producir el enfriamiento deseado.

**Refrigeration** To use an apparatus to cool, keep cool, chill, and keep chilled under controlled conditions by natural or mechanical means as an aid to ensuring personal safety and comfort. To cool the air by removing some of its heat content. The removal of heat by mechanical means.

**Refrigeracion** Utilizar un aparato para enfriar y mantener el frio bajo condiciones controladas por medios naturales o mecanicos para ayudar a asegurar la seguridad y comodidad personales. Enfrier el aire removiendo una porcion de su contenido de calor. La remocion del calor por medios mecanicos.

**Relative humidity** The actual moisture content of the air in relation to the total moisture that the air can hold at a given temperature.

**Humedad relativa** Contenido verdadero de humedad del aire en relacion a la humedad total que el aire puede mantener a una temperatura dada.

**Remote bulb** A sensing device connected to the expansion valve by a capillary tube. This device senses the tailpipe temperature and transmits pressure to the expansion valve for its proper operation.

**Bombilla a distancia** Dispositivo sensor conectado a la valvula de expansion por un tubo capilar. Este dispositivo siente la temperatura del tubo de escape y transmite presion a la valvula de expansion para su funcionamiento correcto.

**Reserve tank** See Overflow tank.

**Tanque de derrame** Véa Overflow tank (tanque de derrame)

**Restriction** A blockage in the air conditioning system caused by a pinched or crimped line, foreign matter, or moisture freeze-up.

**Limitacion** Bloqueo en el sistema de acondicionamiento de aire ocasionado por una linea pellizcada o arrugada, una materia extrana, o la congelacion de humedad.

**Restrictor** Decreases the flow of a liquid or gas.

**Limitador** Disminuye el flujo de un líquido o un gas.

**Retrofit** To modify equipment that is already in service using parts and/or materials made available after the time of original manufacture.

**Retromodificación** Modificar el equipo que ya esta en servicio usando las partes y/o las materiales disponibles después del tiempo de la fabricación original.

**Reverse flow** Direction opposite that of which is considered the standard direction. In engine cooling systems reverse flow systems circulate coolant first through the cylinder head(s) and then through the engine blow.

**Flujjo en reverso** La dirección opuesta de la que se considera la dirección normal. En los sistemas de refrigeración automotivos los sistemas de flujo en reversa circulan el refrigerante primero por la(s) culata(s) de cilindro y luego por el bloque motor.

**Rheostat** A wire-wound variable resistor used to control blower motor speed.

**Reostato** Resistor variable devanado con alambre utilizado para regular la velocidad del motor del soplador.

**Rotary** The turning motion around an axis.

**Rotario** El movimiento de girar alrededor de un eje.

**Saddle valve** A two-part accessory valve that may be clamped around the metal part of a system hose to provide access to the air conditioning system for service.

**Valvula de silleta** Valvula de accesorio de dos partes que puede fijarse con una abrazadera a la parte metalica de una manguera del sistema para proveer acceso al sistema de acondicionamiento de aire para llevar a cabo el servicio.

**SAE** Society of Automotive Engineers.

**SAE** Sociedad de Ingenieros Automotrices.

**SATC** Semiautomatic temperature control.

**SATC** Regulador semi automatico de temperatura.

**Screen** A metal mesh located in the receiver, expansion valve, and compressor inlet to prevent particles of dirt from circulating through the system.

**Cribadora** Malla metalica ubicada en el receptor, la valvula de expansion, y la entrada del compresor para evitar que las particulas de polvo se circulen a traves del sistema.

**Scroll** A spiral, rolled, or convoluted form.

**Arollado** Una forma de espiral, de enrollado o convoluto.

**Sensible heat** Heat that causes a change in the temperature of a substance, but does not change the state of the substance.

**Calor sensible** Calor que ocasions un cambio de temperatura de una sustancia, pero que no cambia el éstado de dicha sustancia.

**Sensor** A temperature-sensitive unit such as a remote bulb or thermistor. See Remote bulb and Thermistor.

**Sensor** Unidad sensible a la temperatura, como por ejemplo una bombilla a distancia o termistor. Ver Remote bulb [Bombilla a distancia] y Thermistor [Termistor].

**Serpentine** Refers to the circuitous and twisted or winding path taken by one drive belt used to turn numerous pulleys.

**Serpentina** Refiere a la senda indirecto y girando o torciendose que un toma una correa de impulso para girar poleas numerosas.

**Serpentine belt** A flat or V-groove belt that winds through all of the engine accessories to drive them off the crankshaft pulley.

**Correa serpentina** Correa plana o con ranuras en V que atraviesa todos los accesorios del motor para forzarlos fuera de la polea del ciguenal.

**Service port** A fitting found on some control devices and in the low- and high-side of an air conditioning system used to gain access into the system for diagnostics and/or service procedures.

**Puerta de servicio** Un montaje que se encuentra en algunos dispositivos de control y en los lados de baja e alta presión de un sistema de aire acondicionado que sirve para dar acceso al sistema para efectuar los procedimientos de diagnóstico y/o el servicio.

**Service valve** See Service port.

**Valvula de servicio** Ver Service Port [Orificio de servicio].

**Shroud** A ductlike cover to ensure that maximum airflow is directed over the engine by the engine-driven fan assembly.

**Gualdera** Cubierta parecida a un conducto para asegurar que un flujo maximo de aire es conducido sobre el moto por el conjunto del ventilador accionado por el motor.

**SNAP** Acronym used for the EPA's Significant New Alternatives Policy program which reviews alternatives to CFC-12 (R-12) refrigerant.

**SNAP** Una sigla de la programa Poliza de Alternativas Nuevas Significantes de la EPA (Agencia de Protección del Medio Ambiente) que revisa las alternativas del refrigerante para el CFC-12 (R-12).

**Snapshot** A feature of OBD II that shows, on various scanners, the conditions that the vehicle was operating under when a particular trouble code was set. For example, the vehicle was at 225°F, ambient temperature was 55°F, throttle position was part throttle at 1.45 volts, rpm was 1,450, brake was off, transmission was in third gear with torque converter unlocked, air conditioning system was off, and so on.

**Instantáneo** Una característica del OBD II que muestra, en varios detectores, las condiciones bajo las cuales operaba el vehículo cuando se registró un código de fallo. Por ejemplo, el vehículo registraba 225 F, la temperatura del ambiente era el 55F, la posición del regulador estaba en una posición parcial de 1.45 voltíos , el rpm era 1,450, el freno estaba desenganchada, la transmisión estaba en la tercera velocidad con el convertidor del par desenclavado, el sistema de acondicionador de aire estaba apagado, y etcétera.

**Specific heat** The quantity of heat required to change one pound of a substance by 1°F.

**Calor especifico** Cantidad de calor requerida para cambiar una libra de una sustancia en un grado Fahrenheit.

**Stabilize** To keep from fluctuating.

**Estabilizar** Prevenir las fluctuaciones.

**Starved** Refers to a condition whereby too little refrigerant is metered into the evaporator.

**Falta de refrigerante** Se refiere a una condicion en la cual no se dosifica la cantidad suficiente de refrigerante al evaporador.

**Strainer** See Screen.

**Colador** Ver Screen [Cribadora].

**Stroke** The distance a piston travels from its lowest point to its highest point.

**Carrera** Distancia que un piston viaja desde el punto mas bajo hasta el mas alto.

**Suction** A negative force or pressure.

**Succion** Fuerza o presion negativa.

**Suction line** The line connecting the evaporator outlet to the compressor inlet.

**Conducto de succion** Linea que conecta la salida del evaporador a la entrada del compresor.

**Suction pressure** Compressor inlet pressure. Reflects the pressure of the system on the low side.

**Presion de succion** La presion de la entrada del compresor. Refleja la presion del sistema del lado de baja presion.

**Suction service valve** See Low-side service valve.

**Valvula de succion de servicio** Ver Low-side service valve [Valvula de servicio del lado de baja presion].

**Suction valve** The low-side service valve is often referred to as the suction valve.

**Válvula de succión** La válvula de servicio del lado bajo de presión suele referirse como la válvula de succión.

**Superheat** Adding heat intensity to a gas after the complete evaporation of a liquid.

**Sobrecalentar** El agregar intensidad calorifica a un gas despues de la evaporacion completa de un liquido.

**Surface temperature** The inner temperature of a body, such as water.

**Temperatura de la superficie** La temperatura interior de un cuerpo, tal como el agua.

**Swash plate** A type of concentric plate found on some compressor crankshafts used to move the pistons to and fro or back and forth.

**Placa oscilante** Tipo de placa concentrica ubicada en algunos ciguenales de compresor y utilizada para mover los pistons de un lado para otro o de un lado a otro.

**Telltale light** A dash lamp to indicate a malfunction such as low oil pressure or overheating.

**Luz indicadora** Una lampara en el tablero de instrumentos para indicar una disfuncion, como por ejemplo la baja presion del aceite o el sobrecalentamiento.

**Temperature** Heat intensity measured on a thermometer.

**Temperatura** Intensidad calorifica medida con un termometro.

**Temperature-pressure relationship** The relationship that exists, in the English system of measure, of the similarities between temperature and pressure readings of refrigerants R-12 and R-134a in a refrigeration system.

**Relacion temperatura-presion** La relacion que existe en el sistema de medida ingles de las similaridades entre las lecturas de temperatura y presion de los refrigerantes R 12 y R 134a in a refrigeration system.

**Temperature switch** A switch actuated by a change in temperature at a predetermined point.

**Interruptor de temperatura** Interruptor accionado por un cambio de temperatura a un punto predeterminado.

**Thermistor** A temperature-sensing resistor that has the ability to change values with a change in temperature.

**Termistor** Resistor sensible a temperatura que tiene la capacidad de cambiar valores al ocurrir un cambio de temperatura.

**Thermostat** A device used to cycle the clutch to control the rate of refrigerant flow as a means of temperature control. The driver has control over the temperature desired.

**Termostato** Dispositivo utilizado para ciclar el embrague para regular la proporcion del flujo de refrigerante como medio de regulacion de temperatura. El conductor puede regular la temperatura deseada.

**Thermostatic expansion valve** The component of a refrigeration system that regulates the rate of flow of refrigerant into the evaporator as governed by the action of the remote bulb-sensing tailpipe temperatures.

**Valvula de expansion termostatica** Componente de un sistema de refrigeracion que regula la proporcion del flujo de refrigerante en el evaporador, lo cual es controlado por la accion de la bombilla a distancia que siente las temperaturas del tubo de escape.

**Toxicity** Toxic or poisonous quality.

**Toxicidad** Calidad toxica o venenosa.

**Ultraviolet (UV) radiation** The invisible rays from the sun that have damaging effects on the earth. Ultraviolet radiation causes sunburns.

**Radiacion ultravioleta** Rayos invisibles del sol que tienen efectos danosos en la tierra. La radiacion ultravioleta es la causa de la insolacion.

**Vacuum** Any pressure below atmospheric pressure.

**Vacio** Cualquier presion inferior a la de la atmosfera.

**Vacuum motor** A device designed to provide mechanical action by the use of a vacuum signal.

**Motor de vacio** Dispositivo disenado para proveer accion mecanica por medio del uso de una senal de vacio.

**Vacuum pot** See Vacuum motor.

**Olla de vacio** Ver Vacuum motor [Motor de vacio].

**Vacuum signal** Level of vacuum received.

**Señal de vacío** El nivel del vacío que se ha recibido.

**Vapor** See Gas.

**Vapor** Ver Gas.

**Variable displacement** To change the displacement of a compressor by changing the stroke of the piston(s).

**Desplazamiento variable** Cambiar el desplazamiento de un compresor al cambiar la carrera del piston o de los pistones.

**Vent** A condition whereby fresh outside air may be introduced into the vehicle.

**Ventilacion** Condicion por medio de la cual el aire fresco exterior puede introducirse al vehiculo.

**Virgin** Newly manufactured or produced, not previously used.

**Virgen** Fabricado o producido ultimamente; no utilizado previamente.

**Visual inspection** An inspection by sight as opposed to smell, hearing, or touch.

**Inspección visual** Una inspección usando el sentido de vista en vez del olfato, el oído o el tacto.

**Wobble plate** An offset plate that is secured to the main shaft and moves the piston(s) to and fro.

**Placa oscilante** Placa de desviacion que se fija al arbol principal y mueve el piston o los pistones de un lado para otro.

**Zener clamping diode** A one-way electrical gate with a threshold voltage used to suppress damaging voltage spikes to integrated circuits.

**Diodo estabilizador zener** Una entrada eléctrica de una vía con un umbral de voltaje que se usa para suprimir los picos dañosos de voltaje en los circuítos integrados.

# INDEX

Midposition, 62
MIX, 236, 242
Mobile air conditioning, 58–59
Mode door adjustment, 255–256
Moisture, 154–155
   prevention of, 154–155
   removal of, 145, 154–155, 156–158
     at high altitudes, 158–159
Molecules, 31
motion of, 32
Montreal Protocol, 9, 184
Mounting brackets, 66
Moving parts, 13, 14
MT-31, 312
Multiwound motor, 272

## N

Negative pressure, 280
Nippondenso compressors, 60–61, 217–218, 219
Nitrogen, 1, 30
Normally closed, 95
Normal operation, 173–174

## O

Odors, 46
OEM (original equipment manufacturer), 232
Oil, 126, 182, 191, 194, 307
Orifice, TXV, 131
Orifice tube, 69, 134–135, 320
O-rings, 168, 319
Outside temperature sensor, 298–299
Overcharge, 182, 162–163
Overcooling, 95
Overflow tank, 89
Overheating, 95–96, 158, 182
Oxygen, 1, 30
OZ-12, 312
Ozone
   in atmosphere, 3
   defined, 1
   destruction (depletion) of, 3–6, 8, 315
   human health, effects of ozone loss on, 7–8, 315
   legislation protecting, 9, 17–18, 51, 312, 315–316
   measurement of, 4

## P

Panel/floor (BI-LEVEL), 236
Panel (NORM), 236
Perspiration, 44
PG. *See* Propylene glycol
Phosgene, 16, 23–24
Pitch, belts, 100–101
Plenum, 231
Polyalkylene glycol (PAG), 192, 326
Polyol ester (POE), 192, 307, 326
Positive pressure, 280–281

Pound can, 190–191
Pour point, 193
Power module, 294–295
Power steering cut-off switch, 300
Pressure cap, 86–88
Pressure controls, 285
Pressure differential, 69, 134–135
Pressure relief valves, 18, 306
Pressure switch
   compressor discharge, 278
   cut-off switch (*See* High-pressure switch; Low-pressure switch)
   cycling switch (*See* Clutch cycling pressure switch (CCPS))
Preventive maintenance, 116, 195–196
Price leader, refrigerant as, 51
Programmer, 291, 294
Propylene glycol (PG), 20, 113–114
Psia, 281
Pump. *See also* Coolant pump
   vacuum, 155
Pump-down, 155
Pure refrigerant, 312–315
Purity test, 315

## Q

Quick-connect valve, 63–64

## R

R-176, 312
R-718, 183
R-134a. *See* HFC-134a
R-405A, 312
Radiation, 40, 43–44
Radiator, 79, 82–86
   cleaning, 64
   cross-flow, 82
   vertical-flow, 82
Radiator cap. *See* Pressure cap
Radiator-condenser fan, 164
R-406A/GHG, 311
Ram air, 79
RB-276, 310
RCD (Refrigerant containment device), 321
Rear heat/cool system, 244–246
Receiver-drier, 65–66, 130, 322
Reciprocating compressor, 123, 217–218
Recirculate, 233, 236
Reclaiming refrigerant, 159, 315
Recovery cylinder, 314
Recovery equipment, 306
Recovery systems, 159–160
   equipment for, 160–162
Recovery tank, 84, 89–90
Recycling refrigerant, 159
Reed valves, 124